AVOTEK®
AERONAUTICAL
DICTIONARY

David Jones

SECOND EDITION

AVOTEK®
INFORMATION RESOURCES

Production Staff

Designer/Lead Illustrator Amy Siever
Designer/Illustrator Dustin Blyer
Senior Designer Roberta Byerly
Production Manager Holly Bonos

Author
David Jones

International Standard Book Number 1-933189-20-7
ISBN 13: 978-1-933189-20-8
Order # T-AVAEDI-0201

For Sale by: Avotek
A Select Aerospace Industries, Inc. company

Mail to:
P.O. Box 219
Weyers Cave, Virginia 24486
USA

Ship to:
200 Packaging Drive
Weyers Cave, Virginia 24486
USA

Toll Free: 1-800-828-6835
Telephone: 1-540-234-9090
Fax: 1-540-234-9399

Second Edition
Printed in the USA

www.avotek.com

Table of Contents

Introduction

English, the universal language of aviation, has a history of being an adaptable and expressive form of communication. A word or group of words can have different meanings based on the context in which they are used. This aspect makes the use of a dictionary so necessary to the proper interpretation of words.

This dictionary contains the terms and definitions that are used by aviation maintenance personnel, ground crews and flight crews on an everyday basis.

Every effort has been made to have the most up-to-date definition possible, given the rapid rate at which changes happen in aviation.

Where a term has a certain meaning as used by the FAA, it has been included and referenced as from FAR 1 Definitions and Abbreviations. The reference is indicated by (FAR 1) at the end of the definition. In all cases the FAA website should be consulted for the most recent changes to FAR 1. All of these definitions were current as of the date of publication.

Illustrations relating to terms with multiple meanings bear a superscript number indicating the definition to which it refers.

Email us at comments@avotek.com for comments or suggestions.

Phonetic Alphabet

A	Alpha	N	November
B	Bravo	O	Oscar
C	Charlie	P	Papa
D	Delta	Q	Quebec
E	Echo	R	Romeo
F	Foxtrot	S	Sierra
G	Golf	T	Tango
H	Hotel	U	Uniform
I	India	V	Victor
J	Juliet	W	Whiskey
K	Kilo	X	X Ray
L	Lima	Y	Yankee
M	Mike	Z	Zulu

Avotek® Aircraft Maintenance Series

Introduction to Aircraft Maintenance

Aircraft Structural Maintenance

Aircraft System Maintenance

Aircraft Powerplant Maintenance

Avotek® Aircraft Avionics Series

Avionics: Fundamentals of Aircraft Electronics

Avionics: Beyond the AET

Avionics: Systems and Troubleshooting

Other Books by Avotek®

Aircraft Corrosion Control Guide

Aircraft Structural Technician

Aircraft Turbine Engines

Aircraft Wiring & Electrical Installation

AMT Reference Handbook

Avotek Aeronautical Dictionary

Fundamentals of Modern Aviation

Light Sport Aircraft Inspection Procedures

Structural Composites: Advanced Composites in Aviation

Aa

A

abeam:
At right angles to the longitudinal axis of the aircraft.

abort:
To terminate an operation prematurely, i.e., to abort the attempt to start the engine, or to abort the aircraft's takeoff roll.

abradable seal:
A knife-edge seal used in turbine engines. Designed to wear away slightly to produce an air-tight fit.

abradable shroud:
A turbine shroud ring made of a honeycomb type material set into the outer turbine case. This material is designed to wear away without damage if the turbine blades creep and contact the shroud.

abrade:
To scrape or rub off.

abrasion:
Wear caused by friction. This is often accelerated by the presence of a foreign substance and is indicated by scratches or marks on the affected parts.

abrasive:
A material containing minute particles of a substance that tends to wear any surface it rubs against.

abrasive blasting:
The process of using a forceful stream of particles, available in varying hardnesses, to remove residue and contaminants from steel surfaces. This may be used to clean turbine engine compressor blades (compressor wash) or to prepare surfaces for painting or plating.

absicissa:
The horizontal reference line of a graph or chart; the X-axis. Opposite of the ordinate (Y-axis).

absolute altitude:
Actual height above the surface of the earth, either land or water.

absolute ceiling:
The altitude where a particular airplane's climb rate reaches zero.

absolute humidity:
The amount of water vapor actually present in an atmosphere, expressed by its weight in grams per cubic foot or grams per cubic meter.

absolute pressure:
Pressure measured relative to zero pressure or to a vacuum.

absolute pressure controller (APC):
Controls the maximum compressor discharge pressure of a reciprocating engine turbocharger system.

absolute temperature:
Temperature referenced from absolute zero. There are two absolute temperature scales used. The Rankine scale uses degrees Fahrenheit, and the Kelvin scale uses degrees Celsius.

absolute value:
The value of a number without considering its sign (whether it is plus or minus).

absolute zero:
The temperature at which molecular motion ceases. This temperature is -459.6°F or -273.18°C.

absorption:
The process of one material (liquid, solid, or gas) merging with a second material by penetrating the particles of the second material.

AC:
See *Advisory Circular*

ACARS:
See *Airborne Communications Addressing and Reporting System*

ACAS:
Airborne Collision and Avoidance System

accelerating agent:
1. A substance that hastens the vulcanization of an elastomer causing it to vulcanize in a shorter time span or at a lower temperature.
2. A substance that speeds up the polymerization of a synthetic resin.
3. The curing agent used in multiple part curing-type sealants.

accelerating pump:
A pump in a carburetion system that momentarily enriches the fuel-air mixture when the throttle is opened suddenly. The pump may be of the plunger type, operated by the throttle, or it may be of the diaphragm type, automatically operated by variation of the air pressure in the induction system.

acceleration:
Defined as the rate of change of velocity, or change in velocity divided by the amount of time over which that change took place.

acceleration due to gravity:
The acceleration of a freely falling body due to the pull of gravity. In a vacuum this will be 32.2 feet per second per second near sea level. Acceleration caused by gravity will decrease with altitude. It becomes zero as a body leaves the earth's gravitational field and enters space.

acceleration well:
An internal cavity provided around the discharge nozzle of some early float-type carburetors. When the throttle is opened quickly, the fuel is discharged from the main discharge nozzle to aid in smooth acceleration of the engine.

accelerator winding:
A series winding used in some vibrating-type voltage regulators. When the points open, this winding decreases the magnetic field immediately, allowing the points to close more rapidly.

accelerometer:
A device that measures the acceleration to which it is subjected and develops a signal proportional to it.

ACCELEROMETER

acceptor atom:
An impurity that when added to a semiconductor accepts one electron from a neighboring atom and creates a hole in the lattice structure of the crystal. Also called *trivalent impurity*.

access door:
A door that provides a normal or emergency entrance or exit route. Also used to describe doors used to provide access to service points and manually operated drains.

access panel:
A panel that is easily removed to provide access for inspection or maintenance.

accessory drive gearbox:
See *accessory section*

accessory section
That part of the aircraft engine that contains the gears and drive mechanism to operate accessories such as fuel pumps, hydraulic pumps, oil pumps, and generators.

accumulator:
Device for storing liquid under pressure, usually consisting of a chamber separated into a gas compartment and a liquid compartment by a bladder, piston, or diaphragm. An accumulator also smoothes out pressure surges in the hydraulic system.

accumulator precharge:
Compressed air that is stored in the air chamber of an accumulator. This pressure does not produce an increase in hydraulic system pressure.

ACDO:
Air Carrier District Office

acetone:
1. A flammable liquid ketone used as a solvent and a constituent in many aircraft finishes.
2. Used in acetylene cylinders to dissolve and stabilize acetylene under high pressure.

acetylene gas:
A highly combustible gas composed of carbon and hydrogen. Used as a fuel gas in the oxyacetylene welding process.

AC fittings:
Air Corps. Replaced by AN (Air Force/Navy) standard and MS (Military Standard) fittings. AN and AC fittings are not interchangeable, although they may appear similar. AN fittings may be identified by a shoulder (unthreaded portion) between the flare and the first thread. An AC fitting does not have this shoulder.

A-check:
More detailed than a service check, an A-check is generally performed after 60 flight hours, about once a week. One or two technicians perform more detailed inspection and functional checks on an overnight stay. The aircraft is not removed from service.

acid:
A chemical substance containing hydrogen, having a sour taste, and reacting with a base (alkali) to form a salt.

acid diluent:
A constituent of wash primer that provides a mild etch to the surface of the metal for a better bond.

acid embrittlement:
A form of hydrogen embrittlement that may be induced in some metals by acid treatment.

acid-resistant paint:
Formulated to withstand the action of acids.

acknowledgement, ISO-alphabet, maintenance (AIM):
An ARINC 429 data word format used for systems that require large amounts of data transfer

ACM:
Air Cycle Machine. See *air cycle cooling system.*

acme thread:
A screw thread having a 29° included angle. Used largely for feed and adjusting screws on machine tools.

acorn nut:
A dome-shaped nut with threads that do not go completely through the nut. Also known as *cap nuts.*

AN FITTING   AC FITTING

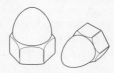

ACORN NUT

3

acoustic emission testing:
A type of nondestructive testing that uses pulses of mechanical frequency at an ultrasonic frequency to detect flaws in materials. Also called *ultrasonic emission testing*.

acrylic:
A glossy, transparent, thermoplastic material used for cast or molded parts. Often seen in aircraft windows and windshields.

acrylic lacquer:
An aircraft finish consisting of an acrylic resin vehicle and certain volatile solvents.

acrylic plastic:
Any of a family of synthetic resins made by the polymerization of esters of acrylic acid and its derivatives.

acrylic resin:
Group of transparent, thermoplastic, polymeric resins used in making molded plastics, paints, textile fibers, etc.

activated charcoal:
A form of highly porous carbon that can easily absorb gases, vapors, and colloidal particles.

active matrix LCD:
A type of LCD with a transistor located at each pixel intersection

activity monitor, data bus:
Monitors the data bus signals to ensure data transmission at regular intervals

actuating cylinder:
An actuator that converts fluid power into linear mechanical force and motion.

actuating cylinder, double-action:
Actuating cylinder in which both strokes are produced by pressurized fluid.

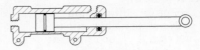

ACTUATING CYLINDER,
DOUBLE ACTION

actuating cylinder, single-action:
Actuating cylinder in which one stroke is produced by pressurized fluid and the other stroke is produced by some other force, such as gravity or spring tension.

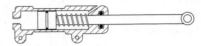

ACTUATING CYLINDER,
SINGLE ACTION

actuator:
A device that converts fluid pressure into mechanical force. The action may be linear, rotary, or oscillating.

acute angle:
An angle that is less than 90°.

AD:
1. See *Airworthiness Directive*

2. Ashless Dispersant. An additive for engine oil.

ADAS:
Aircraft Data Acquisition System

ADC:
Air Data Computer

ADF:
See *Automatic Direction Finder*

ADI system:
Anti Detonation Injection. A method of injecting alcohol into reciprocating engines with the intent of increasing power output without causing detonation.

adhesive:
A substance capable of holding two materials together by surface attachment. Adhesive can be in film, liquid, or paste form.

adiabatic:
Refers to airflow being compressed
without loss or gain of heat.

adiabatic lapse rate:
The decrease in temperature with
altitude when no heat is added
to or taken from the air. This is
normally 5.4°F per 1,000 feet.

adjacent:
The two sides of a triangle that
have a common angle.

adjustable reamer:
A reamer whose size may
be increased or decreased
by tightening or loosening a
centralized expansion screw.

adjustable stabilizer:
A type of horizontal stabilizer that
can be adjusted in flight to reduce
the control pressures needed by
the pilot.

ADMA:
Aviation Distributors and
Manufacturers Association

Administrator:
Federal Aviation Administrator
or any person to whom he has
delegated his authority in the
matter concerned. *(FAR 1)*

adsorption:
The process of one material
(liquid, solid, or gas) merging
with a second material by coating
and being retained on the surface
of the particles (and interstices) of
the second material as opposed
to absorption where the material
penetrates into the particles of the
second material.

**Advanced Cabin Entertainment
Service System (ACESS):**
Software-driven system that
controls and distributes passenger
audio and lighting. ACESS can
easily reconfigure cabin audio and
video signals to compensate for
changes in cabin configuration.
Older systems required changes
in system wiring and components.

advanced composites:
1. Composites made by embedding
   high strength and high-stiffness
   fibers (boron, graphite, and
   aramid) within an essentially
   uniform matrix (thermoset,
   thermoplastic). Advanced
   composites do not include metal
   matrix and ceramic.

2. Composite materials applicable
   to aerospace construction and
   made by embedding high-
   strength and/or high-modulus
   fibers within an essentially
   homogeneous matrix.

advancing blade:
A rotorcraft blade located in the
semicircular part of the rotor disc
where the blade direction is the
same as the direction of flight.

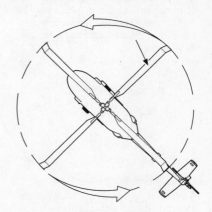

ADVANCING BLADE

advection:
A method of heat transfer by
horizontal movement of air.

adverse yaw:
A condition of flight in which
the nose of the airplane starts to
move in the direction opposite
of that in which the turn is being
made. This is caused by the
drag induced by the downward
deflected aileron (aileron drag).

advisory circular:
A publication of the FAA that is advisory in nature and contains clarification or supplemental information about a regulation or condition.

AEM:
Audio Entertainment Multiplexer

aerated:
Any fluid mixed with or exposed to air.

aerodynamic balance:
The portion of a control surface on an aircraft that extends ahead of the hinge line. This utilizes the airflow to aid in moving the surface.

aerodynamic blockage thrust reverser:
A type of thrust reverser that uses thin airfoils or obstructions placed in the gas stream. These are often called cascade type thrust reversers.

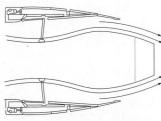

(FORWARD THRUST POSITION)

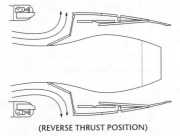

(REVERSE THRUST POSITION)

AERODYNAMIC BLOCKAGE
THRUST REVERSER

aerodynamic braking:
Generating aerodynamic drag by reversing the pitch of the propeller blades or ducting some of the engine exhaust forward to reduce the ground roll after landing.

aerodynamic coefficients:
Non-dimensional coefficients for aerodynamic forces and moments. *(FAR 1)*

aerodynamic drag:
Force that thrust must overcome to move an aircraft forward. Design can lessen aerodynamic drag through streamlining. Drag increases with increased speed.

aerodynamics:
Study of the forces of air acting on objects in motion relative to air.

aerodynamic twisting force:
The force that tries to twist a rotating airfoil to a higher blade angle. Aerodynamic twisting force is produced because the axis of rotation is at the chord line, but the center of lift is ahead of the chord line. This occurs in both helicopter blades and propellers. See *aerodynamic twisting moment.*

aerodynamic twisting moment:
The aerodynamic force that acts on a propeller blade to increase the blade angle.

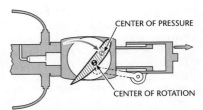

CENTER OF PRESSURE

CENTER OF ROTATION

AERODYNAMIC TWISTING FORCE

Aerofiche®:
The registered trade name for a form of microfiche used in the aircraft industry; 288 frames of information may be placed on a single 4x8 inch card.

Aeromatic® propeller:
A two-bladed, variable-pitch unit that is entirely self-contained. It incorporates a single-piece hub of

chrome-nickel-molybdenum steel and retains the blade flanges on large ball thrust bearings.

aeronautical fixed service:
A radio communication service between specified fixed points provided primarily for the safety of air navigation and for the regular, efficient and economical operation of air transport.

aeronautical fixed station:
A station in the aeronautical fixed service.

aeronautical mobile off-route service:
An aeronautical mobile service intended for communications, including those relating to flight coordination, primarily outside national or international civil air routes.

aeronautical mobile route (R) service:
An aeronautical mobile service reserved for communications relating to safety and regularity of flight, primarily along national or international civil air routes.

AFDS:
Autopilot Flight Director System (also A/P F/D)

AFOLTS:
Automatic Fire Overheat Logic Test System

after bottom center (ABC):
The number of degrees of crankshaft rotation after the piston has passed the bottom of its stroke.

afterburner:
An apparatus for augmenting the jet thrust of a gas-turbine engine, consisting essentially of a duct placed aft of the turbine, into which additional fuel is injected and burned in the presence of the uncombined oxygen in the gases from the turbine. Also called a *tailpipe burner* or *reheat*.

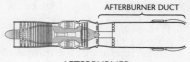

AFTERBURNER DUCT

AFTERBURNER

after cure:
Continuation of vulcanization after the desired cure is effected and the heat source removed.

afterfiring:
Occurs when charges of unburned fuel are present in the exhaust gases. Air from outside the exhaust stacks mixes with this unburned fuel causing it to ignite, which results in an explosion in the exhaust system. This often results when the fuel/air mixture is too rich. Sometimes called afterburning.

after top center (ATC):
The number of degrees of crankshaft rotation after the piston has passed the top of its stroke.

aft-fan engine:
A turbofan engine where the fan section is an extension of the turbine.

age hardening:
Increasing the hardness and possible strength of an alloy by a relatively low temperature heat treatment that causes precipitation of components or phases of the alloy from the supersaturated solid solution. Also known as *precipitation hardening*.

aging:
A metallurgical change in a metal alloy resulting in an increase in mechanical properties. This change can occur in some instances at room temperatures. More often its effects are increased by holding for specified lengths of time at elevated temperatures. Also known as *precipitation hardening*.

AGL:
Above ground level. *(FAR 1)*

aileron:
A primary control surface that extends from about the midpoint of the trailing edge of the wing outward towards the wing tip. They move in opposite directions to deflect airflow and create motion about the longitudinal axis.

AILERON

AIM:
Airman's Information Manual

AIMS:
Aircraft Information Management System

air bleed:
A small hole in the fuel passage between the float bowl and the discharge nozzle through which air is introduced into the liquid fuel. It serves as an aid in atomization.

Airborne Communications Addressing and Reporting System (ACARS):
A digital air/ground communications service. ACARS allows ground to aircraft communications (in a digital format) for operational flight information, such as fuel status, flight delays, gate changes, departure times and arrival times. ACARS can also be used to monitor certain engine and system parameters and downlink relevant maintenance data to the aircraft operator. ACARS can be thought of as e-mail for the aircraft. ACARS is an automatic system, transfer of information requires virtually no flight crew efforts.

air capacitor:
A capacitor that uses air as the dielectric.

air carrier:
A person who undertakes directly, by lease or other arrangement, to engage in air transportation. *(FAR 1)*

air commerce:
Interstate, overseas, or foreign air commerce or the transportation of mail by aircraft or any operation or navigation of aircraft within the limits of any Federal airway or any operation or navigation of aircraft which directly affects, or which may endanger safety in, interstate, overseas, or foreign air commerce. *(FAR 1)*

air-cooled engine:
A reciprocating engine that transfers its waste heat directly into the ambient air by means of cooling fins on the cylinders.

air-cooled turbine blades:
Hollow turbine blades that are cooled by passing compressor bleed air through them.

air cooling/quenching:
Cooling from an elevated temperature in air, still or forced.

air-core transformer:
A transformer composed of two or more coils that are wound around a nonmetallic core.

aircraft:
A device that is used or intended to be used for flight in the air. *(FAR 1)*

aircraft alteration:
The modification of an aircraft, its structure or components which changes its physical or flight characteristics. Alterations are classified as major or minor in accordance with guidelines

established in the Federal Aviation Regulations 14CFR Part 43, Appendix A.

aircraft basic operating weight:
The established basic weight of an aircraft available for flight without its fuel and payload.

aircraft dope:
A colloidal solution of cellulose acetate or nitrate, combined with plasticizers to produce a smooth, flexible, homogeneous film. On some aircraft this dope is used in conjunction with aircraft fabric to cover the structure.

aircraft engine:
An engine used or intended to be used for propelling aircraft, including turbosuperchargers, appurtenances, and accessories necessary for its functioning, but does not include propellers. *(FAR 1)*

Aircraft Listings:
FAA document containing information similar to that found on Type Certificate Data Sheets but applicable to aircraft, engines, etc. that have fewer than fifty listed on the Federal registry.

aircraft log:
A record containing the operational or maintenance history of an aircraft.

aircraft operating weight:
The basic weight of the aircraft plus the weight of crewmembers, equipment, fuel, oil and passengers.

aircraft quality:
Denotes stock of sufficient quality to be forged into highly stressed parts for aircraft or other critical applications. Such materials are of extremely high quality, requiring closely controlled, restrictive practices in their manufacture.

aircraft records:
Documentation of flight time, as well as maintenance that has been performed on an aircraft, its engines and components.

aircraft repair:
Restoring an aircraft, engine or component to a condition of airworthiness after a failure, damage, or wear has occurred.

aircraft rigging:
The adjustment and alignment of the various components of an aircraft to ensure proper operation and aerodynamic characteristics.

aircraft specification:
Documentation that includes the pertinent specification for an aircraft certificated under the Civil Aviation Authority (CAA).

aircraft structural integrity program (ASIP):
A program applied to an aircraft system to improve design, diagnose possible structural failures, give a basis for corrective action, and predict operational life expectancy of the system.

air cycle cooling system:
A simple system that creates air for cabin cooling by passing high pressure engine bleed air through an air-to-air heat exchanger, and then extracting work from this air by passing it through an expansion turbine. This extraction of work removes energy from the air and results in a significant drop in temperature. The cool air may then be used for cabin climate control.

air data computer (ADC):
A system that monitors pitot pressure, static pressure and air temperature to determine various parameters, such as airspeed, altitude, and vertical climb

air density:
The density of the air in terms of mass per unit volume. Dense air has more molecules per unit volume than less dense air. The density of air decreases with altitude above the surface of

the earth and with increasing temperature.

airfoil:
Any surface such as an airplane wing, rudder, aileron, aircraft propeller, or helicopter rotor blade designed to obtain reaction from the air through which it moves.

airframe:
The fuselage, booms, nacelles, cowlings, fairings, air-foil surfaces (including rotors but excluding propellers and rotating airfoils of engines), and landing gear of an aircraft and their accessories and controls. *(FAR 1)*

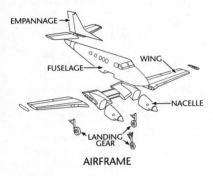

AIRFRAME

air-fuel ratio:
The ratio of air to fuel in an aircraft engine; 15 parts air to 1 part fuel by weight is the typical mixture burned in the combustion chamber.

air gap igniter:
A turbine engine igniter using an air gap, similar to a spark plug, to initiate combustion.

air hardening:
An alloy that does not require quenching from a high temperature to harden. Hardening of the material occurs simply by cooling in air from above critical temperature. The term refers only to the ability of the material to harden in air and does not imply any definite analysis or composition.

air inlet:
Large, smooth aluminum duct to conduct the air into the compressor.

airless painting:
The application of paint without the use of any atomizing air.

Airloc fastener:
A patented form of cowling fastener. Locking action is accomplished by turning a steel pin in a spring steel receptacle.

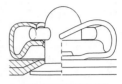

AIRLOC FASTENER

airman:
Any person involved in flying, maintaining or operating aircraft.

air-maze filter:
A type of induction filter that cleans the air by passing it through a series of baffles and turns. Often made of a flock- type material mounted on screens and moistened with oil. Also, in engine oil systems a filter that contains a series of round, fine-meshed screens mounted on a hollow shaft.

air metering force:
One of the forces used in Bendix pressure carburetors and Precision Airmotive fuel injection systems in which venturi and ram air pressures control the amount of fuel metered.

airplane:
An engine-driven fixed-wing aircraft heavier than air that is supported in flight by the dynamic reaction of the air against its wings. *(FAR 1)*

airport:
An area of land or water that is

used or intended to be used for the landing and takeoff of aircraft, and includes its buildings and facilities, if any. *(FAR 1)*

air scoop:
A specifically designed scoop or duct used to conduct air to the fuel metering device and intake manifold of a reciprocating engine induction system.

air seal:
A seal around a rotating shaft designed to keep air from passing out of the housing that holds the shaft. In turbine engines it is usually used to reduce airflow leakage between the gas path and the internal engine or over the blade tips.

airship:
An engine-driven lighter-than-air aircraft that can be steered. *(FAR 1)*

airspeed boom:
A pole or tube extending from a wing or fuselage into the airflow in which instruments are located for measuring airspeed.

airspeed indicator:
A special type of differential pressure gauge designed to compare the impact air pressure and the static air pressure and indicate the speed at which the aircraft is moving through the air.

AIRSPEED INDICATOR

air start:
The process of starting an aircraft engine in flight.

air traffic:
Aircraft operating in the air or on an airport surface, exclusive of loading ramps and parking areas. *(FAR 1)*

air traffic clearance:
An authorization by air traffic control, for the purpose of preventing collision between known aircraft, for an aircraft to proceed under specified traffic conditions within controlled airspace. *(FAR 1)*

air traffic control:
A service operated by appropriate authority to promote the safe, orderly, and expeditious flow of air traffic. *(FAR 1)*

air traffic service route (ATS):
A specified route designated for channeling the flow of traffic as necessary for the provision of air traffic services. The term ATS route refers to a variety of airways, including jet routes, area navigation (RNAV) routes, and arrival and departure routes. An ATS route is defined by route specifications, which may include:

1. An ATS route designator.

2. The path to or from significant points.

3. Distance between significant points.

4. Reporting requirements.

5. The lowest safe altitude determined by the appropriate authority. *(FAR 1)*

air transportation:
Interstate, overseas, or foreign air transportation or the transportation of mail by aircraft. *(FAR 1)*

air turbine starter:
Axial-flow turbine that turns a drive coupling through a reduction gear train and a starter-clutch mechanism. The air to operate an air turbine starter is supplied from either a ground-

operated compressor, the bleed air from another engine or an Auxiliary power unit (APU).

airworthiness certificate:
A certificate issued by the FAA to aircraft that meet the minimum standards for airworthiness as specified in the appropriate regulations.

Airworthiness Directive (AD):
A regulatory notice published by the FAA to notify aircraft owners and subscribers of an unsafe condition. Compliance is mandatory and will be detailed in the text of the AD.

airworthy:
The condition of an FAA Certificated aircraft, engine or component that meets all of the requirements of its original certification.

Alclad:
Coating used on aluminum products that are sometimes coated on one or both surfaces with a metallurgically bonded, thin layer of pure aluminum or aluminum alloy. Specifically for Alclad coating, the combination of core and cladding alloys is selected so that the cladding is anodic to the core. Also designed for corrosion protection.

alert area:
An alert area is established to inform pilots of a specific area wherein a high volume of pilot training or an unusual type of aeronautical activity is conducted. *(FAR 1)*

algorithm:
A specific procedure for solving mathematical problems.

alkali:
A chemical substance, usually the hydroxide of a metal. It has a characteristically bitter taste, and is prone to react with an acid to form a salt.

alkaline cell:
A battery cell that uses potassium hydroxide as its electrolyte.

alkyd resin:
One of the major synthetics formed by polybasic acid reaction with polybasic alcohols. Primarily used for enamels but also in combinations in other types of coatings.

Allen head bolt:
An internal wrenching bolt with a hexagonal hollow in the head.

ALLEN HEAD BOLT

alligator clip:
A spring-loaded clip with a long tapered jaw characterized by rows of jagged teeth. These are generally associated with the temporary attachment of test leads.

alligatoring:
A condition where cracks in the film are caused by contraction of the coating when a sudden change in temperature occurs during drying. It may also occur because of insufficient drying time between lacquer coats, or because of poor penetration or wetting, or when a hard topcoat has been applied over a soft undercoat.

allowance:
The prescribed difference in dimensions of mating parts to provide a certain class of fit.

alloy steel:
A mixture with metallic properties composed of two or more elements of which at least one is a metal. However, a metal is not designated an "alloy" based on elements

incidental to its manufacture. For example, iron, carbon, manganese, silicon, phosphorus, sulfur, oxygen, nitrogen and hydrogen are incidental to the manufacture of plain carbon steel. It does not become an "alloy steel" until the elements are increased beyond regular composition or until other elements (metal) are added in significant amounts for a specific purpose.

alloying agent:
An element added to a metal to create a desired change in its properties.

all-weather spark plug:
A spark plug in which the ceramic insulator is recessed into the shell so that a resilient cigarette on the ignition harness can be installed in such manner as to provide a watertight seal. The plugs may be identified by the ¾ - 20 threads where the lead attaches.

Alnico:
An iron alloy containing aluminum (AL), nickel (NI), and cobalt (CO). This material exhibits an extraordinary ability to retain magnetism and is used in the manufacture of permanent magnets.

Alodine®:
A registered trade name of Amchem Products, Inc., for a conversion coating chemical that forms a hard, unbroken aluminum oxide film, chemically deposited on a piece of aluminum alloy. Alodining serves the same function as anodizing, but does not require an electrolytic bath. It conforms to specification MIL-C-5541B.

alphanumeric:
Consisting of letters and numbers.

alpha particles:
1. A positively charged particle emitted by certain radioactive materials. It is made up of two neutrons and two protons;

hence it is identical with the nucleus of a helium atom.
2. Positively charged particles composed of two protons and neutrons (often referred to simply as *helium atom nuclei*) and characterized by limited penetration.

alpha range of operation:
The governing or flight range of propeller operation. This extends from the flight-idle position to the takeoff position.

ALS:
Approach light system. *(FAR 1)*

ALT:
1. Altitude
2. Alternate

ALT HOLD:
Altitude Hold (usually a function on an autopilot system)

alteration:
A change in the configuration or design of an aircraft, engine or component.

alternate airport:
An airport at which an aircraft may land if a landing at the intended airport becomes inadvisable. *(FAR 1)*

alternate air source:
A selectable second source for the air necessary for the operation of an aircraft system. This is commonly seen as an alternate source of static air for the pitot-static system, and an alternate source of induction air for engine combustion. Generally, these systems provide a backup in icing conditions.

alternating current (AC):
An electrical current that constantly changes amplitude, and periodically changes direction.

alternation:
One half of the cycle of alternating current.

alternator:

Common term for a special type of generator in which alternating current electricity is generated in the fixed windings and is converted to direct current by solid-state rectifying diodes. Used on light aircraft, ground equipment and automobiles.

altimeter:

Any of various types of instruments for measuring altitude. Specifically, an instrument similar to an aneroid barometer that utilizes the change of atmospheric pressure with altitude to indicate the approximate elevation above a given point or plane used as a reference.

ALTIMETER

altitude:

The vertical distance of an aircraft or object above a given reference, such as ground or sea level.

altitude engine:

A reciprocating aircraft engine having a rated takeoff power that is producible from sea level to an established higher altitude.

altitude sickness:

Illness caused by lack of oxygen in thin air above 6,000 ft. The symptoms are headache, nausea, vomiting and trouble sleeping.

aluminum alloy:

A physical mixture of metals in which aluminum is the base and other metals are added for specific characteristics.

aluminum ore:

Most commonly bauxite, it is plentiful and occurs mainly in tropical and sub-tropical areas: Africa, the West Indies, South America and Australia. There are also some deposits in Europe. Bauxite is refined into aluminum oxide trihydrate (alumina) and then electrolytically reduced into metallic aluminum.

aluminum paste:

Extremely small flakes of aluminum metal suspended in a vehicle and used to make aluminum dope, which is applied over clear dope to exclude the ultraviolet rays of the sun.

aluminum wool:

Shavings of aluminum metal formed into a pad. This product can be used to remove corrosion from aluminum alloy parts, and to smooth out minor scratches in aluminum parts.

AM:

See *Amplitude Modulation*

amalgamate:

To form an alloy with mercury.

ambient:

Surrounding, adjacent to, or next to. For example, ambient conditions are physical conditions of the immediate area such as ambient temperature, ambient humidity, ambient pressure, etc.

AMC:

See *Automatic Mixture Control*

American Wire Gauge (AWG):

The standard adopted in the United States for the measurement of wire size.

ammeter:

An instrument for measuring the amount of electron flow (in amperes).

ampere:

This is the unit of electrical current. One ampere is the current that flows through a conductor having a resistance of one ohm, at a potential of one volt.

ampere-hour capacity:
A rating of the capacity of a battery. One ampere-hour is the product of the current flow in amps, multiplied by the length of time, in hours, that the battery can supply this current. A five hour standard is common.

ampere turn:
A measure of magnetomotive force (MMF) of an electromagnet. This is the force produced when one amp of current flows through one turn of wire in a coil. One ampere turn is equal to 1.26 gilberts.

amphibian (amphibious aircraft):
An airplane designed to take off and land on either water or land.

amplifier:
The device that provides amplification (the increase in current, voltage, or power of a signal) without appreciably altering the original signal.

amplitude:
The size of a signal as measured from a reference line to a maximum value above or below the line. Generally used to describe voltage, current, or power.

amplitude modulation (AM):
Any method of varying the amplitude of an electromagnetic carrier frequency in accordance with the information to be transmitted.

AMT:
Aviation maintenance technician

AN:
Air Force/Navy (standard or specification).

anaerobic resin:
A single-component polyester resin that hardens when all air is restricted from it.

analog:
A physical variable that keeps a fixed relationship with another variable as it changes.

AND gate:
A binary circuit with two or more inputs and a single output in which the output is a logic 1 only when all inputs are a logic 1. The output is a logic 0 when any one of the inputs is a logic 0.

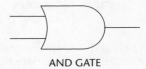

AND GATE

anemometer:
Instrument used to measure the speed of wind.

aneroid:
A sealed flexible container that expands or contracts in relation to the surrounding air pressure. Used in altimeters and other pressure measuring instruments.

angle of attack:
Acute angle measured between the chord of an airfoil and the relative wind.

angle-of-attack system:
Consists of an airstream direction detector (transmitter), and an indicator located on the instrument panel. The airstream direction detector contains the sensing element that measures local airflow direction relative to the true angle of attack by determining the angular difference between local airflow and the fuselage reference plane. The sensing element operates in conjunction with a servo-driven balanced bridge circuit that converts probe positions into electrical signals.

angle of incidence:
The angle between the chord line of the wing and the longitudinal axis of the airplane.

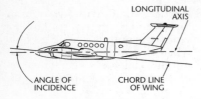

ANGLE OF INCIDENCE

angstrom:
Unit of length usually reserved for the expression of wavelength. One Angstrom equals 10^{-8} cm. Under the standard system of units, the Angstrom will be replaced by the nanometer (1.0 A = 0.10 nm). This is the standard unit for measuring wavelengths of light.

anhedral:
The downward or negative slope of the wing.

anhydrous:
Containing no water.

anion:
A negatively charged ion, especially the ion that migrates to an anode in electrolysis.

anneal:
The controlled heating and cooling of a metal to remove stresses and to make it softer and easier to work with.

annual inspection:
An inspection performed once each twelve calendar months to determine if an aircraft is airworthy.

annular combustor:
Two-part combustion chamber made up of an annular liner and a housing assembly. Used with axial-flow and dual compressors.

annunciator panel:
Electrically controlled signal board or indicator.

anode:
The positive electrode of an electrochemical device toward which negative ions are drawn.

anodizing:
The formation of a hard oxide film on the surface of aluminum alloys by an electrolytic process. Anodizing protects against corrosion and forms a good base for primers.

antenna:
A conductor or set of conductors used to radiate radio frequency energy into space or to collect radio frequency energy from space, or both.

antenna coupler:
A device used for impedance matching between an antenna and a transmitter or receiver.

anti-collision light:
A safety light used to warn other aircraft, especially in congested areas. Frequently referred to as a rotating beacon, because of the construction and operation of the most common type. These lights may also utilize high energy strobes or other new technologies. They are usually installed on the top (or bottom, if two are installed) of the aft fuselage, or on top of the vertical stabilizer. All airplanes certified for night flight must have at least one.

ANTI-COLLISION LIGHT

antifreeze:
Ethylene glycol. A type of alcohol added to a liquid (usually water) to lower the freezing point.

antifriction bearings:
Ball or roller bearings that have a very low drag quality.

16

A

antiglare paint:
Flat black or dark paint applied to surfaces to prevent glare from interfering with the function of the flight crew.

anti-icing:
Preventing the formation of ice on aircraft surfaces.

anti-knock rating:
The rating of gasoline that refers to its ability to resist detonation.

antiseize compound:
A silicon-based, high-temperature lubricant applied to threaded components to aid in their removal after they have been subjected to rapid heating and cooling.

anti-servo tab:
An adjustable tab on the trailing edge of a control surface. It moves in the same direction as the primary control.

anti-skid system:
A system of controls for the aircraft brakes that senses wheel motion and acts to prevent lock up or skidding.

anti-tear strips:
Strips of fabric of the same material the airplane is covered with, laid over the wing rib under the reinforcing tape.

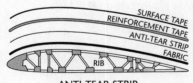

ANTI-TEAR STRIP

anti-torque pedals:
The foot pedals that are used to control the pitch of the anti-torque rotor on the tail of a single-rotor helicopter.

AOA:
1. Angle-of-attack.
2. Airport Operations Area.

AOPA:
Aircraft Owners and Pilots Association

APC:
Absolute pressure controller

APCDU:
APU Power Conversion and Distribution Units

API:
American Petroleum Institute

API Scale:
A scale developed by the American Petroleum Institute to measure the specific gravity of a liquid.

apparent power:
In an AC circuit it is the simple product of the voltage and current, and is expressed in volt-amps.

appliance:
Any instrument, mechanism, equipment, part, apparatus, appurtenance, or accessory, including communications equipment, that is used or intended to be used in operating or controlling an aircraft in flight, is installed in or attached to the aircraft, and is not part of an airframe, engine, or propeller. *(FAR 1)*

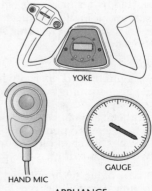

YOKE

HAND MIC

GAUGE

APPLIANCE

applicability:
Something that applies to and / or affects another.

approved:
1. A technician has approved or stated that the aircraft has met all applicable airworthiness requirements and is ready for flight.

2. Information is approved by the FAA such as found on the back of the Form 337.

3. Unless used with reference to another person, refers to being approved by the Administrator. *(FAR 1)*

approved inspection system:
A maintenance program consisting of the inspection and maintenance necessary to maintain an aircraft in airworthy condition.

APU:
See *Auxiliary Power Unit*

approved parts:
Those parts produced by an aircraft manufacturer in accordance with its specifications, produced by a sub-contractor for the manufacturer and carrying a manufacturer's part number, manufactured by a third party under a Parts Manufacturing Approval (PMA) or Technical Standard Order (TSO) or fabricated by an air carrier with the authorization to produce the part to the manufacturer's specifications.

aramid:
1. A manufactured fiber in which the fiber-forming substance consists of a long-chain synthetic aromatic polyamide with at least 85 percent of the linkages attached directly to two aromatic rings.

2. A type of highly oriented organic material derived from polyamide (nylon) but incorporating aromatic ring structure. Kevlar® and Nomex are examples of aramids.

arbor press:
A hand-operated machine tool designed for applying high pressure for the purpose of pressing together or removing parts.

ARBOR PRESS

Archimedes' Principle:
Idea that the buoyant force that a fluid exerts upon a submerged body is equal to the weight of the fluid the body displaces.

arc welding:
A group of welding processes in which fusion is obtained by heating with an electric arc or arcs, with or without the use of filler metal.

area:
The surface of anything; the measure of its extent.

area navigation (R-NAV):
A method of navigation that permits aircraft operations on any desired course within the coverage of station-referenced navigation signals or within the limits of self-contained system capability. *(FAR 1)*

area navigation route (R-NAV route):
An ATS route based on R-NAV that can be used by suitably equipped aircraft.

ARINC:
1. Aeronautical Radio Incorporated.

2. One of the two major corporations that provide ACARS services worldwide. It is a global corporation based in the United States with primary stockholders consisting of various U.S. and international airlines and aircraft operators. It also provides services and standards related to a variety of aviation communication and navigation systems.

ARINC 629:
Also called *629*.

A digital data bus format that permits up to 120 receiver/transmitters to share a bidirectional serial data bus.

arm:
The distance, in inches, from the datum to the item being considered in a weight and balance calculation.

armature:
1. In a relay, the movable portion of the relay.
2. The windings in which the output voltage is generated in a generator or in which input current creates a magnetic field that interacts with the main field in a motor.

armature losses:
Copper losses, eddy current losses, and hysteresis losses that act to decrease the efficiency of armatures.

armature reaction:
The effect in a DC generator of current in the armature creating a magnetic field that distorts the main field and causes a shift in the neutral plane.

armed:
The condition in which a device is ready for actuation.

armed forces:
The Army, Navy, Air Force, Marine Corps, and Coast Guard, including their regular and reserve components and members serving without component status. *(FAR 1)*

aromatics:
An organic chemical possessing the benzene ring structure. Benzene, toluol andxylol are typical aromatic hydro-carbons.

articulated rotor:
A helicopter rotor in which each blade is connected to the hub in such a manner that it is able to move up and down, back and forth, and change its pitch angle.

articulating rod:
A link rod that connects the pistons in a radial engine to the master rod.

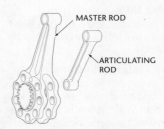

ARTICULATING ROD

artificial aging:
This process involves solution heat treating an aluminum alloy and then holding it at an elevated temperature for a specified length of time to increase its strength. Also called *precipitation heat treating*.

artificial feel:
A type of force feedback system used with some fly-by-wire flight control systems. This system produces an opposition to the movement of the control that is proportional to the aerodynamic loads acting on the control surface.

ARTS:
Automated Radar Terminal System

as cast:
Condition of a casting as it leaves the mold with no heat treatment.

as forged:
The condition of a forging as it comes out of the finisher cavity without any subsequent operations.

ashless dispersant oil (AD):
A mineral oil with additives that is used as a lubricant in aircraft reciprocating engines. Ashless dispersant oil does not contain any metallic ash-forming ingredients. The additives will keep contaminants that form in the oil in suspension so that they will not join together and clog the oil filters.

aspect ratio:
Ratio of the span to the chord of the airfoil (span divided by chord).

Asp® Fastener System:
This assembly consists of a pin, threaded sleeve, and a locking collar. ASP® stands for Adjustable clamping force, Self-sustaining, Positive lock. Their primary use is in assemblies where common fasteners might crush softcore panels and fastener clamp-up tension must be limited. A sleeve driver is used to install and torque the collar and the specified puller is used to set the locking collar and break the pintail.

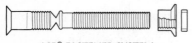

ASP® FASTENER SYSTEM

asphaltum:
A bituminous or tar-based material sometimes used as a coating on battery boxes.

ASR:
Airport surveillance radar. *(FAR 1)*

ASRS:
Aviation Safety Reporting System. Aviation incident reporting system run by NASA for FAA.

assembly drawing:
A drawing that shows a group of parts in the same relationship that they will have when they are assembled.

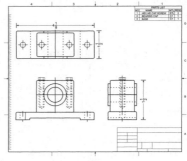

ASSEMBLY DRAWING

assigned frequency band:
The frequency band within which the emission of a station is authorized.

astable multi-vibrator:
A multi-vibrator that has no stable state. Also called *free-running* because it alternates between two different output voltage levels during the time it is on. The frequency is determined by the RC time constant of the coupling circuit.

A-stage:
1. An early stage in the reaction of thermosetting resins in which the material is still soluble in certain liquids and may be liquid or capable of becoming liquid upon heating. Sometimes referred to as resol.

2. An early stage in the polymerization reaction of certain thermosetting resins (especially phenolics) in which the material is still linear in structure, soluble in some liquids and fusible.

A

ASTM (Specifications):
The American Society for Testing and Materials.

as welded:
The condition of weld metal, welded joints, and weldments after welding and prior to any subsequent thermal, mechanical, or chemical treatments.

ATA:
1. Air Transport Association

   a. An organization that represents airlines, aircraft manufacturers, and various system manufactures in an effort to ensure uniformity in various facets of the aviation industry

2. Actual Time of Arrival.

ATA specification:
The standardized format for aircraft maintenance manuals developed by the Airline Transport Association.

ATC:
Air Traffic Control. A generic term for a joint civil/military system for controlling traffic within a specific area. *(FAR 1)*

ATHR:
Auto Thrust System

ATIS:
Automatic Terminal Information Service. Recorded voice message that provides weather and airport services.

atmospheric pressure:
The pressure due to the weight of the earth's atmosphere. One standard atmosphere equals 14 p.s.i.

ATN:
Aeronautical Telecommunications Network. The collection of ground subnetworks, air/ground subnetworks and airborne subnetworks interconnected by ATN routers that support computer-to-computer, inter-network communication and message transfer between host computers using the OSI ISO protocol architecture.

atom:
The smallest particle of an element that can exist alone or in combination.

atomic number:
An integer that expresses the positive charge of the nucleus in multiples of the fundamental electronic charge. In present theory, it is the number of protons in the nucleus.

atomic weight:
The relative weight of the atom of an element, referred to some element taken as a standard. An atomic weight of 16 for oxygen is the one usually adopted as a basis for reference.

ATP:
Airline Transport Pilot

ATS:
Automatic Throttle System

attenuation:
Reduction or division of signal amplitude while retaining the characteristic waveform. It implies deliberately throwing away or discarding a part of the signal energy for the sake of reduced amplitude.

attitude gyro:
An instrument that senses an aircraft's pitching and rolling movements about the lateral and longitudinal axes.

ATTITUDE GYRO

augmenter tube:
See *exhaust augmenter*

aural warning system:
A bell or horn that alerts the
pilot to an abnormal situation.
This may be a part of the takeoff,
landing, pressurization, speed,
fire, or crew calling systems.

austenite:
A solid solution of iron carbide
in gamma iron. It forms when
the metal solidifies and remains
a solution until it cools to about
1350°F (732°C). Addition of
certain alloying elements such as
nickel and manganese preserves
austenite below 0°F (17°C).

autoclave:
A closed vessel for producing an
environment of fluid pressure,
with or without heat, to an
enclosed object that is undergoing
a chemical reaction or other
operation.

autoclave molding:
A process similar to the pressure
bag technique. The lay up is
covered by a pressure bag, and
the entire assembly is placed in
an autoclave capable of providing
heat and pressure for curing the
part. The pressure bag is normally
vented to the outside.

auto-feather:
A portion of the propeller control
system that will cause the
propeller to feather automatically
if the engine is shut down in
flight.

autogyro:
A rotary-wing aircraft whose rotor
is turned throughout its flight
by air forces resulting from the
motion of the craft through the air
with lift over the rotor equalized
by vertical oscillation (flapping)
of the sustaining airfoils. Forward
propulsion is independent of the
rotor.

AUTOGYRO

auto-lean:
A lean mixture whose air/fuel
ratio is maintained automatically
by a sensing mechanism in the
carburetor.

automatic adjusters:
A portion of the return system of
a brake that maintains a constant
clearance between the disk and
the linings when the brake is
released.

automatic direction finder (ADF):
A type of radio compass which
when properly tuned to a radio
transmitting station automatically
indicates the direction of the
station in relation to the heading
of the aircraft. The automatic
direction finder is sometimes
called an automatic radio compass
or radio compass.

**automatic flight control system
(AFCS):**
A system that couples the
automatic pilot to the radio
navigation and approach
equipment.

**automatic frequency control
(AFC):**
A radio receiver circuit that keeps
the receiver tuned to the desired
frequency within design limits.

automatic gain control (AGC):
A circuit used to vary radar
receiver gain for best reception of
signals that have widely varying
amplitudes.

automatic mixture control (AMC):
A device actuated by air density
that controls the fuel-air mixture
ratio.

automatic reset circuit breaker:
A circuit protection device that will open the circuit when a current overload occurs, and when the overload is no longer present it will reset itself automatically.

automatic volume control (AVC):
A circuit used to limit variations in the output signal strength of a receiver.

autoration:
A rotorcraft flight condition in which the lifting rotor is driven entirely by action of the air when the rotorcraft is in motion.

auto-rich:
A rich mixture whose air/fuel ratio is maintained automatically by a sensing mechanism in the carburetor.

autosyn:
A type of remote indicating system using an electromagnet powered by 3-phase AC power.

autotransformer:
A special type of transformer in which the output voltage can be easily varied.

auxiliary flight surfaces:
Lift modifying devices such as flaps, slots, and slats.

auxiliary power unit (APU):
A self-contained power unit used to provide electrical and/or pneumatic power for aircraft use.

auxiliary rotor:
A rotor that serves either to counteract the effect of the main rotor torque on a rotorcraft or to maneuver the rotorcraft about one or more of its three principal axes.

availability:
The capability of the GPS system to be used for navigation whenever it is needed, and the ability to provide that service throughout the entire flight.

AVGAS:
Aviation Gasoline. It consists almost entirely of hydrocarbons, namely compounds consisting of hydrogen and carbon. Some impurities in the form of sulphur and dissolved water will also be present. This gasoline is used in virtually all reciprocating engines.

aviation shears (snips):
Compound-action hand shears for cutting sheet metal. Normally sold as a set of three. One for cutting left, one for cutting right, and one for cutting straight. Also called *Dutchman Shears*.

aviator's breathing oxygen:
Oxygen that meets Federal Specification BB-0-925A, Grade A, or its equivalent, and is used in aircraft breathing oxygen systems.

avionics:
Aviation electronics

avionics standard communication bus (ASCB):
A bidirectional data bus operating at 0.667 MHz.

Avogadro's principle:
A principle of physics that states that under equal pressure and temperature, equal volumes of all gases will contain equal numbers of molecules.

AWAS:
Automated Weather Advisory Station

AWG:
See *American Wire Gauge*

awl:
Sharp pointed tool used to make holes in soft materials such as leather, wood or plastic.

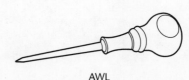

AWL

axial:
In the same direction as the shaft centerline.

axial-centrifugal flow compressor:
A combination axial and centrifugal compressor. Usually they are constructed so that the axial stages are at the front and the centrifugal portion is at the rear. This is a popular design for turboprop engines and APUs.

axial flow compressor:
A rotary compressor having intervening rows or stages of rotary and stationary blades, through which the movement or flow of fluid is substantially parallel to the rotor's axis of rotation.

axial load:
A load on a bearing that acts parallel to the shaft supported in the bearing. Axial loads are generally carried by ball bearings or tapered roller bearings.

axial piston pump:
The cylinder bores lie parallel to, and are evenly spaced around, the pump axis. The piston pump is then called an axial piston pump.

azimuth:
1. Horizontal direction or bearing, as in, to find the azimuth (of something).

2. Navigation. The horizontal direction of a celestial body with respect to a terrestrial reference direction, usually measured clockwise from a northern reference direction through 360°.

3. A vertical plane as in, to establish a flight path in azimuth, or the stability of a rotor blade in azimuth.

4. The measure of azimuth, i.e., azimuth angle.

5. Angular measurement in the horizontal plane in a clockwise direction.

Bb

babbit:
An antifriction metal alloy used for bearing inserts; made of tin, antimony, lead, and copper.

back drilling:
Drilling of a hole from the back of the sheet. Drilling rivets from the shop head side when it is not possible to drill the head.

backfire:
1. A burning or explosion in the cylinder of a reciprocating engine when the fuel/air mixture in the induction system is ignited by gases that are still burning inside the cylinder when the intake valve opens.

2. The momentary backward flow of the gases at the tip of a welding torch that causes the flame to go out. This may be caused by overheating the tip, touching the tip to the work, or by incorrect operating pressure.

backhand welding:
A welding technique in which the flame is directed towards the completed weld.

backing plate:
A reinforcing plate for a sheet metal repair, a doubler.

backlash:
1. In an aircraft control system, a looseness or play in the linkage between the cockpit controls and the control surfaces or the cockpit controls and a mechanical feel system.

2. The lost motion between two machine parts that transmit motion one to the other, such as between gear teeth, or lead screw and nut.

back pressure:
Pressure caused by the exhaust system of a reciprocating engine that opposes the evacuation of the burned gases from the cylinders.

backsaw:
A wood cutting saw with a stiffened back and fine teeth. The stiff back helps make straight cuts.

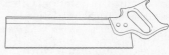

BACKSAW

back suction mixture control:
A type of float carburetor mixture control. The fuel-air ratio is controlled by varying the air pressure above the fuel in the carburetor float bowl.

backswept wing:
See *swept back wing*

backup ring:
An anti-extrusion device consisting of a ring of relatively hard and tough material placed in the gland between the O-ring and the groove sidewalls to prevent extrusion of the O-ring.

back voltage:
Counter electro-motive force (CEMF) generated in a conductor by the action of changing lines of flux across that conductor.

BAe:
British Aerospace. An aircraft manufacturer.

baffle:
1. A plate, wall, or the like in a fuel tank or other liquid container used especially to prevent sloshing of the contents.

2. A plate or wall, as around an air-cooled engine, to direct, deflect, or retard the flow of air for cooling.

bagging:
Applying an impermeable layer of film over an uncured part and sealing edges so that a vacuum can be drawn.

bag side:
The side of the part that is cured against the vacuum bag.

Bakelite:
A phenol resin manufactured by the Bakelite Corporation. Often used as electrical insulation.

balance:
A state of equilibrium when all the positive and negative moments are equal.

balance cable:
The cable linking the up side of both ailerons together.

balanced actuator:
A hydraulic or pneumatic actuator having the same area on both sides of the piston.

balanced construction:
Equal parts of warp and fill in fiber fabric.

balanced control surface:
A primary control surface with an overhang ahead of the hinge line to provide an aerodynamic assist to help the pilot in moving the control.

balanced design:
In filament-wound reinforced plastics, a winding pattern so designed that the stresses in all filaments are equal.

balanced laminate:
A composite laminate in which all laminae at angles other than 0° and 90° occur only in ± pairs (not necessarily adjacent) and are symmetrical around the centerline.

balanced-type relief valve:
A type of relief valve that balances system pressure against preset spring pressure to relieve excess system pressure.

balance point:
Point at which the nose-heavy moments and the tail-heavy moments are of equal magnitude. This point may also be known as center of gravity.

balancing tab:
A tab so linked that when the control surface to which it is attached is deflected the tab is deflected in an opposite direction, creating a force that aids in moving the larger surface. Sometimes called a geared tab.

ballast:
Any substance (usually sand or water) put aboard an airship or balloon to help stabilize it or to afford a means of altitude control. Any substance, object, or accumulation of objects used to weight an airplane, rocket, etc., so as to achieve a desired trim or balance in flight. Ballast is sometimes used in test flights in place of passengers, cargo, etc.

ball bearing:
A bearing assembly consists of grooved inner and outer races, one or more sets of balls and, in bearings designed for disassembly, a bearing retainer. They are used for supercharger impeller shaft bearings and rocker arm bearings in some engines. Special deep-groove ball bearings are used in aircraft engines to transmit propeller thrust to the engine nose section.

ball check valve:
A valve used in fluid systems to allow flow in one direction only. It generally utilizes a spring loaded steel ball and seat. Fluid flowing in one direction will overcome spring pressure and force the ball off of its seat, allowing flow. Fluid in the opposite direction will be blocked by the ball, which is firmly seated by the spring.

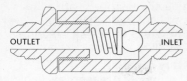

BALL CHECK VALVE

ball joint:
A flexible expansion joint used in exhaust systems to allow small amounts of movement.

balloon:
A lighter-than-air aircraft that is not engine driven, and that sustains flight through the use of either gas buoyancy or an airborne heater. *(FAR 1)*

ball peen hammer:
A hammer with one side of its head shaped like a ball.

balun:
A type of transformer used to match a balanced antenna to an unbalanced transmission line.

band-pass filter:
A filter that allows a narrow band of frequencies to pass through the circuit. It rejects or attenuates frequencies that are either higher or lower than the desired band of frequencies.

band-reject filter:
A filter that rejects a specific band of frequencies while allowing those above and below that band to pass.

bandwidth:
1. In electronic communications, bandwidth is the width of a band or continuous group of frequencies. It is expressed in terms of the difference between the highest frequency signal component and the lowest frequency signal component.

2. In computer networks, bandwidth is the amount of data that can be carried from one point to another in a given time period (usually one second). It is usually expressed in bits per second (bps) or occasionally in bytes per second (Bps).

bank:
A flight maneuver in which one wing points toward the ground and the other to the sky.

bank indicator:
See *inclinometer*

bar:
A section hot rolled from a billet to a form, such as round, hexagonal, octagonal, square or rectangular, with sharp or rounded corners or edges, with a cross-sectional area of less than 16 square inches.

bar folder:
A folding machine used to make bends or folds along the edge of metal sheets.

bare conductor:
An electrical conductor that is not protected by insulation.

barometer:
An instrument that measures the pressure of the atmosphere.

barometric pressure:
Atmospheric pressure.

barrel:
The cylinder, excluding the cylinder head, of a reciprocating engine.

base earth station:
An earth station in the fixed-satellite service or, in some cases, in the land mobile-satellite service.

base metal:
The metal to be welded or cut. In alloys it is the metal present in the largest proportion.

baseball stitch:
An FAA-approved hand-sewn seam used to join two pieces of fabric that butt together but do not overlap.

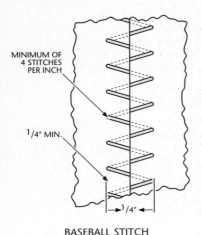

MINIMUM OF 4 STITCHES PER INCH

1/4" MIN.

1/4"

BASEBALL STITCH

base station:
A land station in the land mobile service.

basic weight:
A weight determined by the manufacturer. It typically consists of weighing every tenth aircraft prior to adding any optional equipment.

basswood:
Satisfactory low-density species of wood for use in plywood and for filler blocks and corner blocks. It is light in weight, low in strength, straight-grained, easily workable and can be nailed without splitting. The heartwood of basswood is creamy brown, and the sapwood is creamy white. Basswood has a slight, characteristic odor, even when dry.

bastard file:
A standard coarse cut file.

battery:
A device for converting chemical energy into electrical energy.

battery analyzer:
A device equipped with a timer, load bank and monitoring equipment used for servicing batteries.

battery capacity:
The amount of energy available from a battery. Expressed in ampere-hours.

battery cart:
A vehicle containing one or more batteries used for starting an aircraft while on the ground. Sometimes used generically to refer to any ground power unit for starting an aircraft including those that use a generator to supply electrical power.

baud:
A measurement of speed based on the number of code elements or units per second.

bauxite:
Aluminum ore that is plentiful and occurs mainly in tropical and sub-tropical areas. Bauxite is refined into aluminum oxide trihydrate (alumina) and then electrolytically reduced into metallic aluminum.

bay:
Part of an antenna array.

B-check:
A complete A-check and a more extensive inspection of certain systems specified for the aircraft.

BDC:
Bottom dead center

bearing:
A device fitted into a hole to reduce the friction present when a shaft rotates in the hole.

bearing misalignment:
A misalignment that results when the bearings supporting a shaft are not aligned with each other. The bearings may not be mounted in parallel planes, may be cocked relative to the shaft, or may be distorted due to

foundation settling or thermal growth.

bearing strength:
The ability of a material to resist the forces that tend to damage it at the point of an applied load.

Bessemer process:
A process for making steel by blowing air through molten pig iron contained in a suitable vessel. The process is one of rapid oxidation primarily of silicon and carbon.

best angle-of-climb airspeed:
The best angle-of-climb airspeed (V_x) will produce the greatest gain in altitude for horizontal distance traveled.

best rate-of-climb airspeed:
The best rate-of-climb airspeed (V_y) produces the maximum gain in altitude per unit of time.

bead:
A groove or depressed portion of a sheet-metal structure for the purpose of stiffening. Also used on tube ends for sealing low pressure systems.

bead heel:
The outer bead edge of a tire that fits against the wheel flange.

bead seat:
The highly stressed portion of a wheel where the bead of the tire seats against the wheel.

bead toe:
The inner bead edge of a tire closest to the centerline.

bearing cage:
A thin sheet-metal separator that holds the bearing rollers equally spaced around the races. The cage should not contact either of the races.

bearing cone:
An assembly that consists of a tapered, hardened steel, cone-shaped bearing race that fits over the axle, and the rollers, and the cage that holds the rollers in position.

bearing cup:
The steel race of a roller bearing that is shrunk into the bearing cavity of the wheel.

bearing race:
The hardened steel surface that anti-friction bearings ride on.

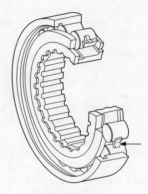

BEARING CAGE

bearing strength:
The ability of a material to resist the forces that tend to damage it at the point of an applied load.

beat-frequency oscillator:
An additional oscillator used in a receiver when it is receiving a continuous wave signal. It provides an audible tone.

beef up:
To strengthen or reinforce a structure or component.

beehive spring:
The retaining spring used to prevent the rivet set from separating from a pneumatic rivet gun. The name comes from the shape of the spring.

beep button:
A switch on the collective control of a turbine powered helicopter used to trim the engine by increasing or decreasing the steady state r.p.m.

before bottom dead center (BBDC):
The number of degrees of crankshaft travel before the piston stops at the bottom of its stroke.

before top dead center (BTDC):
The number of degrees of crankshaft travel before the piston stops at the top of its stroke.

bel:
A unit expressing the relative intensity of a sound, equal to ten decibels.

bell gear:
The central gear in planetary gearing, within which the planetary gear and sun gear rotate. The bell gear is fixed to the engine case. Also called *stationary gear*.

bellcrank:
1. A component in a control system that converts rotary motion to linear motion.

2. A mechanical device having two arms and a central fulcrum, normally used to transmit or change the direction of a force from one assembly or control to another, as in the steering system of an airplane's nose wheel, certain types of aileron controls, etc. Bell cranks are usually V-shaped, but in any shape the principle of two arms having a central fulcrum is present.

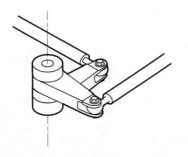

BELL CRANK

Belleville washer:
A special type of spring made in the form of a cupped steel washer. It has a great deal of compressive force, but a limited amount of travel.

bellmouth inlet:
A convergent shaped turbine engine inlet.

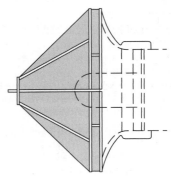

BELLMOUTH INLET

bench check:
A modified service test in which the service conditions are approximated, but the equipment is conventional laboratory equipment and not necessarily identical to that in which the product will be employed.

bench plate:
A super flat plate made of polished granite or cast iron that is used for making precision measurements. Also a cast iron plate built into a bench that is used with bench stakes for working sheet metal.

bench test:
A test of a component made with the component removed from the aircraft. Often done on a workbench or special test apparatus designed for that purpose.

bench timing:
The procedure used to adjust the breaker points and check the rotor of a magneto for e-gap position.

bend allowance:
The term referring to the flat distance or allowance of the curved section of metal within the bend (the portion of metal, which will be curved in bending). The bend allowance may be considered as being the length of the curved portion of the neutral line. Bend allowance can be determined by the use of either formulas or a chart.

Bendix fuel injection:
A continuous-flow fuel metering system utilizing a diaphragm-type regulator unit. This design and technology may appear on products from several manufacturers as a result of multiple sales of the production rights.

bend radius:
When sheet metal is bent the angle formed will not be sharp but will follow the arc of a circle. The radius of this arc is called the bend radius. The bend radius is measured from the radius center to the inside surface of the bent sheet metal.

bend tangent line:
Lines where the bent and unbent metal meets drawn across flat metal that indicate the boundaries of a bend to be made. Such lines must be located where the surface of the unbent section is tangent to the arc of the radius. Dimensions that give the length of the unbent section are known as Bend Tangent Line Dimensions (BTLD).

Bernoulli's principle:
The basic principle of fluids in motion. When the total energy remains constant, any increase in kinetic energy in the form of velocity will result in a decrease in potential energy in the form of pressure.

beryllium bronze:
An alloy of copper that contains approximately 3 percent beryllium.

best economy mixture:
The fuel-air mixture in a reciprocating engine that will achieve the greatest range of flight.

best power mixture:
The fuel-air mixture in a reciprocating engine that will produce the maximum power.

beta range:
The operating range of a turbo-propeller system used for ground operations and reversing.

bevel gear:
Gears that can be used to change direction and speed.

bezel:
The rim that holds the glass in an instrument case.

BFO:
Beat Frequency Oscillator

BHP:
Brake Horsepower

bias:
Difference of potential applied to a vacuum tube or transistor to establish a reference operating level.

bias current:
Current that flows through the base-emitter junction of a transistor and is adjusted to set the operating point of the transistor.

bias-cut surface tape:
Fabric tape that is cut at a 45° angle to the length of the manufactured fabric. This allows the tape to conform to curves more easily.

bias tires:
Tires constructed with plies laid at angles between 30° to 60° to the direction of rotation. Each succeeding ply is laid with the cord angle opposite to the last one. This provides a balanced carcass that is very strong. Until the advent of radial tires, all tires were bias tires.

bicarbonate of soda:
Baking soda. Used to neutralize battery acid.

bifurcated duct:
A split exhaust duct. Used on turbofan or lift fan engines.

bilge:
Nautical term applied to the lowest part of the aircraft structure where water and dirt may accumulate.

billet:
A semi-finished, cogged, hot-rolled, or continuous-cast metal product of uniform section, usually rectangular with radiused corners. Billets are relatively larger than bars. See *bloom*.

bill of material:
A list of the parts and materials needed to manufacture or assemble a component.

BIM:
Blade inspection method

bimetallic strip:
Dissimilar metals that are in close proximity or joined together. They are used for a variety of temperature sensing devices.

binary:
1. A number system that uses a base of 2. Two digits (1 and 0) are used in the binary system.
2. Pertaining to a characteristic that involves the selection, choice, or condition in which there are only two possibilities.

binary coded decimal (BCD):
A specific ARINC 429 data word format

binary state:
A dual configuration or set of circumstances that characterizes a function.

binomial:
Algebraic expression with two terms connected by a plus or minus sign.

biocidal action:
The function of certain fuel additives that kill microbes living in water in aircraft fuel tanks. This prevents scum that would promote corrosion in these tanks.

biplane:
An airplane with two wings, one above the other.

BIPLANE

bipolar:
A digital data format that reverses polarity (two-polarity) when it changes from binary 1 to binary 0

bisect:
To divide into two equal sections.

bistable:
A device that is capable of assuming either one of two stable states.

bistable multi-vibrator:
A multi-vibrator that has two stable states. It remains in one of the states until a trigger is applied. It then flips to the other stable state and remains there until another trigger is applied. Also referred to as a flip-flop.

bit:
Short for binary digit. A number expressed in binary notation utilizing the digits 1 and 0. Any number can be expressed with combinations of these two digits.

bite:
Amount of the die in contact with the work piece throughout one entire forging reduction, e.g., heavy bite is three-quarter to full width of the die.

BITE:
Built-in-test-equipment.
Aircraft systems containing a
computerized ability to perform
some internal self-checking.

BITE systems:
A system that uses built-in-
test-equipment to record EGT
information, spool speeds, fuel
flow, EPR, and other engine
parameters, which can then be
displayed for both flight deck and
maintenance personnel.

bituminous paint:
See *asphaltum*

black box:
1. A term used to describe any
   piece of electronic equipment
   that may be removed and
   replaced as a single unit.

2. The flight data or cockpit voice
   recorder.

black light:
Ultraviolet light whose rays are
in the lower end of the visible
spectrum. While more or less
invisible to the human eye,
they excite or make visible such
materials as fluorescent dyes.

blacksmith welding:
See *forge welding*

bladder-type fuel tank:
A non-self-sealing vessel that is
used to reduce weight. It depends
entirely upon the structure of the
cavity in which it is installed to
support the weight of the fuel
in it. These cells are removable
and employ a variety of retaining
systems.

blade:
A rotating airfoil.

blade angle:
The angle that a blade makes with
some reference plane, as in:

1. The angle between the
   geometric chord of a
   propeller blade and a plane
   perpendicular to the axis of

rotation of the propeller.

2. The angle between the chord
   of a rotor blade, usually the
   zero lift chord, and a plane
   perpendicular to a reference
   axis through the rotor.

blade back:
The side of a propeller blade that
faces forward, corresponding to
the upper surface of a wing.

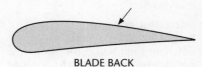

BLADE BACK

blade blending:
A process used to remove small
shallow scratches or dents in
turbine blades. Blending must be
accomplished in accordance with
the profile and dimensional limits
established by the manufacturer.

blade butt:
The end of the propeller arm on
certain types of propellers that is
fastened to the hub.

blade chord:
The straight line between the
leading edge and trailing edge of
the blade.

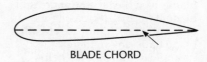

BLADE CHORD

blade climbing:
The condition in a rotorcraft
where one or more blades are
not operating in the same plane
of rotation during flight. This
condition may or may not exist on
the ground.

blade coning:
The acute angle between the
span-wise axis of the rotor blade
of a helicopter and the plane of
rotation.

blade cuff:
A metal, wood or plastic structure designed for attachment to the shank end of the blade, with an outer surface that will transform a round shank into an airfoil section. The cuff is designed primarily to increase the flow of cooling air to the engine nacelle. The cuffs are attached to the blades by mechanical clamping devices or by using bonding materials.

blade dampener:
A shock absorber installed between the main rotor blade of a helicopter and the hub to dampen blade movement on the lead-lag axis.

blade face:
The side of a propeller opposite the blade back, corresponding to the lower surface of a wing. Sometimes called the load face or thrust face.

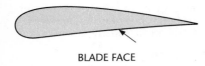

BLADE FACE

blade flapping:
Movement of the helicopter rotor blades in which the advancing blade flaps up, decreasing its angle of attack, and the retreating blade flaps down, increasing its angle of attack. This helps to compensate for the asymmetry of lift.

blade inspection method (BIM):
A system used by Sikorsky Helicopter to detect rotor cracking. It utilizes inert gas and an indicator.

blade leading and lagging:
Sometimes called hunting, the movement of rotor blades in the plane of rotation when approaching and leaving the pure radial position (90° to the helicopter longitudinal axis on the advancing half of the rotor disc). Blades lead when moving away from the pure radial position; they lag when approaching pure radial position. Leading and lagging is caused by increase and decrease in drag on the blades. It is limited by hydraulic dampers on fully articulated rotor systems and by rigidity of blades on all other types.

blade loading:
The amount of weight each square foot of helicopter rotor blade supports. Blade loading is the ratio of the helicopter weight to the total blade area.

blade neck:
The blade shank

blade pitch:
See *blade angle*

blade shank:
Base end of a propeller blade, which must be thick to withstand bending and torque forces; usually cylindrically shaped.

blade slip:
Difference between effective and geometric pitch.

blade station:
Reference point on a propeller blade or rotor blade measured in inches from the center of the hub.

blade tabs:
Fixed tabs mounted on the trailing edge of some helicopter blades for adjusting tracking.

blade tips:
That part of the propeller blade that is farthest from the hub.

blade tracking:
The process of determining the positions of the tips of the propeller blades relative to each other. Tracking shows only the relative position of the blades, not their actual path. The blades should all track one another as closely as possible. The difference

in track at like points must not exceed the tolerance specified by the propeller manufacturer.

blade twist:
The change in angle of incidence of a propeller blade between the root and the tip. This is used to compensate for the variation in thrust due to the change in speed from hub to tip.

blanket method (of aircraft covering):
This method applies the fabric to the wing by wrapping it around the structure and attaching it with a combination of hand sewing and cement.

blast gate:
See *waste gate*

bleed air:
Hot, high-pressure air taken from the compressor section of a jet engine.

bleeder cloth:
A nonstructural layer of material used in the manufacture or repair of composite parts to allow the escape of excess gas and resin during the cure.

bleeder materials:
Absorbent, very porous and typically made of polyester random mat-type material. Typically placed on top of a porous release film/fabric next to a part so as to allow removal of excess resins, air and volatile gases from the patch. This aids compaction and helps to produce a void-free structure.

bleeder resistor:
A resistor used to draw a fixed current.

blemish:
A mark, deformity, or injury which impairs the appearance.

blending:
A filing and stoning procedure used to re-contour damaged compressor and turbine blades.

blimp:
A non-rigid airship

blind hole:
A hole made in a work piece that does not pass through it.

blind rivet:
A special fastener designed to be installed from one side only.

block diagram:
A type of drawing used to show the relationship and function of each item in a diagram.

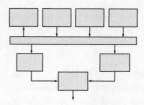

BLOCK DIAGRAM

blocking:
A condition in an amplifier caused by overdriving one or more stages, in which the amplifier is insensitive to small signals immediately after reception of a large signal.

block test:
The operational test of an aircraft engine, usually following overhaul. This is accomplished in a calibrated test cell.

bloom:
A semi-finished product of square, rectangular, or even round cross section; hot rolled, or forged. For steel, the width of a bloom is not more than twice its thickness, and the cross sectional area is usually not less than about 36 square inches. No inviolable rule prevails for distinguishing between blooms and billets. The two terms are used interchangeably.

blooming:
Also known as *hazing*. The appearance of blooming is similar to blushing, though

the underlying reasons are different. Blooming is the result of rubbing the finish too soon after application, the use of too coarse an abrasive or too hard a rubbing stroke. When blooming does occur, it may be removed by washing with a mild soap solution and warm water, followed by drying with a chamois skin. Properly dried and hardened surfaces will not bloom when rubbed or polished.

blowback:
The forcing of exhaust gas into the intake manifold of an engine during the period when intake and exhaust gases are open at the same time.

blowby:
The escape of gases past the valves, piston rings or head gasket of an engine during the compression and power strokes.

blower:
A device designed to give greater pressure to the fuel/air fixture in the induction system to charge the cylinders more fully. Also called a *supercharger*, it is driven through a gear train from the crankshaft. The impeller is located centrally within the diffuser chamber.

blower section:
The section of the crankcase that houses the internal supercharger.

blow-out plug:
Frangible disc installed in oxygen and fire extinguishing systems. In the case of dangerous over-pressure situations, this type of disc will rupture and discharge the system to prevent further damage. Generally located on the outside skin of the aircraft so that it will be visible during walk-around inspections.

blueprint:
A pen or ink line drawing reproduced (printed) on sensitized paper by direct exposure. The original blueprint process has largely been replaced by modern copy technologies. However, the term blueprint continues to be used to describe technical drawings produced by any copy process.

blush:
The white or grayish cast that forms on a lacquer or dope film that has been applied under conditions of too high humidity. It is actually nitrocellulose that has precipitated from the finish.

BMEP:
Brake Mean Effective Pressure. That portion of IMEP that produces brake horsepower.

BNC connector:
A small quick disconnect connector developed for coaxial cable. BNC stands for Bayonet, Neil Concelman who developed the connector.

B-nut:
A nut used to connect a piece of flared tubing to a threaded fitting.

Boeing:
The Boeing Company. A manufacturer of civilian airliners and military aircraft.

bob weight:
A weight in the elevator control system of some aircraft used to apply a nose-down force. An aerodynamic force caused by the elevator trim tab counteracts this. If the aircraft slows down enough that the force on the trim tab is lost, the bob weight forces the nose down, and the aircraft's speed increases.

bogie landing gear:
1. A type of landing-gear unit consisting of two sets of wheels in tandem with a central strut.
2. A supporting and aligning wheel or roller on the inside of an endless track, used, e.g., in certain types of landing gear.

B

BOGIE LANDING GEAR

bogus parts:
Improperly manufactured, rejected or out-of-date parts that have been repackaged and sold to represent legitimate parts. The use of bogus parts can seriously compromise the integrity of an aircraft repair or servicing operation.

boiling point:
The temperature at which a liquid changes to vapor. The boiling point of water is 212°F (100°C).

bolt:
A fastener that consists of a head, thread and grip. The head is the larger diameter of the bolt and may be one of many shapes or designs. The head keeps the bolt in place in one direction, and the nut used on the threads keeps it in place in the other direction.

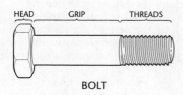

HEAD   GRIP   THREADS

BOLT

bolthole scanner:
An eddy current device designed to provide automatic, uniform inspection of walls of fastener holes.

bomb tester:
A spark plug tester in which the plug is exposed to approximately 200 p.s.i of air pressure, and high voltage is applied to the center electrode. Plugs that can spark in this atmosphere are considered to be acceptable.

bond:
An attachment of one material to another, or of a finish to the metal or fabric.

bonded structure:
A structure that is held together by chemical means rather than mechanical fasteners.

bonding:
1. Specifically, a system of connections between all metal parts of an aircraft or other structure forming a continuous electrical unit and preventing jumping or arcing of static electricity.

2. Gluing or cementing together for structural strength. Bonds may be classified by type as follows:

   a. *Mechanical Bond* - Purely physical attachment accomplished by such means as "through" holes, interlocking fingers, envelope design, riveting, etc.

   b. *Cold Bond* - Adhesion of previously vulcanized elastomer to another member through use of suitable contact cements.

   c. *Vulcanized Bond* - Adhesion of an elastomer to a previously primed surface using heat and pressure, thus vulcanizing the elastomer at the same time.

bonding agent:
An adhesive used to join parts together.

bonding jumper:
A very low resistance wire used to electrically connect a component or structure to the airframe.

bonnet assembly:

The operating head of a fire extinguishing system. The bonnet contains an electrically ignited powder charge that is used to rupture a frangible disk and release the extinguishing agent.

Boolean algebra:

A system of logic dealing with on-off circuit elements associated by such operators as the AND, OR, NAND, NOR, and NOT functions.

Boolean logic:

See *Boolean algebra*

boost charge:

A constant charge applied to batteries while installed in the aircraft to restore their charge sufficiently to start the aircraft.

boost pump:

A fuel pump that is used to provide a positive pressure to the inlet side of the engine drive pump. Central to starting, takeoff, landing and high altitude operations.

boost system:

A hydraulically actuated system that aids the pilot in operating the flight controls.

boosted brake:

A form of brake power source using a master cylinder in which the hydraulic pressure from the aircraft hydraulic power system is used to aid the pilot in applying force to the master cylinder. This boost, or assistance, is automatically applied when the pressure required at the brake is greater than the pilot can produce with foot pressure alone.

booster coil:

A system using a transformer coil and vibrator to produce a high voltage spark for starting.

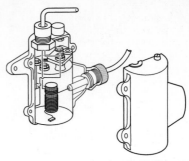

BOOSTER COIL (CUTAWAY)

booster magneto:

A small magneto used to produce a hot spark for starting reciprocating engines. On older aircraft, this is normally turned by hand during startup.

bootstrapping:

1. The technique with which something is brought into the desired state through its own action.

2. The continued drifting of the settings on a supercharged engine installation. This is an undesirable condition.

bore:

1. The cavity, or diameter, of an engine cylinder.

2. To enlarge and finish the surface of a cylindrical hole by the action of a rotating boring bar (cutting tool) or by the action of a stationary tool pressed (fed) against the surface as the part is rotated.

BORE[1]

38

B

borescope:
An optical tool with which a visual inspection can be made inside an area where it is impossible to get the eye. It consists of a light, mirrors, and lenses.

boric acid:
A weak acid solution used to neutralize spilled electrolyte from NiCad batteries.

boron fibers:
Fibers made by using a 0.0005-inch tungsten filament, heated to about 2,200°F and drawn through a gaseous mixture of hydrogen and boron trichloride. A coating of black boron is deposited over the tungsten filament. The resulting fiber is about 0.004 inch in diameter, has excellent compressive strength and stiffness, and is extremely hard.

boss:
An enlarged or thickened part of a forging or casting that provides additional material for strength.

bottom dead center:
The dead center position of an engine piston and its crankshaft arm when at the bottom of its stroke.

bottoming tap:
A tap used to cut full threads to the bottom of a blind hole. The bottoming tap is not tapered. It is used after a tapered tap has been used to partially tap the hole.

boundary layer:
The layer of fluid in the immediate vicinity of a bounding surface. In fluid mechanics, the layer affected by viscosity of the fluid, referring ambiguously to the laminar, turbulent, planetary, or surface boundary layers.

Bourdon tube:
Curved metal tube used to measure pressure and temperature changes. As the temperature changes it expands or contracts and, through a gear mechanism, rotates a pointer. The pointer registers the movement on a calibrated dial. The Bourdon tube is used in many direct-reading pressure and temperature indicators.

bow:
The forward end of an aircraft.

bow wave:
A shock wave that forms immediately ahead of an aircraft that is flying faster than the speed of sound.

bowline knot:
A knot commonly used to tie down aircraft, and to start rib stitching. A properly tied bowline will not slip.

TYING A BOWLINE KNOT

box brake:
A metal forming machine similar to a cornice brake. It utilizes removable sections (fingers) to adjust to a variety of box sizes. Also called a *finger brake*.

boxing (of a) paint:

Procedure in which pigmented paint is thoroughly mixed by pouring it back and forth between two containers.

box spar:

Any hollow spar of square or rectangular cross section.

box wrench:

A wrench with an enclosed end having six, eight, or twelve points.

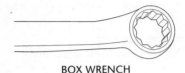

BOX WRENCH

Boyle's law:

A statement in physics—the product of the pressure and the specific volume of a gas at constant temperature is constant.

braced wing:

A wing that requires external bracing.

brad:

A thin wire nail.

brake back plate:

A retaining plate to which the wheel cylinder and brake shoes attach.

brake caliper:

The clamp in a disc brake system that holds the brake linings. When pressure is applied to the brake pedal, the caliper applies pressure to the linings to produce the braking action.

brake debooster cylinder:

Device used to reduce the pressure to the brake and increase the volume of fluid flow. In some power brake control valve systems, debooster cylinders are used in conjunction with the power brake control valves. The unit is mounted on the landing gear shock strut in the line between the control valve and the brake.

brake disc:

A disc on a landing gear wheel that receives the braking pressure.

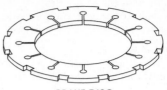

BRAKE DISC

brake horsepower (BHP):

The horsepower actually delivered to the propeller shaft of an aircraft engine. (*FAR 1*)

brake lining:

A material with a high coefficient of friction and the ability to withstand heat. It is the wear surface of a brake system.

brake mean effective pressure (BMEP):

A computed value (not measured) of the average pressure that exists in the cylinder of an engine during the power stroke.

brake puck:

A circular brake lining.

brake specific fuel consumption:

Number of pounds of fuel burned per hour to produce one brake horsepower.

branch:

An individual current path in a parallel circuit.

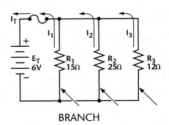

BRANCH

brass:

A nonferrous alloy consisting essentially of copper and zinc.

Brayton cycle:
The operating cycle of a gas turbine engine; the constant pressure cycle.

brazing:
Joining metals by the fusion of nonferrous alloys having a melting temperature above 800°F, but below that of the metals being joined.

break corners:
To remove sharp edges.

breakdown:
The phenomenon occurring in a reverse-biased semiconductor diode. The start of the phenomenon is observed as a transition from a high dynamic resistance to one of substantially lower dynamic resistance. This is done to boost the reverse current.

breakdown voltage:
The voltage at which equipment will arc over to a structural member. Also the voltage at which an insulation fails.

breaker assembly:
Electrical contacts in a magneto that are opened and closed by the action of a cam. The opening of the contacts causes the magneto to generate a spark.

breaker point bounce:
A condition caused by weak breaker point springs. This causes the points to bounce open when the cam follower moves off of the cam lobe.

break line:
A break line indicates that a portion of the object is not shown on the drawing. Short breaks are made by solid, freehand lines. For long breaks, solid ruled lines with zigzags are used. Shafts, rods, tubes, and other such parts, which have a portion of their length broken out, have the ends of the break drawn as indicated.

BREAK LINE (SHORT)

B

breather:
A vent in the engine oil system that keeps pressure within the tank the same as the atmosphere.

breather cloth:
A loosely woven material, such as glass fabric, that will serve as a continuous vacuum path over a part or the repair area.

breather tube:
A tube providing an opening in the crankcase of an engine to equalize the pressure in the crankcase with atmospheric pressure.

bridging:
A welding defect caused by poor penetration. A void at the root of the weld is spanned by weld metal.

bright annealing:
A process of annealing, usually with reducing gases, such that surface oxidation is reduced to a minimum, thereby yielding a relatively bright surface.

brightness control:
The name given to the potentiometer used to vary the potential applied to the control grid of a CRT.

brine:
A solution of salt (NaCl) and water (H_2O). Used as a quenching medium for certain heat treating operations. Brine quenches are generally most severe and result in a harder product.

Brinell hardness test:
The hardness of a metal or part, as represented by the number obtained from the ratio between the load applied on and the spherical area of the impression made by a steel ball forced into the surface of the material

tested. The Brinell Hardness Number (BHN) is determined by measuring the diameter of the impression using a low power microscope, then matching this diameter with the load on a standard table.

brinelling:
Indentations in bearing races usually caused by high static loads or improper installation or removal techniques.

British Thermal Unit (BTU):
The amount of heat energy required to raise the temperature of one pound of water one degree Fahrenheit.

brittle fracture:
Fracture with little or no plastic deformation.

brittleness:
The property of a material that permits little bending or deformation without fracture. Brittleness and hardness are closely associated.

broach:
A metal cutting tool having a series of teeth in a straight line. Each tooth is slightly higher than the preceding one, except the last few which are the same height and finish the cut.

broaching:
The process of removing metal by pushing or pulling a cutting tool, called a broach, along the surface of the part.

broadcasting satellite service:
A radio communication service in which signals transmitted or retransmitted by space stations are intended for direct reception by the general public.

broad goods:
A term loosely applied to prepreg material greater than about 12 inches in width, usually furnished by suppliers in continuous rolls. The term is currently used to

designate both collimated uniaxial tape and woven fabric prepregs.

bronze:
A nonferrous alloy consisting essentially of copper and tin.

brushes:
Sliding contacts, usually carbon, that make electrical connection to the rotating part of a motor or generator. Also used to transmit electrical power across moving connections—as in power to propeller deicing boots.

B-stage:
An intermediate stage in the reaction of a thermosetting resin in which the material softens when heated and swells when in contact with certain liquids but does not entirely fuse or dissolve. Materials are usually precured to this stage to facilitate handling and processing prior to final cure. Sometimes referred to as *resistol*.

BTU:
See *British Thermal Unit*

bucket:
1. A turbine blade.
2. Any of the cups on the rim of an air-driven gyroscope rotor.

bucking bar:
A tool held against the shank end of a rivet while the shop head is being formed.

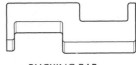

BUCKING BAR

buff:
To polish to a smooth finish of high luster with a cloth or fabric wheel to which a compound has been added.

buffer amplifier:
An amplifier that isolates one circuit from another. It decreases

the loading effect on an oscillator by reducing the interaction between the load and the oscillator.

buffeting:
The irregular shaking or oscillation of an aircraft component owing to turbulent air or to separated flow.

built-in-test-equipment:
See *BITE*

bug:
1. An unexpected malfunction.
2. An arrow or pointer on an instrument that can be rotated to a specific point by the operator.

bulb angle:
An angular piece of extruded metal having the outer edge of one flange enlarged in a circular manner, which gives additional stiffness to the parts.

bulb root:
A means of attaching turbine blades to the hub. The base of the blade is cylindrical and larger than the rest of the blade. This fits into a mated hole in the rotor hub.

bulkhead:
A structural partition in the fuselage or wing. Bulkheads usually divide the structure into bays, and provide additional strength.

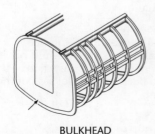

BULKHEAD

bumping:
Forming sheet metal by hammering or pounding.

bump testing:
A single channel approximation to a two channel impact test. This method works because the impacting force approximates an impulse and imparts broadband excitation over a limited frequency range. Since the Fourier Transform of the impulse response function is the frequency response function, it provides a good method of estimating the natural frequencies of the structure.

Buna-N:
Same as nitrile rubber.

Buna-S:
A general term for the copolymers of butadiene and styrene. Also known as *SBR* and *GRS*.

bundled cable:
Any number of individually insulated electrical wires tied together with lacing cord or special wire-wrapping straps.

bungee cord:
A shock absorbing medium composed of numerous rubber bands enclosed in loosely woven fabric.

buoyancy:
1. The property of floating on or in a fluid.
2. The upward force exerted on a body, such as a lighter-than-air aircraft or a seaplane float or hull, by the fluid it displaces.
3. The amount of this force, expressed in units of weight and equal to the weight of the fluid displaced by a body.

burn point:
The lowest temperature at which a petroleum product in an open container will continue to burn when ignited by an open flame held near its surface.

burner cans:
Term associated with the combustion chambers on a turbine engine.

burnishing:
The process of finishing a metal surface by contact with another harder metal to improve it. To make smooth or glossy by, or as if by, rubbing or polishing.

burr:
1. The sharp edge left on metal after cutting or punching.
2. A rotary cutting tool designed to be attached to a drill.

bus bar:
A heavy copper strap or bar used to connect several circuits together when a large current-carrying capacity is required.

bus hierarchy:
A design concept to ensure that the most critical electrical systems are the least likely to fail

bushing:
A sleeve or a lining for a bearing, or a drill jig to guard against wear.

butterfly valve:
A flat disk-shaped valve used to control the flow of fluid in a round pipe or tube.

butt joint:
A welded joint where the two pieces of metal are placed edge to edge so that there is no overlap.

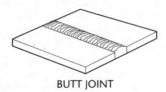

BUTT JOINT

butt line:
A vertical reference plane, which divides the aircraft front to rear through the center of the fuselage

butt rib:
The last rib at the inboard end of an airfoil.

butyrate dope:
A shortened version of Cellulose Acetate Butyrate (CAB) dope. A finish for aircraft fabric consisting of a film base of cellulose fibers dissolved in solvents with the necessary plasticizers, solvent, and thinners. Generally considered a replacement for earlier Nitrate dope, which was very flammable.

butyl:
The trade name of a synthetic rubber product made by the polymerization of isobutylene. It withstands such potent chemicals as Skydrol hydraulic fluid.

buzz:
A condition that occurs when a shock wave is alternately swallowed and expelled by the inlet of a jet engine. This can result in violent fluctuations of pressure great enough to cause damage to the engine inlet or the engine itself.

bypass capacitor:
A capacitor used to transfer unwanted signals out of a circuit; for example, coupling an unwanted signal to ground. Also called a *decoupling capacitor*.

bypass duct:
The cold airstream duct of a turbofan engine. Also called the *fan exhaust duct*.

bypass ratio:
The ratio of the air passing through the fan to the air passing through the core of a turbofan engine.

bypass valve:
A valve used to maintain a specific pressure in a fluid power system by bypassing some of the fluid back to the inlet side of the pump.

byte:
A group of binary digits consisting of eight bits.

Cc

CAA:
Civil Aviation Authority (Great Britain)

CAAC:
Civil Aviation Authority of China

CAB:
Civil Aeronautics Board

CAB dope:
See *butyrate dope*

cabin:
The passenger compartment of an aircraft.

cabin altitude:
The simulated altitude condition in a pressurized aircraft cabin.

cabin interphone system (CIS):
Provides communications between flight attendant stations, and from flight attendant stations to the flight deck. A handset, which resembles a telephone receiver, is located at each flight attendant's station. From the flight deck, the pilots can interface with the CIS using either the flight deck handset or the flight interphone system.

cabin supercharger:
A mechanical air pump used to supply air for the cabin pressurization system on some aircraft.

cable:
Either a stranded conductor (single-conductor cable) or a combination of conductors insulated from one another (multiple conductor cable). Small sizes are commonly referred to as stranded wire or as cords.

cable tensiometer:
A device used to check the tension of cables that operate

flight control surfaces. Each type is designed for different kinds of cable, cable sizes and cable tension.

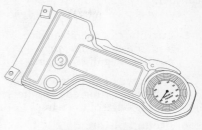

CABLE TENSIOMETER

cadmium-plating:
Electrolytically deposited silver gray plating. It provides exceptionally good protection against corrosion, particularly in a salty atmosphere, but it is not recommended in applications where the temperature exceeds 450°F.

calendar month:
A measure of time often specified by the FAA. A calendar month ends at midnight on the last day of the month, regardless of the day it began.

calendaring:
The process of ironing fabric by threading it, wet, between a series of hot and cold rollers. Produces a smooth finish.

calibrate:
To make adjustments to a meter or other instrument so that it will give the correct indications with respect to its inputs.

calibrated airspeed:
The indicated airspeed of an aircraft, corrected for position and instrument error. Calibrated airspeed is equal to true airspeed in standard atmosphere at sea level. *(FAR 1)*

caliper:
A device used to measure inside or outside dimensions.

cam:
An eccentric plate or shaft used to impart motion to a follower riding on its surface or edge.

camber:
Also *cambre*.

1. Curvature of airfoil surfaces from the chord line; may be positive, negative, or zero.

2. The curve of an airfoil section from the leading edge to the trailing edge of the wing.

cam-ground piston:
An aircraft engine piston ground in such a way that its diameter parallel to the wrist pin boss is less than its diameter perpendicular to the boss. When the piston reaches its operating temperature, the difference in mass has caused the piston to expand to a perfect circular form.

camlock fastener:
A type of turnlock fastener that consists of a receptacle, a grommet, a retaining ring, and a stud assembly.

cam pump:
Type of hydraulic pump that utilizes a cam to cause stroking of the pistons.

camshaft:
A rotating shaft used to operate the valve mechanism of an opposed engine. The camshaft always rotates at one-half the crankshaft speed. As the camshaft revolves, lobes cause the tappet assembly to rise in the tappet guide, transmitting the force through the push rod and rocker arm to open the valve.

can-annular combustor:
A combustor with characteristics of both the annular types. It has an outer shell and a number of individual cylindrical liners.

canard:
1. Pertaining to an aerodynamic vehicle in which horizontal surfaces used for trim and control are forward of the main lifting surface; the horizontal trim and control surfaces in such an arrangement.

2. The forward wing of a canard configuration and may be a fixed, movable, or variable geometry surface, with or without control surfaces. *(FAR 1)*

CANARD

canard configuration:
A configuration in which the span of the forward wing is substantially less than that of the main wing. *(FAR 1)*

cannibalize:
To take salvageable parts from one machine for the use in repairing or building another machine.

cantilever wing:
A wing attached without external bracing.

can-type combustor:
One type of turbine engine burner arrangement. This type of combustor consists of multiple individual combustor assemblies arranged radially around the engine. Each combustor assembly can be removed individually.

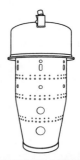

CAN-TYPE COMBUSTOR

capacitive reactance:
The opposition, expressed in ohms, offered to the flow of an alternating current by capacitance. The symbol for capacitive reactance is X_C.

capacitor:
An electrical device capable of storing electrical energy in an electrostatic field.

capacitor discharge ignition system:
A type of high-energy ignition system associated with turbine engines. Large quantities of electrons are stored in capacitors and then released to proved a particularly intense spark.

capacitor start induction motor:
A type of AC motor employing a second winding to assist in startup. In the second winding the phase is shifted by a capacitor to provide a rotating field. When the motor gets up to speed, a centrifugal switch deactivates the starter winding.

capillary action:
The tendency of certain liquids to travel or climb when exposed to small openings, cracks, fissure, etc., due to factors such as surface tension, cohesion, adhesion and viscosity.

capillary cementing:
Solvents for Plexiglas® (ethylene dichloride or 1-1-2 trichloroethylene) are applied with a brush, pipe cleaner or eyedropper to the butted edges to be joined. Wherever possible, the solvent should be applied to both sides of the joint to be cemented.

capillary tube:
A tube with a very small internal diameter. These may be used to supply fluids to instruments or as a metering device.

cap nut:
A dome-shaped nut with threads that do not go completely through the nut. Also known as an *acorn nut.*

cap screw:
A type of threaded fastener. The head of a cap screw is generally turned with a wrench and not a screwdriver.

carbide drill:
A cutting tool to which carbide tip inserts have been brazed, to provide cutting action on harder materials than the high-speed drills are capable of.

carbon:
The element that provides the backbone for all organic polymers. Graphite is a more ordered form of carbon.

carbonaceous:
Consisting of or containing carbon.

carbon brakes:
One of the newest developments in aircraft brakes required for extremely high energy dissipation. Both the rotating and stationary disks are made of pure carbon.

carbon-carbon:
A composite material consisting of carbon or graphite fibers in a carbon or graphite matrix.

carbon dioxide (CO_2):
A colorless, odorless, nonflammable gas often used as a fire extinguishing agent. Associated with conventional on-board extinguishing systems as well as hand-held extinguishers.

carbon fibers:
Also called *graphite fibers.*

1. Fibers produced by graphitizing filaments of rayon or other polymers in a high-temperature furnace. The resulting fibers are black in color and only a few microns in diameter. They are strong, stiff and brittle; through control of the process, graphite of higher tensile strength

can be produced at the cost of lower stiffness. Aircraft parts are generally produced with fibers of intermediate strength and stiffness. Carbon fiber is stiff, black fabric that is very good for primary structural applications. It has a good compressive strength, is highly rigid when in a matrix and has a high fatigue resistance. Because it is carbon, it is conductive and requires lightning protection.

2. Fibers produced by the pyrolysis of organic precursor fibers, such as rayon, polyacrylonitrile (PAN), and pitch in an inert environment.

CARBON FIBER

carbon fouling:
Sooty deposits on spark plugs associated with over-rich fuel/air mixtures. This is especially likely to happen when the idle mixture is not properly adjusted and during prolonged ground operations.

carbon monoxide (CO):
A colorless, odorless, highly toxic gas formed as the result of incomplete combustion of hydrocarbon fuels. Some carbon monoxide is present in all exhaust fumes and represents the primary danger of exhaust system failure for flight crews and passengers.

carbon pile voltage regulator:
A type of voltage regulator that utilizes a stack of thin carbon disks as a resistor regulating generator field current. The resistance of the carbon stack

varies inversely with the pressure applied. Pressure on the carbon stack depends on spring pressure opposed by the pull of an electromagnet that senses generator voltage. When generator voltage varies the pull of the electromagnet changes, increasing or decreasing the resistance of the carbon stack. This change in resistance will change the output of the generator.

carbon resistor:
A device inserted in a circuit to limit current flow. Carbon resistors are manufactured from a rod of compressed graphite and a binding material, with wire leads, called pigtails, attached to each end of the resistor.

carbon steel:
Steel that does not contain significant amounts of alloying elements other than carbon. Also known as *straight carbon, ordinary steel,* or *plain carbon steel.*

carbon tracking:
A fine line of carbon left inside a magneto from internal arcing at high altitude. May cause loss of engine power, misfiring of the spark plugs and engine damage.

carborundum:
A trade name for a manufactured aluminum oxide abrasive similar to natural emery. It is used for grinding wheels and for abrasive papers.

carburetor heater:
A unit designed to provide heat to engine intake air to prevent the formation of carburetor ice. This is normally accomplished by drawing warm air from within the engine compartment.

carburetor ice:
Ice which forms inside of a carburetor as a result of the temperature drop that occurs due to the air pressure drop in the carburetor venturi. This

temperature drop may be sufficient to condense and freeze moisture present in the induction air.

carburizing:
To produce surface hardness on low carbon steels by heating above the critical range while in contact with a suitable material containing carbon.

carburizing flame:
An oxyacetylene flame that has an excess of unburned acetylene.

cardinal headings:
The four main compass points: north, south, east, west.

cardiopulmonary resuscitation (CPR):
Procedure designed to restore breathing after cardiac arrest. Includes clearing air passages to lungs and chest compressions for heart massage.

carrier power (of a radio transmitter):
The average power supplied to the antenna transmission line by a transmitter during one radio frequency cycle taken under the condition of no modulation.

carrier wave:
High frequency alternating current that can be modulated to carry intelligence by propagation as a radio wave.

CAS:
Calibrated airspeed. *(FAR 1)*

cascade thrust reverser:
See *aerodynamic blockage thrust reverser*

CASE:
Computer Aided Software Engineering

case hardening:
A combination of heat treatments in which the surface layer of an iron-based alloy is made substantially harder than the interior by altering its composition by carburizing, cyaniding, or nitriding.

casein glue:
A form of powdered glue made from milk.

cast iron:
A generic term for a large family of cast ferrous alloys.

casting:
A part made by pouring molten metal into a mold.

castle nut:
Commonly used general purpose nut shaped like a castle. The slots between the turrets are used for locking the nut to the bolt with cotter pins.

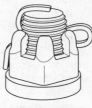

CASTLE NUT

CAT I:
Facility providing operation down to 200 feet decision height and runway visual range not less than 2,600 feet. *(FAR 1)*

CAT II:
1. Category II.
2. Facility providing operation down to 100 feet decision height and runway visual range not less than 1,200 feet. *(FAR 1)*

CAT IIa:
Facility providing operation with no decision height limit to and along the surface of the runway with external visual reference during final phase of landing and with a runway visual range not less than 700 feet. *(FAR 1)*

catalyst:
A substance that changes the rate of a chemical reaction without itself undergoing permanent change in its composition.

catalyzed material:
A material whose cure is initiated by the addition of a catalyst.

category:
1. As used with respect to the certification, ratings, privileges, and limitations of airmen: a broad classification of aircraft. Examples include: airplane, rotorcraft, glider, and lighter-than-air.
2. As used with respect to the certification of aircraft: a grouping of aircraft based upon intended use or operating limitations. Examples include: transport, normal, utility, acrobatic, limited, restricted, and provisional. *(FAR 1)*

category II operations:
With respect to the operation of aircraft: a straight-in ILS approach to the runway of an airport under a Category II ILS instrument approach procedure issued by the Administrator or other appropriate authority. *(FAR 1)*

category III operations:
With respect to the operation of aircraft: an ILS approach to, and landing on, the runway of an airport using a Category III ILS instrument approach procedure issued by the Administrator or other appropriate authority. *(FAR 1)*

category IIIa operations:
An ILS approach and landing with no decision height (DH), or a DH below 100 feet (30 meters), and controlling runway visual range not less than 700 feet (200 meters). *(FAR 1)*

category IIIb operations:
An ILS approach and landing with no decision height, or with a DH below 50 feet (15 meters), and controlling runway visual range less than 700 feet (200 meters), but not less than 150 feet (50 meters). *(FAR 1)*

category IIIc operations:
An ILS approach and landing with no decision height and no runway visual range limitation. *(FAR 1)*

category A:
With respect to transport category rotorcraft: multi-engine rotorcraft designed with engine and system isolation features specified in Part 29 and utilizing scheduled takeoff and landing operations under a critical engine failure concept which assures adequate designated surface area and adequate performance capability for continued safe flight in the event of engine failure. *(FAR 1)*

category B:
With respect to transport category rotorcraft, a single-engine or multi-engine rotorcraft which does not fully meet all category A standards. Category B rotorcraft have no guaranteed stay-up ability in the event of engine failure and unscheduled landing is assumed. *(FAR 1)*

cathode:
The negative plate of an electrochemical combination. Electrons are attracted from the anode to the cathode.

cathode-ray tube (CRT):
An electron tube that has an electron gun, a deflection system, and a screen. This tube is used to display visual electronic signals.

cathodic protection:
Another name for sacrificial corrosion. A material more anodic than the material being protected is attached to or plated on the material, which then becomes the cathode and is not corroded.

cation:
A positive charged ion that moves toward the cathode in the process of electrolysis.

caul plates:
Smooth metal plates, free of surface defects, the same size and shape as a composite lay-up, used immediately in contact with the lay-up during the curing process to transmit normal pressure and to provide a smooth surface on the finished laminate.

caustic material:
Any substance having the ability of burning, corroding, or eroding other substances by chemical action.

caution:
A notation that will call attention to any methods, materials, or procedures, which must be followed to avoid damage to equipment on the aircraft

cavitation:
The formation of bubbles in a liquid, occurring whenever the static pressure at any point in the fluid flow becomes less than the fluid vapor pressure.

C-check:
A major inspection that covers the airframe, engines and systems. C-checks are performed once a year, or about every 3,000-5,000 flight hours. Some airlines categorize these inspections as C1, C2, up to C7. A C1 inspection typically is less in-depth and requires less disassembly of panels and cowlings, and may take a week to perform. C2, C3 and C4 inspections may cover different areas of the aircraft structure, with repeat inspections of areas prone to damage or corrosion.

C-clamp:
A metal clamp in the general shape of the letter C. It is used to temporarily hold objects together.

Ceconite:
A registered trade name for a fabric woven from polyester fibers.

ceiling:
The height above the earth's surface of the lowest layer of clouds or obscuring phenomena that is reported as broken, overcast, or obscuration, and not classified as thin or partial. *(FAR 1)*

Celsius (C):
A temperature scale using 0 as the freezing point of water and 100 as the boiling point. The scale has 100 equal divisions between the 0 and 100, with each division designating a degree. A reading is usually written in an abbreviated form, for example, 75°C. This scale was formerly known as the centigrade scale, but it was renamed in recognition of Anders Celsius, the Swedish astronomer who devised the scale.

cement:
A type of adhesive, that comes in many forms. Rubber and gasket adhesive is a general-purpose type that is flexible when cured, and is useful for most applications except upholstery. There is also de-icer cement, which is used around the edges of de-icing boots to provide an electrical bond to the airframe. This prevents static electricity from building up and causing pinholes in the de-icers.

center-feed method:
Connecting the center of an antenna to a transmission line that is then connected to the final (output) stage of the transmitter.

center head:
A part of a combination square set that is used to find the center of, or to bisect a round or square work piece.

center line:
A center line is made up of alternate long and short dashes. It indicates the center of an object or part of an object. Where center lines cross, the short dashes intersect symmetrically. In the case of very small circles, the center lines may be shown unbroken. A center line may also be used to indicate the travel of a center and as an extension line.

CENTER LINE

center of gravity:
Point within an airplane or airfoil (blade) through which, for balance purposes, the total force of gravity is considered to act.

center of gravity (CG) range:
The distance between the forward and rearward CG limits indicated in the pertinent Aircraft Specification or Type Certificate Data Sheets.

center of pressure:
The aerodynamic center of an airfoil; the point where all forces act.

center punch:
A pointed hand tool made of hardened steel and shaped somewhat like a pencil.

center-tapped winding:
A winding on a transformer that has a connection located at its electrical center (a tap). This tap may be used to divide the winding in half, with each half having opposite polarity.

centigrade scale:
A temperature scale that is constructed by using the freezing and boiling points of water, under standard conditions, as fixed points of 0° and 100°, respectively, with 100 equal divisions between. See also *Celsius*.

centistoke:
A unit of kinematic viscosity. Water has a viscosity of about one centistoke.

centralized fault display interface unit (CFDIU):
The main computer that manages the CFDS information

centralized fault display system (CFDS):
Is the advance diagnostic system used on Airbus Industries transport category aircraft. See *built-in test equipment*

central maintenance computer system (CMCS):
The advanced built-in troubleshooting systems found on Boeing aircraft

centrifugal casting:
A casting made in a mold (sand, plaster, or permanent mold) that rotates while the metal solidifies under the pressure developed by centrifugal force.

centrifugal clutch:
A type of friction clutch that engages when the drive wheel reaches a certain speed. The clutch is engaged by the centrifugal force on a flyweight mechanism.

centrifugal compressor:
A compressor having one or more vaned rotary impellers that accelerate the incoming fluid radially outward into a diffuser, compressing by centrifugal force.

centrifugal force:
The force that a rotating object exerts on the body constraining the object and that acts outwardly away from the center of rotation.

centrifugal pump:
A type of pump that uses a high speed impeller to sling the fuel outward by centrifugal action. Commonly used as fuel boost pumps.

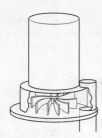

CENTRIFUGAL PUMP

centrifugal twisting moment (CTM):
The force acting on a propeller blade that tries to decrease blade angle. Centrifugal twisting moment is produced because all parts of the blade try to move in the exact same plane of rotation as the blade centerline. This force opposes aerodynamic twisting moment.

centripetal force:
The force that deflects an object from a straight path and forces it to travel in a curved path.

ceramic fibers:
Made from ceramic materials that are drawn into fibers and combined with a metal. Used in high temperature areas of up to 2,200°F.

chafing:
Rubbing action between adjacent or contacting parts under light pressure that results in wear.

chafing tape:
Cloth or paper tape placed over any metal seam or protruding screw head that is to be covered with fabric. It is used to protect the fabric from wear.

chamfer:
The bevel or angular surface cut on the edge or a corner of a machined part.

chamfered tooth:
The tooth of a gear on a rotating magnet or distributor gear, which is beveled to identify it for use when timing a magneto.

channel nuts:
Self-locking nuts that are mounted in a channel that can be riveted in place.

character generator:
Avionics processor circuitry used to produce letters, numbers, and symbols

characteristic frequency:
A frequency which can be easily identified and measured in a given emission.

Charles' Law:
An empirical generalization that in a gaseous system at constant pressure, the temperature increase and the relative volume increase stand in approximately the same proportion for so-called perfect gases.

$$V_1T_2 = V_2T_1$$

or

$$\frac{V_1}{T_1} = \frac{V_2}{T_2}$$

CHARLES' LAW

chasing threads:
Cutting threads in a lathe or screw machine.

chattering:
A vibration in the cutting tool that leaves shallow ridges or chatter marks in the work. The chattering may be small enough to cause only a light mark in the work or it may be severe enough to break the tool.

chattering brakes:
A heavy vibration in the brakes produced by the brake friction varying as the discs rotate. Chattering is caused by glazed discs.

check nut:
These nuts are used in locking devices for non self-locking plain hex nuts, setscrews and threaded rod ends.

check valve:
A valve that permits fluid flow in one direction, but prevents flow in the reverse direction.

cheesecloth:
Lightweight cotton gauze that has no sizing in it. Often used to strain liquids such as paint, or as a polishing cloth.

chemical etching:
1. A process used to detect small cracks in aluminum by the application of caustic soda.

2. A chemical process used to roughen the surface of metal in preparation for painting.

chem-milled skin:
A method of machining large sheets of metal by chemically etching away part of their surface.

chemical milling:
A chemical etching process used to shape large sheets of metal.

chemical salt:
The result of the combination of an alkali with an acid. Salts are generally porous and powdery in appearance and are the visible evidence of corrosion in a metal.

cherry rivet:
A type of hollow shank blind rivet manufactured by the Cherry Rivet division of Townsend, Inc. The upset head is formed by pulling the tapered stem through its hollow shank.

chevron seal:
A single-direction seal used in hydraulic or pneumatic actuators. The name is derived from its V-shaped (chevron) cross-section.

CHEVRON SEAL

chine:
The longitudinal member on the side of an aircraft float or seaplane hull where the bottom and the side meet.

chine tire:
A tire that has a deflector molded into the sidewall. This type of tire is normally mounted on the nose wheel of a jet aircraft to prevent water, ice, slush, etc., from getting into the intake of the engines.

CHINE TIRE

chip detector:
Device that contains a magnetic plug that collects ferrite particles in the scavenged oil prior to the oil being returned to the engine oil tank assembly

chipping:
Breaking away of pieces of material by excessive stress or careless handling.

chisel:
Any one of a variety of small hand cutting tools, generally wedge-shaped.

chlorofluorocarbons (CFCs):
Since they were developed in the 1930s, they have been widely used as air conditioner (A/C) and refrigerator coolants, aerosol can propellants, electronic parts cleaners and foam-blowing agents. Common CFCs may appear under the names of Halon, and Freon. Environmental concerns have resulted in a ban on manufacturing these materials. However, existing supplies may continue to be used.

chock:
A block of wood or other material placed under the tires of an aircraft to prevent rolling.

choke:
An inductor used to smooth the pulsations in rectified AC.

choke bore:
A method of boring a cylinder of an aircraft engine in which the top, that portion affected by the mass of the cylinder head, has a diameter slightly less than that of the main bore of the barrel. When the cylinder reaches operating temperature, the mass of the head has caused the bore to expand so it is straight throughout its length.

choked nozzle:
The exhaust nozzle on a turbine engine whose flow rate has reached the speed of sound.

choo-choo:
A mild compressor surge condition.

chord:
An imaginary straight line between the leading and trailing edges of an airfoil section.

chromate:
A salt or ester of chromic acid.

chromel-alumel:
A combination of metals often associated with thermocouples. Alumel contains an excess of electrons, which when heated move into the chromel lead. The current flow resulting from this reaction can be calibrated to measure the temperature change.

chrome-moly:
A commonly used term for chrome molybdenum steel.

chrome molybdenum steel:
An alloy steel containing chromium and molybdenum. SAE 4130 chrome-moly steel is commonly used in aircraft work and valued for its strength, toughness and weldability.

chrome plating (cylinders):
An electrolytically deposited coating of hard chrome (not the shiny decorative type) on walls of aircraft engine cylinders. The surface contains thousands of tiny cracks that will hold oil to provide for cylinder wall lubrication.

chrome vanadium steel:
An alloy steel containing chromium and vanadium. The SAE 6100 series is often used in the manufacture of tools.

chromic acid etch:
A solution of sodium dichromate, nitric acid, and water. This is used to etch or roughen the surface of a metal to make it better for paint adherence.

chugging:
A mild audible compressor stall condition, which usually can be controlled by proper throttle movement.

circuit:
The complete path of an electric current.

circuit breaker:
A circuit protection device that will open a circuit having an excessive flow of current. Circuit breakers may normally be reset in flight.

circular magnetism:
Magnetism induced when an electric current is passed through a solid magnetic conductor. A circular magnetic field is developed not only around the conductor, but also within the conductor. The conductor may be a component being tested using the magnetic particle inspection method. This is the magnetism induced by a head shot.

circular mil:
An area equal to that of a circle with a diameter of 0.001 inch. It is used for measuring the cross-sectional area of wires.

circumference:
The distance around the outside of a circle.

CIS:
Commonwealth of Independent States (formerly USSR)

civil aircraft:
Aircraft other than public aircraft. *(FAR 1)*

clad aluminum:
A method of protecting aluminum alloys from corrosion by cold rolling a coating of pure aluminum onto the surface of the alloy. This is done in the rolling mill and it reduces the strength of the material somewhat. See *Alclad.*

clamshell thrust reverser:
Turbine engine reverser similar in diameter to the engine nacelle cowling when in use, and when not in use it fits neatly around engine exhaust duct. It has the added advantage of splitting the exhaust gas discharge, which tends to prevent flow instability and severe buffeting.

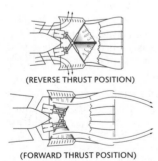

(REVERSE THRUST POSITION)

(FORWARD THRUST POSITION)

CLAMSHELL THRUST REVERSER

class:
1. As used with respect to the certification, ratings, privileges, and limitations of airmen, means a classification of aircraft within a category having similar operating characteristics. Examples include: single engine, multi-engine, land, water, gyroplane, helicopter, airship, and free balloon.
2. As used with respect to the certification of aircraft, means a broad grouping of aircraft having similar characteristics of propulsion, flight, or landing. Examples include: airplane, rotorcraft, glider, balloon, landplane, and seaplane. *(FAR 1)*

class A amplifier operation:
The type of operation in which the amplifier is biased so that variations in input signal polarities occur within the limits of cutoff and saturation.

class AB amplifier operation:
The type of operation in which the amplifier is biased so that collector current is cut off for a portion of the alternation of the input signal.

class A fire:
A fire that involves ordinary combustible materials, paper or wood.

class B amplifier operation:
The type of operation in which the amplifier is biased so that collector current is cut off for one-half of the input signal.

class B fire:
A fire that involves combustible liquids, gasoline or oil.

class C fire:
A fire that involves energized electrical circuits.

class D fire:
A fire that involves metals.

class K fire:
A fire that involves cooking oil or fat.

class of emission:
The set of characteristics of an emission designated by earth stations, beyond which the level of permissible interference will not be exceeded and

coordination is therefore not required.

clearance:
The allowable space between two parts.

clearance cut:
A cut made to provide clearance between adjacent parts.

clearway:
1. For turbine engine powered airplanes certificated after August 29, 1959: an area beyond the runway, not less than 500 feet wide, centrally located about the extended centerline of the runway, and under the control of the airport authorities. The clearway is expressed in terms of a clearway plane, extending from the end of the runway with an upward slope not exceeding 1.25 percent, above which no object nor any terrain protrudes. However, threshold lights may protrude above the plane if their height above the end of the runway is 26 inches or less and if they are located to each side of the runway.

2. For turbine engine powered airplanes certificated after September 30, 1958, but before August 30, 1959: an area beyond the takeoff runway extending no less than 300 feet on either side of the extended centerline of the runway, at an elevation no higher than the elevation of the end of the runway, clear of all fixed obstacles, and under the control of the airport authorities. *(FAR 1)*

cleco fastener:
Sheet metal fasteners that can be quickly installed in or removed from a single side of a material that has to be held tightly in place and with hole alignment maintained. Used while the holes are being drilled and fasteners installed.

clevis:
The forked end of a push-pull tube that is usually attached to a bell crank in an aircraft control assembly.

clevis bolt:
A special-purpose type of bolt designed for shear loads and normally seen in aircraft control systems. They utilize a round head that is slotted to accept a screwdriver, and the threaded portion of the bolt is very short.

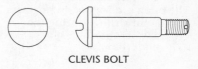

CLEVIS BOLT

clevis pin:
See *flathead pin*

climbout speed:
With respect to rotorcraft: a referenced airspeed that results in a flight path clear of the height-velocity envelope during initial climbout. *(FAR 1)*

climb power:
Power output of the engine reduced by decreasing the manifold pressure and increasing the blade angle to lower the r. p. m. for climb after takeoff. Torque (horsepower absorbed by the propeller) is reduced to match the reduced power of the engine.

clockwise rotation:
The direction in which the hands of a clock rotate.

closed-center valve:
Type of hydraulic valve that has its pressure passage blocked to fluid flow when the valve is in the OFF position.

close-tolerance bolt:
An aircraft bolt with a shank diameter that has been ground to a tolerance of +0.000 – 0.0005. It is identified by a triangle on the head enclosing the material identification mark.

cloud point:
The temperature of an oil at which its wax content, normally held in suspension, begins to solidify and separate into tiny crystals, causing the oil to appear cloudy or hazy.

clove hitch:
Two half-hitches tied around aircraft wiring bundles to hold them.

club propeller:
A stubby propeller used for testing engines after overhaul. The pitch is designed to provide additional airflow during the ground operation.

CLUB PROPELLER

CNS:
Communications Navigations and Surveillance

coaxial cable:
A cable in which the center conductor is separated from an outer conductor by a dielectric material; used in RF transmission.

coaxial rotor:
A rotor system that has two rotors turning in opposite directions, to counteract torque, with the same center of rotation. Mounted on concentric shafts.

cockpit:
The portion of the inside of the airplane occupied by the person(s) operating the airplane and contains the instruments and controls. The flight deck.

Cockpit Resource Management:
Human factors research aimed primarily at cockpit and flight crew research.

cockpit voice recorder (CVR):
Several microphones installed in the cockpit that can record all voice communication between the crew members. The cockpit voice recorder can also record any other sounds that may be present.

co-curing:
The act of curing a composite laminate and simultaneously bonding it to some other uncured structure, or to a core material such as honeycomb or foam.

coefficient of thermal expansion:
The linear expansion or contraction per unit length per degree Fahrenheit between specified lower and upper Fahrenheit temperatures. If aluminum is involved, such values are multiplied by one million for easier reading.

coil shot:
A term used colloquially to indicate a shot of magnetizing current passed through a solenoid or coil surrounding a part, for the purpose of establishing a longitudinal field.

coke deposits:
A carbon buildup often seen in the waste gate unit of turbocharged engines. It may cause erratic system operation. Excessive deposit buildups may cause the waste gate valve to stick in the closed position, causing an over-boost condition. Coke deposit buildup in the turbo itself will cause a gradual loss of power in flight and a low manifold pressure reading prior to takeoff.

cold cathode fluorescent tube:
A highly efficient fluorescent tube often used to illuminate a transmissive LCD.

C

cold-cylinder check:
Procedure that identifies those cylinders that may be running cold, and are usually the cause of backfiring in the engine.

cold flow:
Continued deformation under stress. Seen in the extrusion of rubber hose through and around hose clamps.

cold joint:
A soldered connection in electrical wiring in which the wires were moved before the solder solidified. Often results in high electrical resistance at the joint.

cold lap:
A flaw that results when a workpiece fails to fill the die cavity during the first forging. A seam is formed as subsequent dies force metal over this gap to leave a seam on the workpiece surface.

cold-rolled steel:
The permanent deformation of metal below its re-crystallization temperature by rolling. This process is frequently applied in finishing rounds, sheets, strip, and tin plate.

cold spark plug:
A spark plug in which the nose insulator provides only a short path for heat to travel from the center electrode to the shell. This type of spark plug is normally associated with high-compression engines to minimize the danger of pre-ignition.

cold stream reverser:
Device that reverses thrust by utilizing only the cold fan air of a turbine engine.

cold working:
Any mechanical process that increases the hardness of a metal. This may include hammering, rolling or pulling through a die (as in wire forming).

collective pitch control:
The helicopter control that changes the pitch of all of the rotor blades at the same time. This is normally associated with vertical movement.

collector:
The electrode through which conventional current leaves a transistor.

collector ring:
A type of exhaust system associated with radial engines. The exhaust gases are collected into a single ring and then routed overboard.

collet:
A device similar to a chuck employed to hold a tool or piece of stock during a machining operation. It consists of a split sleeve with a tapered end to fit into a tapered seat. A lengthwise movement of the collet causes either expansion or contraction of the sleeve that clamps the tool or stock.

colloid:
A very finely divided (but not molecular) dispersion of a solid in a liquid. Colloidal dispersions do not settle and the particles are too small to be observed by an ordinary microscope.

color wheel:
A means of visualizing the color that will result when the basic colors are mixed.

combination compressor:
A compressor that combines elements of the centrifugal-flow and the axial-flow compressors. It usually consists of several stages of the axial-flow compressor and one stage of the centrifugal-flow compressor. Also called *dual compressor*.

combustion heater:
An aircraft cabin heater in which fuel from the aircraft's fuel tanks is burned to produce heat that is directed to the cabin area.

combustion liner:
Engine part usually constructed of welded, high-nickel steel, subjected to flames of extremely high temperature. It is behind the compressor and receives the compressed air, which is mixed with fuel and ignited.

coming-in speed:
The speed of rotation of a magneto that is sufficient to produce the voltage required to fire all of the spark plugs consistently.

Comité Consultatif International des Radio Communications (CCIR):
French International Radio Consultative Committee

commercial operator:
A person who, for compensation or hire, engages in the carriage by aircraft in air commerce of persons or property, other than as an air carrier or foreign air carrier or under the authority of Part 375 of this title. Where it is doubtful that an operation is for compensation or hire, the test applied is whether the carriage by air is merely incidental to the person's other business or is, in itself, a major enterprise for profit. *(FAR 1)*

commercial standard digital bus (CSDB):
A one way data bus system between one transmitter and a maximum of 10 receivers.

common base:
A transistor circuit in which the base electrode is the common element to both input and output circuits.

common-base detector:
An amplifying detector in which detection occurs in the emitter-base junction and amplification occurs at the output of the collector junction.

common collector:
A transistor circuit configuration

in which the collector is the element common to both the input and the output circuits.

common emitter:
A circuit configuration in which the emitter is the element common to both the input and the output circuits.

common-emitter detector:
Often used in receivers to supply detected and amplified output. The emitter-base junction acts as the detector.

commutative law:
In Boolean algebra this law states that changing the order of the terms in an equation will not affect the value of the equation. Example:
$A + B = B + A; A \cdot B = B \cdot A$

commutator:
The copper bars on the end of a generator armature to which the rotating coils are attached. Alternating current is generated in this armature, and brushes riding on the commutator act as a mechanical switch to convert it into direct current.

compass:
An instrument used to determine direction.

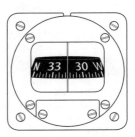

COMPASS

compass correction card:
A card mounted near the magnetic compass, in full view of the pilot, to indicate the difference between the compass reading and the magnetic heading.

compass rose:
A circle marked on a flat surface of the airport, away from magnetic interference. This circle is marked every thirty degrees of magnetic direction. The aircraft is placed on the compass rose and the magnetic compass is adjusted to agree with the heading on each of the marks. Any deviations are recorded on the compass correction card.

compass swinging:
The process of adjusting the magnetic compass according to the marks on the compass rose.

compensated relief valve:
An oil pressure relief valve with a thermostatic valve to decrease the regulated pressure when the oil warms up. High pressure is allowed to force the cold oil through the engine, but the pressure automatically decreases when the oil warms up.

compensating port:
A port inside a brake master cylinder that vents the wheel cylinder to the reservoir when the brake is not applied. This prevents fluid expansion due to heat from causing the brakes to drag.

compensating winding:
Windings embedded in slots in pole pieces, connected in series with the armature, whose magnetic field opposes the armature field and cancels armature reaction.

compensator unit:
Avionics unit used to correct for magnetic errors and flux detector misalignment

complex wave:
1. A waveform other than a sine wave.
2. A wave that is produced by combining two or more pure tones at the same time.

compliance:
To accomplish as required by regulation or directive.

COMPOSI-LOK®:
A brand name of a particular type of bolt made for specific applications. This particular bolt uses a different standard (tenths of an inch) and requires a completely different grip gauge.

composite material:
1. Combinations of materials differing in composition or form on a macro scale. In most cases, neither the reinforcement-type fiber itself nor the matrix has an independent functional utility. Each phase contributes essential benefits that the other phase lacks to the usefulness of the composite materials.
2. A combination of two or more materials (reinforcing elements, fillers, and composite matrix binder), differing in form or composition.

compound-wound generator:
Machines that have a series field in addition to a shunt field. Such machines have characteristics of both series- and shunt-wound machines.

compression ratio:
The ratio of the volume of an engine cylinder with the piston at bottom center to the volume with the piston at top center.

compression ring:
The top piston ring used to provide a seal for the gases in the cylinder, and to transfer heat from the piston into the cylinder walls.

compression riveters:
Commonly called rivet squeezers, these tools are one of the best ways to drive, or squeeze, a solid rivet. Available in a wide variety of sizes and styles, both hand and power operated, they are relatively inexpensive. They all

use interchangeable tooling and can be used for many different jobs.

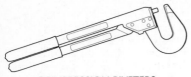

COMPRESSION RIVETERS

compressive strength:
The maximum stress developed in a material when located in compression. For practical purposes, the compressive yield strength is considered as the maximum compressive strength, particularly in the case of wrought metals.

compressor bleed air:
Air taken from the compressor section of a turbine engine to prevent compressor stall and/or to operate certain other systems.

compressor inlet guide vanes:
The guide vanes in the compressor section of a turbine engine that prepare the air for the next stage of compression.

compressor stall:
A condition occurring in a rotary air compressor when some of the blades or vanes meet the airflow at such an angle that there is a reversal of flow, often leading to flameout in a gas turbine engine.

compressor surge:
A severe compressor stall across the entire face of the compressor. Can cause a flameout or structural damage.

computed tomography:
A method by which a radiograph (X-ray) of a predetermined interior plane of a thick material is obtained through the use of a computer. The images resulting from a series of exposures at different angles are stored and reconstructed into a single image

by the computer. In medical terms, a CAT Scan.

concave:
Hollowed or rounded inward like the inside of a bowl.

concentration cell corrosion:
A type of corrosion in which the electrode potential difference is caused by a difference in ion concentration of the electrolyte instead of a difference in galvanic composition within the metal.

concentric:
Accurately centered or having a common center.

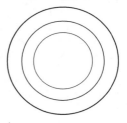

CONCENTRIC

concurrent:
Pertaining to the occurrence of two or more events or activities within the same specified interval of time.

condenser:
1. The component in a vapor cycle air conditioning system where heat energy is given up to the air and the refrigerant vapor is turned into a liquid.

2. Another name for a capacitor.

condition lever:
One of the engine control levers in some turboprop installations. On some aircraft it serves as the propeller control lever during flight, on others it serves only as a fuel shutoff.

conductance:
The ability of a material to conduct or carry an electric current. It is the reciprocal of the

resistance of the material and is expressed in mhos or siemens.

conduction:
The transfer of heat by actual contact between two objects in which the heat energy moves from the higher level to the lower.

conduit:
A tubular raceway, usually metal or plastic, for holding wires or cables.

configuration strapping:
Also known as *pin programming*

Specific electrical connections used to determine various display, input/output signal formats and other system parameters

conformity inspection:
An inspection performed to determine if an aircraft meets all of the requirements of its original or properly altered conditions as specified in the Type Certificate Data Sheets and the manufacturer's specifications.

congealed oil:
Oil that has become solid because of contaminants or low temperatures.

coning:
The upward bending of helicopter rotor blades in flight.

connecting rod:
The link that transmits forces between the piston and the crankshaft.

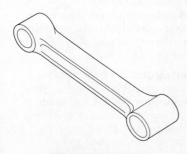

CONNECTING ROD

consensus standard:
For the purpose of certificating light-sport aircraft, an industry-developed consensus standard that applies to aircraft design, production, and airworthiness. It includes, but is not limited to, standards for aircraft design and performance, required equipment, manufacturer quality assurance systems, production acceptance test procedures, operating instructions, maintenance and inspection procedures, identification and recording of major repairs and major alterations, and continued airworthiness. *(FAR 1)*

CONSOL:
A kind of low or medium frequency long range navigational aid. *(FAR 1)*

CONSOLAN:
See *CONSOL*

constant current charge:
A method of charging batteries where the voltage is adjusted during the charge cycle to maintain a constant charging current.

constant displacement pump:
A pump that displaces a constant amount of fluid each time it turns. The faster the pump turns, the more it puts out.

constant speed drive (CSD):
A hydraulic transmission unit used to ensure that the alternator of a large aircraft is always turning at a constant speed and maintaining a constant frequency output regardless of the engine r.p.m.

constant speed propeller:
Controllable pitch propeller used in a system that automatically changes propeller pitch (and drag) to maintain a constant engine r.p.m. and increases engine efficiency.

CONSTANT-SPEED PROPELLER

constant voltage charge:
A method of charging batteries where the voltage remains constant but the charging current varies with the state of charge. At the beginning the charging current will be high, but it should taper off as the battery is restored to full charge.

constituent:
In general, an element of a larger grouping. In advanced composites, the principal constituents are the fibers and the matrix.

contact cement:
A syrupy adhesive applied to both surfaces and bonds on contact.

contact testing:
Ultrasonic testing with transducer assembly in direct contact with material through a thin layer of couplant.

contact transducer:
A transducer that is coupled to a test surface either directly or through a thin film of couplant.

conterminous United States:
The contiguous 48 states and the District of Columbia (DC).

continuous airworthiness program:
A maintenance program consisting of the inspection and maintenance necessary to maintain an aircraft or a fleet of aircraft in airworthy condition and is usually used on large or turbine powered aircraft.

continuous-element type detector:
A type of fire detection system consisting of a small stainless steel tube containing a discrete element

that contains gas. At a certain temperature the gas will be released causing a pressure rise in the tube and activating a pressure switch. This switch activates the fire warning lights and alarm bell.

continuous flow oxygen system:
An oxygen system that provides a continuous flow of oxygen at a constant rate for any give altitude.

continuous ignition system:
A secondary ignition system used with some turbine engine installations. This is generally a lower powered system used to fire one igniter during takeoff, landing, extreme weather and in-flight emergencies.

continuous loop fire detector system:
A type of fire detection system which provides better coverage of large areas than spot-detector type systems. They generally employ two conductors separated by a thermistor-type material. At normal temperatures, this material acts as a resistor and current cannot flow between the conductors. Above a certain temperature, this material becomes conductive and signals the presence of a fire.

continuous method (magnetic particle inspection):
The method in which the inspection medium is applied while the magnetizing current is on.

continuous wave:
An electromagnetic wave that is continuously repeating with constant amplitude and frequency.

contrarotating propellers:
Two propellers mounted on concentric shafts and turning in opposite directions. This is designed so that the rotation will cancel the torque forces.

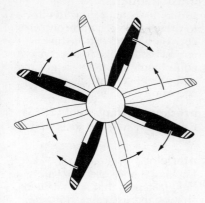

CONTRAROTATING PROPELLERS

control cable:
A cable especially for transmitting controlling movement. A cable for moving the control surfaces of an airplane, either directly or through intermediate mechanisms, or a cable connecting two or more control surfaces.

control display unit (CDU):
An LRU containing a display and alphanumeric keyboard typically used to control the auto-flight and other system functions

controllable pitch propeller:
A propeller whose blade angle may be changed from the cockpit while the propeller is rotating.

controlled airspace:
An airspace of defined dimensions within which air traffic control service is provided to IFR flights and to VFR flights in accordance with the airspace classification. Note: Controlled airspace is a generic term that covers class A, class B, class C, class D, and class E airspace. *(FAR 1)*

controlled firing area:
An area established to contain activities, which if not conducted in a controlled environment, would be hazardous to nonparticipating aircraft. *(FAR 1)*

convection:
The transfer of heat by its absorption by a fluid at one point, followed by motion of the fluid and rejection of the heat at another point.

conventional current:
Also known as a *"Franklin" current.* Dating to the 1700s, this theory assumes current flow to be from positive to negative. Electron flow has been determined to be from negative to positive, but the conventional current thinking continues to be used in some descriptions.

conventional gear:
A landing gear arrangement consisting of two primary main gear with a small tail wheel or tail skid at the rear of the aircraft. Sometimes referred to as a taildragger.

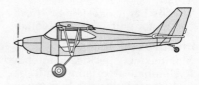

CONVENTIONAL GEAR

convergent duct:
Duct that decreases or tapers to the exit. Often used in turbine engines to control the hot gas, pressure, speed and density.

conversion coating:
A chemical solution used to form a dense, non-porous oxide or phosphate film on the surface of aluminum or magnesium alloys.

cooling fin:
Any one of a number of fins or flat surfaces used for cooling, such as one machined or cast into, or fastened to, an air-cooled engine cylinder or other air-cooled machine, offering its surface area to the air to provide more effective cooling.

coordinated universal time (UTC):
Time scale, based on the second (SI), as defined in Recommendation ITU–R TF.460–6.

copper crush gasket:
A copper gasket with a fiber core that is designed for a single use only. When installed, the gasket takes the shape of the mating surface and provides a leak-free seal.

coriolis force:
A deflective force that is created by the difference in rotational velocity between the equator and the poles of the earth. It deflects air to the right in the northern hemisphere and to the left in the southern hemisphere.

cornice brake:
A sheet metal forming tool used to make straight bends. Also called a *leaf brake*.

corona:
The discharge of electricity from a conductor with a high potential.

corrective maintenance:
Maintenance specifically intended to eliminate an existing fault. Includes location and repair of equipment failures.

corrosion:
The deterioration of material due to electrochemical or chemical attack resulting from exposure to natural or induced environmental conditions or from the destructive attack of fungi or bacteria.

Corrosion Prevention Advisory Board (CPAB):
A board of subject matter experts in the fields of aerospace materials, aircraft structural maintenance, depot and fielded production. The board reviews contractual requirements, prepares design guidance for the system, and periodically surveys contractor activities to provide whatever technical guidance is necessary to ensure the contractor conforms to the goals of the program.

corrosion program:
A planned and organized effort to prevent, detect, and control corrosion in order to reduce corrosion damage to any system, equipment, or aerospace ground equipment susceptible to corrosion damage.

corrosion-resistant steel (CRES):
Commonly referred to as stainless steel.

cotter pin:
Locking device used for safetying only fasteners that have drilled shanks and use castle nuts or on free fitting pins. They are produced in both carbon and stainless steel.

COTTER PIN

coulomb:
A measure of the quantity of electricity. One coulomb is equal to 6.28 x 1,018 electrons.

Coulomb's Law:
States that charged bodies attract or repel each other with a force that is directly proportional to the product of their individual charges and inversely proportional to the square of the distance between them.

counter EMF:
The voltage generated within a coil by a moving magnetic field cutting across the coil itself. This voltage is in opposition (counter) to the moving field that created it. Counter EMF is present in every motor, generator, transformer, or other inductance winding whenever an alternating current flows.

counterbore:
1. To enlarge the part of a hole to a specific size, as for the head of a socket-head cap screw.

2. The tool that is used for this operation.

counterpoise:
A network of wire connected to a quarter-wave antenna at one end. The network provides the equivalent of an additional one-fourth wavelength.

counter-rotating propellers:
A twin-engine propeller configuration where the propellers on the left engine rotate in the opposite direction from those on the right. When configured with the left hand engine turning clockwise and the right turning counter-clockwise, this improves single-engine handling in the event of an engine failure.

countersink:
1. To enlarge the part of a hole at an angle for a flat-head screw.

2. Also, the tool that is used for this operation.

3. To set the head of a screw at or below the surface.

counterweight:
A concentrated mass used to balance a weight or load. Often used on the movable control surface of an airplane to prevent the surface from fluttering. Used in propeller governors to offset the speeder spring.

couplant:
A substance (usually liquid) used when performing ultrasonic inspection. It is placed between the search unit and test part to permit or improve transmission of ultrasonic energy into the test part.

coupling capacitor:
A capacitor used to couple signals.

Course Deviation Indicator (CDI):
Instrument part of Omni navigation system that displays intelligence from the VOR receiver.

cowl flaps:
A system of shutters in an aircraft engine cowling used to regulate the flow of cooling air around the engine.

cowling:
1. A removable cover or housing placed over or around an aircraft component or section, especially an engine.

2. The material or parts used in a cowling. Also called a *cowl*.

CPDLC:
Controller-Pilot Datalink Communications

CPU:
Central Processing Unit

crack:
A discontinuity that has a relatively large cross section in one direction and a small or negligible cross section when viewed in a direction perpendicular to the first.

crankcase:
The foundation of an engine. It contains the bearings in which the crankshaft revolves and also provides support for attachment of the cylinder assemblies.

crankpin:
The part of the crankshaft where the connecting rods attach.

crankshaft:
A shaft forged from a very strong alloy and composed of one or more cranks located at specified points along its length. Its main purpose is to transform the reciprocating motion of the piston and connecting rod into rotary motion for rotation of the propeller.

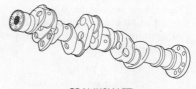

CRANKSHAFT

craze:
A surface irregularity characterized by many hairline indentions or ridges.

crazing:
Region of ultrafine cracks, which may extend in a network on or under the surface of a resin or plastic material.

creep:
The time dependent part of strain resulting from an applied stress.

CRES:
Corrosion-resistant steel.

crewmember:
A person assigned to perform duty in an aircraft during flight time. *(FAR 1)*

critical altitude:
The maximum altitude at which in standard atmosphere it is possible to maintain at a specified rotational speed, a specified power or a specified manifold pressure. Unless otherwise stated, the critical altitude is the maximum altitude at which it is possible to maintain, at the maximum continuous rotational speed, one of the following:

1. The maximum continuous power, in the case of engines for which this power rating is the same at sea level and at the rated altitude.

2. The maximum continuous rated manifold pressure in the case of engines, the maximum continuous power of which is governed by a constant manifold pressure. *(FAR 1)*

critical engine:
The engine whose failure would most adversely affect the performance or handling qualities of an aircraft. *(FAR 1)*

critical operating range:
For a particular engine-propeller combination there may exist an r.p.m. range at which point vibrational forces are too great to allow for constant operation. This range will be marked with a red arc on the tachometer.

critical part:
The part in an assembly that would prevent function should it fail.

crocus cloth:
An abrasive cloth having a very fine, dark red abrasive on its surface. It is used for polishing metals.

cross-coat:
A double coat of dope or paint. It is sprayed on in one direction, and then immediately after the solvent flash off, it is sprayed at right angles to the first coat.

crossover tube:
Duct carrying flame to the individual cylindrical liners of the can-annular combustion chamber.

cross section:
A view showing an internal structure as it would be revealed by cutting through the piece in any plane.

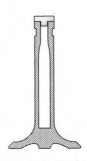

CROSS-SECTION

crystal microphone:
A microphone that uses the piezoelectric effect of crystalline matter to generate a voltage from sound waves.

C

CSD:
A unit used to maintain a constant rotational speed of aircraft AC alternators even though the engine speed varies. See *also constant speed drive.*

C-stage:
The final stage in the reaction of certain thermosetting resins in which the material is practically insoluble and infusible.

Cuno filter:
The proprietary name of a fluid filter made up of a stack of discs separated by scraper blades. Contaminants collect on the edge of the discs and are periodically scraped out and collected in the bottom of the filter case.

cure:
1. A chemical change that takes place in a finishing or adhesive system which produces the desired results.
2. To irreversibly change the properties of a thermosetting resin by chemical reaction.

cure cycle:
The schedule of time periods at specified conditions to which an acting thermosetting material is subjected in order to reach a specified property level.

curie (RT):
A unit of measure to express the rate at which a radioactive material decays. It is defined as that quantity of any radioactive material in which 3.7 x 1,010 disintegrations per second are occurring. Under the new International System (SI) of Units.

current-fed antenna:
A half-wave antenna fed at its center.

current flow:
Electrons in motion.

current limiter:
A device that limits generator output to a level within that rated by the generator manufacturer.

current mode coupler (CMC):
An inductive coupling device, which connects the LRU to the 629 data bus

customer bleed air:
High-pressure hot air taken from the compressor of a turbine engine for use in other systems such as air conditioning, pressurization, deicing, etc.

cutout switch:
An electrical switch that interrupts the flow of power to a motor or actuator when the desired limit of travel is reached (the gear is up, the flaps are down, etc.)

cutting plane line:
A line on a mechanical drawing used to indicate the surface of an auxiliary view.

CUTTING PLANE LINE

cycle:
A complete set of events that occur regularly. The series ends at the same condition as it started.

cyclic pitch control:
The helicopter control used to change the pitch of the rotor blades at a specific point in their rotation. This is associated with lateral, forward, and reverse motion.

cylinder baffles:
Thin sheet metal covers and deflectors attached to air-cooled cylinders to force air through the cooling fins to remove the maximum amount of heat.

cylinder barrel:
The portion of the cylinder where the piston moves up and down.

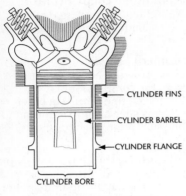

CYLINDER COMPONENTS

cylinder bore:
The diameter of the cylinder barrel.

cylinder fins:
Metal fins on the barrel and head of the cylinder of an air cooled engine to increase the surface area for cooling purposes.

cylinder flange:
The heavy portion on the base of a cylinder barrel which is machined to provide for attachment of the cylinder to the crankcase.

cylinder head temperature:
The temperature of the head of a reciprocating aircraft engine during operation. This is usually measured using a thermocouple replacing the spark plug gasket on one or more cylinders.

Dd

Dacron:
The registered trade name for polyester fibers made by DuPont.

Dalton's law:
Theory that says a mixture of several gases that do not react chemically exerts a pressure equal to the sum of the pressures that the several gases would exert separately if each were allowed to occupy the entire space alone at the given temperature.

dampen:
To lessen, reduce, or deaden.

damper:
A device used to limit movement.

D'Arsonval meter movement:
The permanent magnet moving coil movement used in most analog meters.

dash number:
Numbers following, and separated from, a part number by a dash. These may be used to identify variations in model, size, application, or other variables.

dashpot:
A mechanical damper using a viscous fluid to cushion or slow down movement.

data:
A representation of facts, concepts, or instructions in a formalized manner suitable for communication, interpretation, or processing by humans or by automatic means.

data bus analyzer:
Test equipment used to troubleshoot digital systems

data plate:
An identification plate permanently attached to an aircraft, engine, or accessory.

data plate speed:
The speed at which the manufacturer determines the rated power of an engine. This is normally stamped on the data plate and permanently affixed to the engine.

data transmission:
The transfer of information from one place to another or from one part of a system to another.

datum:
A vertical reference line established by the manufacturer from which all horizontal measurements are made when determining the moments for weight and balance computations.

dB:
See *decibel*

DCAS:
Digital Controlled Audio System

D-check:
The most in-depth inspection of an aircraft. May include the removal of certain major sub-sections like engines and landing gear.

DCMS:
Data Communication Management System

dead smooth:
The term applied to the finest cut of a file.

debond:
A separation of a bonded joint or interface. May be done for repair or rework purposes as well as referring to accidental damage. See *disbond*.

debooster:
A component in a power brake system used to reduce aircraft hydraulic system pressure to brake pressure and permit rapid release of the brakes.

71

debulking:
Compacting of a thick laminate under moderate heat and pressure to remove most of the air and to prevent wrinkles.

decalage:
The difference in the angle of incidence between the upper and lower wings of a biplane. If the angle of incidence of the upper wing is greater than the lower wing, the decalage is positive.

decalcomania:
The process of transferring to glass, wood, etc., prepared copy, decorative pictures or designs printed on specially prepared paper.

decibel:
A measure of sound intensity equal to $^1/_{10}$ of a bel.

decimal:
A proper fraction in which the denominator is a power of ten.

decision height:
With respect to the operation of aircraft, the height at which a decision must be made, during an ILS or PAR instrument approach, to either continue the approach or to execute a missed approach.

dedicated serial data line (DSDL):
A digital bus structure unique to Airbus aircraft

deep cycling:
A service action associated with nickel cadmium batteries where the battery is completely discharged, the cells shorted out and allowed to rest. The battery is then recharged to 140 percent of its ampere-hour capacity.

defect:
A discontinuity that interferes with the usefulness of a part.

de-fueling:
The process of removing fuel from an aircraft with gravity or by pumping the fuel out of the tanks.

degenerative feedback:
Feedback in which the feedback signal is out of phase with the input signal; also called *negative feedback*.

degradation:
A gradual deterioration in performance. The synonym "drift" is often used in electronic equipment.

dehydrator plug:
A plastic plug screwed into the spark plug opening of an aircraft engine cylinder. This plug is filled with a material designed to absorb moisture to prevent corrosion and will change color to indicate when moisture is present.

deicing:
Systems designed to remove ice that has already formed on the propeller or wing.

delaminated:
The separation of the layers of material in a laminate. This may be local or may cover a large area of the laminate. It may occur at any time in the cure or subsequent life of the laminate and may arise from a wide variety of causes.

delamination:
Term used to describe a delaminated area, either local or covering a wide area.

delta:
Change or differential.

delta winding:
A three-phase connection in which windings are connected end-to-end, forming a closed loop that resembles the Greek letter delta (Δ). A separate phase wire is then connected to each of the three junctions.

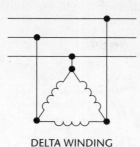

DELTA WINDING

demagnetization:
The reduction in the degree of residual magnetism in ferromagnetic materials to an acceptable level following magnetic particle inspection.

demand oxygen system:
A type of oxygen system where the delivery rate of oxygen is determined by the requirement of the individual user.

demodulator:
A circuit used in servosystems to convert an AC signal to a DC signal. The magnitude of the DC output is determined by the magnitude of the AC input signal, and its polarity is determined by whether the AC input signal is in or out of phase with the AC reference voltage.

demultiplexer (DEMUX):
A circuit that converts serial data into parallel data

denier:
A yarn and filament numbering system in which the yarn number is numerically equal to the weight in grams of 9,000 meters of yarn.

denominator:
The part of a fraction below the line.

density:
Mass of material per unit volume. It is commonly expressed in terms such as pounds per cubic foot, or cubic inch.

density altitude:
Pressure altitude corrected for nonstandard temperature variations. Performance charts for many airplanes are based on this value.

dent:
Small hollow in a surface.

depleted uranium:
Slightly radioactive material used in the counter weights of larger aircraft. Depleted uranium has a heavier mass than lead, therefore counterweights (or bobweights) can be made smaller and still retain the same weight. This reduction in size makes it easier to design the weights so that they are not exposed to the airstream.

depletion area:
The region in a semiconductor where essentially all free electrons and holes have been swept out by the electrostatic field which exists there.

depth micrometer:
A type of micrometer used to measure the depth of a recess.

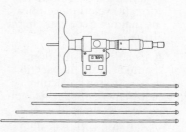

DEPTH MICROMETER

descaling:
Removing the thick layer of oxides formed on some metals at elevated temperatures.

desiccant:
Any form of absorbent material, such as that used in the receiver-dryer of a vapor cycle air conditioning system to remove moisture from the refrigerant.

detail drawing:
A type of drawing that describes a single part in detail.

detergents:
Water-soluble chemicals that emulsify contamination and allow it to be washed away.

detonation:
The almost instantaneous release of heat energy from fuel in an aircraft engine caused by the fuel-air mixture reaching its critical pressure and temperature. It is an explosion rather than a smooth burning process.

developer:
Material, wet or dry, which will draw or absorb penetrant from a surface crack or defect to the extent the defect will be visible under natural, artificial, or black light, as applicable.

deviation:
1. A compass error caused by magnetic disturbances from electrical and metal components in the airplane. The correction for this error is displayed on a compass correction card placed near the magnetic compass in the airplane.

2. A specific authorization, granted before the fact, to depart from a particular requirement of specifications or related documents.

3. Variation from a specified dimension or requirement, usually defining the upper and lower limits.

dew point:
The temperature to which air must be cooled to become saturated.

DH:
Decision height. *(FAR 1)*

dial indicator:
Instrument used to measure amounts of motion or

displacement in thousandths of an inch (mils).

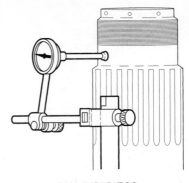

DIAL INDICATOR

diaphragm switch:
A switch whose action is controlled by the movement of a diaphragm.

die:
A tool used to form or stamp out metal parts. Also, a tool used to cut external threads.

die casting:
1. A casting made in a die.

2. A casting process where molten metal is forced under high pressure into the cavity of a metal mold.

dielectric:
An insulator; a term applied to the insulating material between the plates of a capacitor.

dielectric constant:
The ratio of a given dielectric to the dielectric value of air.

dielectric strength:
The ability of an insulator to withstand a potential difference without breaking down (usually expressed in terms of voltage).

diesel engine:
A type of internal combustion engine where ignition is obtained by the heat of compression.

differential aileron travel:
The situation where the ailerons

do not move the same amount in the up and down direction. The up aileron produces extra parasitic drag which is balanced by the increased deflection of the down aileron. The balancing of these forces minimizes adverse yaw during turns.

differential amplifier:
A circuit that amplifies the difference between two input signals.

differential compression check:
A test used to check the compression of aircraft engines by measuring the leakage through the cylinders caused by worn or damaged components. Operation of the compression tester is based on the principle that, for any given airflow through a fixed orifice, a constant pressure drop across that orifice will result.

differential global positioning system (DGPS) station:
A differential RNSS station for specific augmentation of GPS.

differential GPS (DGPS):
A design concept to increase the accuracy, availability, integrity and continuity of the basic GPS to a level sufficient for complete aircraft navigation

differential pressure:
The pressure difference between two systems or volumes. Expressed as: Delta P or Δ P.

differential radio navigation satellite service (differential RNSS) station:
A station used for the transmission of differential correction data and related information as an augmentation to an RNSS system for the purpose of improved navigation accuracy.

differential transducer:
A device that is capable of simultaneously following the voltages across or from

two separate signal sources and providing a final output proportional to the difference between the two signals.

diffuser:
A specially designed duct, chamber, or section, sometimes equipped with guide vanes, that decreases the velocity of a fluid, such as air, and increases its pressure, as in a jet engine, a wind tunnel, etc.

digital data bus:
A bus where exclusively digital data is collected and distributed. A wire that can transmit multiple signals at the same time.

dihedral:
The upward or positive slope of the wings or horizontal tail surfaces. The opposite of anhedral.

DIHEDRAL

dikes:
Diagonal cutting pliers. Often used to cut safety wire.

diluter-demand oxygen system:
A type of oxygen system which delivers oxygen mixed with air to maintain a constant oxygen partial pressure as the altitude changes.

dimensional inspection:
The physical inspection of parts against the established standard (usually the manufacturer's overhaul manual) to determine serviceability.

dimension line:
A dimension line is a light solid line, broken at the midpoint for insertion of measurement indications, and having opposite pointing arrowheads at each end

to show origin and termination of a measurement. Dimension lines are generally parallel to the line for which the dimension is given, and are usually placed outside the outline of the object and between views if more than one view is shown. A dimension lines should not contact the outline of the object.

DIMENSION LINE

dimpling:
1. Stretching a relatively small, shallow indentation into sheet metal.
2. In aircraft, stretching metal into a conical flange for the use of a countersunk head rivet.

diode:
A two-element electron control valve.

diode detector:
A demodulator that uses one or more diodes to provide a rectified output with an average value that is proportional to the original modulation.

dipole:
A common type of half-wave antenna made from a straight piece of wire cut in half. Each half operates at a quarter wavelength of the output.

dipstick:
A graduated rod or stick for measuring the contents of a tank or similar container.

direct-cranking electric starter:
A high-torque DC motor used to rotate an aircraft engine for starting.

direct current:
An electric current that flows in one direction only.

directional gyro:
An instrument that senses yaw movement about the vertical axis. It indicates a change in direction relative to the magnetic north pole.

DIRECTIONAL GYRO

directional stability:
Stability of an aircraft around the vertical axis.

direct sequence systems:
A spread spectrum system in which the carrier has been modulated by a high speed spreading code and an information data stream.

direct short:
Same as short circuit.

disbond:
An area within a bonded interface in which an adhesion failure or separation has occurred.

discontinuity:
An interruption in the normal physical structure or configuration of a part such as cracks, laps, seams, inclusions, porosity. A discontinuity may or may not affect the usefulness of a part. See *defect*.

discrete word format:
An ARINC 429 data word format used to transmit the status of several individual components

dissimilar metals:
Different types of metal, usually considered to be in contact with each other, which produce an electrical potential difference and are susceptible to corrosion.

dissymmetry of lift:
Uneven distribution of lift in the rotor disc area normally encountered in forward flight of a helicopter; caused by the increased velocity of the advancing half of the rotor disc creating more lift, and the decreased velocity of the retreating half reducing lift.

Distance Measuring Equipment (DME):
A radio aid to navigation which provides distance information by measuring total round-trip time of transmission from an interrogator to a transponder and return.

distortion:
An unwanted change in waveform. Principal forms of distortion are inherent nonlinearity of the device, nonuniform response at different frequencies, and lack of constant proportionality between phase-shift and frequency. (A wanted or intentional change might be identical, but it would be called modulation.)

distributor:
That part of a high-tension magneto which distributes high voltage to each spark plug at the proper time. Distributors for low-tension ignition systems distribute low voltage to the transformers at each plug, at their proper time.

dive:
A steep angle of descent.

divergent area:
Place where air flows from a smaller into a larger area.

DLP:
Data Link Processor (the FAA's ground automation system that supports the Mode S sub network (GDLP), internet work (ATN router) and non-ATC data link application processes).

DME:
1. Distance measuring equipment compatible with TACAN.

2. Designated mechanic examiner. *(FAR 1)*

dock:
An enclosed work area where aircraft can be placed for repairs.

donor:
An impurity that can make a semiconductor material an N-type by donating extra free electrons to the conduction band.

dope:
A general term applied to the finishing material used on aircraft fabric covering. Originally it served to tauten and strengthen the fabric as well as make it weatherproof. New types of heat shrinking fabric may be associated with non-tautening products.

doped-on fabric repair:
A repair scheme permitted on certain small repairs to fabric covered aircraft where adhesives and dope are used exclusively to secure the repair.

dope roping:
A condition in the application of dope in which the surface dries while the dope is being brushed. This results in a stringy, uneven surface.

doppler effect:
Also called *Doppler shift*.

1. The apparent change in frequency or pitch when a sound source moves either toward or away from a listener.

2. In radar, the change in frequency of a received signal caused by the relative motion between the radar and the target.

3. The change in frequency with which energy reaches a receiver when the receiver and the energy source are in motion relative to each other.

D

dorsal fin:

The vertical surface extending from the top of the fuselage to the vertical fin. The dorsal fin is used to increase directional stability of the aircraft.

DORSAL FIN

dosimeter:

1. A device worn by persons working in close proximity to radioactive material which indicates the dose of radiation to which they have been exposed.

2. An instrument for measuring the ultraviolet component in solar and sky radiation.

DOT:

Department of Transportation

double-acting actuator:

A linear actuator that is moved in both directions by fluid power.

double-acting hand pump:

A type of pump that moves fuid with both the forward and rearward movement of the handle.

double flare:

A flare made in aluminum or steel tubing where the tube is doubled back on itself to produce a double thickness of metal in the flared portion.

doubler:

1. A piece of sheet metal placed against another piece of sheet metal to provide extra strength or stiffness. This may be used for repairs or for the installation of additional components.

2. A reinforcing strip of metal which has the same contour as the part to which it is fastened.

double-pole, double-throw switch (DPDT):

An electrical switch capable of establishing three conditions in two circuits.

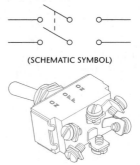

(SCHEMATIC SYMBOL)

DOUBLE-POLE,
DOUBLE-THROW SWITCH

double-pole, single-throw switch (DPST):

An electrical switch capable of establishing two conditions in two circuits.

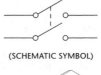

(SCHEMATIC SYMBOL)

DOUBLE-POLE,
SINGLE-THROW SWITCH

doublet signal:

A short positive and negative pulse (spike) on the bus whenever the data value changes from binary one to binary zero or back

Douglas fir:
Wood from the Pacific coast that is somewhat heavier than spruce, but its strength is equal or higher to that of spruce. It is excellent for spars, particularly routed or laminated blanks. Large, solid sizes should be avoided because they are difficult to inspect internally. More likely to develop checks, Douglas fir can split and splinter during fabrication.

down converter:
A circuit found in GPS receivers used to filter out any extraneous signals and converts the RF input to a given intermediate frequency (IF).

downwash:
Air forced down by aerodynamic action below or behind a wing or rotor of a helicopter.

drag:
A force that opposes an aircraft's thrust, retarding the forward motion and limiting the speed of that aircraft.

drag hinge:
The hinge on a helicopter rotor blade that is parallel to the axis of rotation of the blade. It allows the blade to move back and forth on a horizontal plane, minimizing blade vibrations.

drag wire:
A diagonal, load-carrying member of a Pratt truss wing. It runs from the front spar inboard to the rear spar outboard, and carries tensile loads tending to drag back on the wing.

drape forming:
Procedure where a Plexiglas® sheet is heated and then draped over a form to achieve its final contour.

draw filing:
A method of hand filing used to produce a very smooth surface. The file is held with both hands and moved crosswise over the work.

draw set:
A riveting tool used to force sheets of metal together before they are riveted.

drift punch:
A pin punch with a long straight shank.

drill bushing:
A hardened steel guide inserted in jigs, fixtures or templates for the purpose of providing a guide for the drill in drilling holes in their proper or exact location.

drill chuck:
A device used to grip drills and attach them to a rotating spindle.

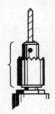

DRILL CHUCK

drill press:
An upright, power-driven machine for drilling holes in metal, wood, or other material.

drip-stick gauge:
A visual means of checking fuel levels from the bottom of the wing of some transport category aircraft. The stick is pulled downward until fuel drips from its end. The quantity of fuel in the tank may then be read at the point where the drip-stick enters the wing.

drive coupling:
A coupling between an accessory and the engine designed to absorb torsional shock. These couplings may also be designed to shear in case of accessory failure to prevent engine damage.

drive fit:
Also known as an *interference fit*. The dimensions of mating parts

are such that the parts must be forced together. This is often designed to be simply the single blow of a hammer.

driver head:
The head of a bolt or screw that is designed to be installed by means of a tool other than a wrench.

drive screw:
Plain head, self-tapping screws installed by tapping in with a hammer. These screws are used to install data plates and to seal holes in aircraft tubular structures after being treated for corrosion.

drop forging:
Metal forming accomplished by placing heated stock in closed or impression dies under a drop or steam hammer and subjecting them to repeated blows.

dross:
The scum that forms on the surface of molten metals largely because of oxidation but sometimes because of the rising of impurities to the surface. The oxide scum present on the surface of molten solder.

dry cell:
An electrical cell in which the electrolyte is not a liquid. In most dry cells the electrolyte is in the form of a paste.

dry-charged battery:
A common method of shipping lead-acid batteries. The battery is fully charged, drained, the cells washed, dried and the battery sealed. To place the battery in service, electrolyte is added and the battery is given a topping charge.

dry-sump engine:
One in which the oil is stored separate from the engine.

dry weight:
The weight of a vehicle or component without fuel or lubricating oil.

dual ignition:
Ignition in which the cylinders of an engine are fired by two separate and complete ignition systems.

dual inline package (DIP):
A component (usually an IC package) which terminates in two straight rows of pins or leads wires.

dual magneto:
Two magnetos incorporated in one housing. One rotating magnet and a cam are common to two sets of breaker points and coils. Two separate distributor units are mounted on the engine apart from the magneto or within the magneto housing.

duckbill pliers:
Flat nosed pliers often used in safety wiring.

ductility:
The property of a metal that permits it to be drawn, rolled, or hammered without fracturing or breaking.

dump valve:
1. Also known as a *fuel jettison valve*. May be used to dump fuel overboard when needed to reduce the weight of an aircraft for landing.

2. One function of the pressurizing and dump valve (P&D Valve) of a turbine engine. This valve drains the fuel manifold after engine shutdown to prevent fuel boiling in the lines.

duplex fuel nozzle:
A type of fuel nozzle that discharges its fuel into the combustion burner in two different patterns and flow rates to match different airflow conditions.

duplex operation:
Operating method in which transmission is possible

simultaneously in both directions of a telecommunication channel.

dutch roll:
A low amplitude oscillation about both the yaw and roll axis of an aircraft. Dutch roll is minimized by the use of yaw dampers.

dutchman shears:
Common name for compound action aviation metal cutting shears. Available in three variations, they are often sold in sets with left cutting, right cutting, straight cutting shears.

dwell time:
The period of time that the liquid penetrant remains on the surface of the part.

dye penetrant inspection:
A form of penetrant inspection in which a dyed oil is applied to the part and allowed to penetrate any cracks. The dye is then removed from the surface and the surface is covered with a white, chalk-like developer to draw the penetrant from any cracks, and with visual penetrants, provide contrast for the inspection.

dynafocal engine mount:
A type of engine mount where the extended centerline of the mount bolts would cross at the center of gravity of the engine-propeller combination.

dynamic balance:
The condition which exists in a rotating body when the axis about which it is forced to rotate, or to which reference is made, is parallel with a principal axis of inertia. No products of inertia about the center of gravity of the body exist in relation to the selected rotational axis.

dynamic damper:
A counter-weight on a crankshaft of an aircraft engine. It is attached in such a way that it can rock back and forth while the shaft is spinning, and absorb dynamic

vibrations. In essence, it changes the resonant frequency of the engine propeller combination.

dynamic microphone:
A device in which sound waves move a coil of fine wire that is mounted on the back of a diaphragm and located in the magnetic field of a permanent magnet.

dynamic pressure:
The difference between pitot pressure and static pressure

dynamic stability:
The characteristics of a body such as an aircraft or rocket, that causes it, when disturbed from an original state of steady flight or motion, to damp the oscillations set up by restoring moments and gradually return to its original state; specifically, the aerodynamic characteristics.

dynamometer:
An instrument used to measure torque force or power, often associated with an engine test cell.

dynamotor:
An electrical device used to convert low voltage DC into high-voltage DC. The dynamotor contains two rotating armatures on the same shaft: basically it is a motor driving a generator.

Dzus® fastener:
A patented type of cowling fastener which uses a slotted stud locking on to a spring steel wire.

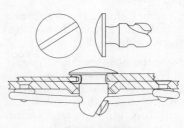

DZUS FASTENER

Ee

EAA:
Experimental Aircraft Association.

EAS:
Equivalent airspeed. *(FAR 1)*

easy-out:
Also known as *EZ out*. A type of screw extractor manufactured from hardened steel with a tapered shape and a left-hand spiral thread. An appropriate sized hole is drilled in the screw to be removed and the easy-out is inserted and turned to the left to extract the broken screw.

eccentric:
A circle not having a geometric center. Also, a device such as a crankshaft or a cam for converting rotary motion to reciprocating motion.

ECM:
Electronic counter measures.

economizer system:
A system in a carburetor which is closed at throttle settings below 60-70 percent so that an engine can develop maximum power at full throttle.

economizer valve:
The valve in a carburetor economizer system that meters the fuel flow to economize on fuel at low power settings.

eddy current:
Current induced in the core of a transformer by current flowing in the windings.

eddy current inspection:
A type of nondestructive inspection that is used to detect cracks, pitting, discontinuities and corrosion in metals both on the surface and below the surface.

Eddy currents are induced into the part being inspected. The presence of a defect is indicated by a difference in the amount of current needed to induce the eddy current.

edge delamination:
A separation of the detail parts along an edge after the assembly has been cured.

edge distance:
The distance from the center of a rivet or bolt hole to the edge of the material.

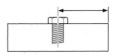

EDGE DISTANCE

edge-grain wood:
See *quarter sawn wood*

Edison effect:
The phenomenon wherein electrons emitted from a heated element within a vacuum tube will flow to a second element that is connected to a positive potential. Also called the *Richardson effect*.

effective pitch:
The actual distance a propeller moves forward through the air in one revolution.

effective propeller thrust:
The net thrust developed by a propeller mounted on an aircraft.

effective radiated power (ERP):
The product of the power supplied to the antenna and its gain relative to a half-wave dipole in a given direction.

effective value:
The root mean square (RMS) value of alternating current. This corresponds to the DC value that would produce the same amount of heat. Effective voltage is equal to 0.707 times the peak value.

effectivity:
Used to determine if the aircraft is covered by the information stated in that section (page) of a manual

EFIS:
See *electronic flight instrument system.*

EFVS:
Enhanced flight vision system. *(FAR 1)*

E-gap angle:
The number of degrees of magnet rotation beyond its neutral position at which the primary breaker points in a magneto open. It is at this point that the primary current flow is the greatest, and therefore the rate of collapse of the primary field will induce the greatest voltage into the secondary winding.

E-glass:
A family of glasses with a calcium aluminoborosilicate composition. A general purpose fiber that is most often used in reinforced plastics, and is suitable for electrical laminates because of its high resistivity.

EICAS:
Engine Indicating and Crew Alerting System

ejector:
The aft portion of a turbojet engine shroud, which permits the escape of cooling air.

ejector pump:
Device used to scavenge fuel from remote areas of fuel tanks, and to provide fuel pressure to an operating engine fuel control unit. Also called a *fuel ejector.*

EJECTOR PUMP

elastic limit:
The maximum stress to which a material may be subjected without any permanent strain remaining upon complete release of stress.

elastic stop nut:
A self-locking nut that utilizes a locking collar of plastic material that is slightly smaller than the outside diameter of the bolt on which it is installed. The pressure exerted by the locking collar prevents the nut from backing off.

elastomeric bearing:
A metal and rubber composite bearing used to carry oscillating loads where complete rotation is not necessary. These bearings can be designed to take radial, axial, and torsional loads and may be associated with some types of helicopter rotor systems.

Elco connector:
A special terminal for aircraft batteries. This is a slip on connector secured with the turn of a hand screw. Also called an *Elcon connector.*

electrical wiring diagram:
A schematic of an electrical system.

electric propeller:
A propeller in which the pitch is regulated by electrical power.

electric servo:
Utilizes an electric motor and clutch assembly to move the aircraft's control surface according to autopilot commands

electrochemical action:
The corrosive results of the electrode potential difference of two metals in contact with each other in the presence of an electrolyte.

electrode:
A terminal or surface at which electricity passes from one material or medium into another.

E

electrodynamometer:
A meter using an electrodynamic movement to measure an electric current.

electrogalvanizing:
The process of coating metal with zinc by electroplating. Used for corrosion prevention.

electrolyte:
A chemical which will conduct electrical current by releasing ions to unite with ions in the electrodes.

electrolytic capacitor:
A capacitor that uses metal foil for the electrodes and a thin film of metallic oxides as the dielectric.

electromagnet:
A magnet created by electrical current flowing through a coil of wire.

electromagnetic induction:
Transfer of electrical energy from one conductor to another by means of a moving electromagnetic field. The value of the voltage produced is proportional to the number of magnetic lines of force cut per second.

electromotive force (EMF):
The work or energy that causes the flow of an electric current. Expressed as volts. It should be noted that the term force is a misnomer. However, the term is so well established that its use continues in spite of its being incorrect.

electron:
The elementary negative charge that revolves around the nucleus of an atom.

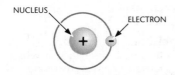

ELECTRON (HYDROGEN ATOM)

electron beam welding:
A welding process where heat is produced by a high-speed stream of electrons striking the metal.

electronic flight display (EFD):
An LRU used to provide primary flight and navigation data on a LCD or CRT display

electronic flight instrument system (EFIS):
Employs two or more CRTs or LCDs to present alphanumeric data and graphical representations of aircraft flight instruments

electronics:
The branch of physics which deals with the emission, transmission, behavior and effects of electrons. Practical applications are made through devices such as transistors, computer chips, photo-electric cells, capacitors and the like.

electroplating:
An electrochemical method of depositing a film of metal on an object. The object to be plated is the cathode, the metal to be deposited is the anode, and the electrolyte is a material which will form ions of the plating metal.

electrostatic discharge:
The discharge (movement of electrons) created when any material containing a static charge is exposed to a material containing a different or neutral charge

electrostatic coupling:
Coupling between two circuits that is effected by a capacitor included in a common branch, or by a capacitor connected between appropriate points in the two circuits.

electrostatic field:
The field of influence between two differently charged bodies.

element:
One of the 110 known chemical

substances that cannot be divided into simpler substances by chemical means. Examples: hydrogen, lead, and uranium.

elevator:
A control surface that is attached to the back of the horizontal stabilizer and used to deflect air lift upward and downward in order to cause the airplane to pitch.

ELEVATOR

elevator station (ES) or nacelle station (NS):
Used on larger aircraft to help technicians find components in specific areas of the aircraft

elevon:
A control surface that combines the function of the elevator and the aileron.

elongate:
To lengthen or stretch out.

emergency locator transmitter (ELT):
A self-contained, battery powered radio transmitter that will automatically activate upon the impact of a crash and transmit an emergency signal to aid in locating the aircraft.

emergency position-indicating radio beacon station:
A station in the mobile service whose emissions are intended to facilitate search and rescue operations.

emission:
Radiation produced, or the production of radiation, by a radio transmitting station.

empennage:
See *tail section*

empty weight:
The weight of an aircraft including the weight of its power plant, trapped fuel and oil, coolant (if any), fluid in the hydraulic system, ballast normally carried, fixed equipment and furnishings, and other weight as may be defined in context; also sometimes applied to a rocket less the weight of its propellants and load.

empty weight center of gravity (EWCG):
The CG of an aircraft in its empty weight condition. It is an essential part of the weight and balance record of the aircraft. It has no usefulness in itself, but serves as a basis for other computations, and not as an indication of what the loaded CG will be. The EWCG is computed at the time of weighing.

emulsion type cleaner:
A type of solvent that can be rinsed off with water after it is applied or used as a solvent wipe remover.

encapsulate:
To completely cover or surround something.

encoding altimeter:
An altimeter coupled with the radar transponder to report the aircraft's altitude.

end play:
Longitudinal back-and-forth play of a shaft.

engine cradle:
A framework for the support of an unmounted aircraft engine.

engine logbook:
A record of time in service, inspections and maintenance performed, etc., for an aircraft engine.

engine mount:
Framework or device used to mount an engine to an airframe. Can be a welded assembly or a built-up sheet metal assembly.

engine pressure ratio (EPR):
Instrument that measures the engine pressure ratio as a measure of the thrust being developed by the engine.

engine station:
Numeric designations for locations along the length of a turbine engine. This normally begins at the inlet (station 1) and ends at the jet nozzle (station 10).

enhanced flight visibility (EFV):
The average forward horizontal distance, from the cockpit of an aircraft in flight, at which prominent topographical objects may be clearly distinguished and identified by day or night by a pilot using an enhanced flight vision system. *(FAR 1)*

enhanced flight vision system (EFVS):
An electronic means to provide a display of the forward external scene topography (the natural or man made features of a place or region especially in a way to show their relative positions and elevation) through the use of imaging sensors, such as a forward looking infrared, millimeter wave radiometry, millimeter wave radar, low light level image intensifying. *(FAR 1)*

enrich:
To increase the amount of fuel in the mixture without increasing the amount of air.

entrained water:
Water held in suspension in aircraft fuel. It is in such tiny droplets that it passes through filters and will do no damage until the temperature of the fuel drops to the point that these tiny particles accumulate or coalesce to form free water in the tank.

envelope method of recovering:
A method of installing fabric on aircraft structure using a pre-sewn envelope. This method has the advantage of minimizing the amount of hand sewing required.

EPCS:
Electronic Propulsion Control System

ephemeris:
A table showing the precalculated position of a satellite at any given time.

epoxy:
Resins which may be of widely different structures but are characterized by the presence of the epoxy group. The epoxy or epoxide group is usually present as a glycidyl ether, glycidyl amine, or as part of an aliphatic ring system. The aromatic type epoxy resins are normally used in composites.

epoxy resin:
A thermoset polymer containing one or more epoxide groups. An important matrix resin in composites and structural adhesives.

EPROM:
Erasable Programmable Read-Only Memory

EPR-rated gas turbine engine:
A method of expressing the thrust of a gas turbine engine in terms of the engine pressure ratio.

equalizer circuit:
A circuit in a multiple generator voltage-regulator system that is designed to equalize the current output of the generators by controlling the field current of the generators.

equatorial orbit:
An orbit that occurs when the plane of a satellite coincides with the plane of the earth at the equator.

EQUATORIAL ORBIT

equipment identifier:
Part of the ARINC 429 data word used to further define the word label.

equivalent airspeed:
The calibrated airspeed of an aircraft corrected for adiabatic compressible flow for the particular altitude. Equivalent airspeed is equal to calibrated airspeed in standard atmosphere at sea level. *(FAR 1)*

equivalent shaft horsepower (ESHP):
A means of measuring power output of turboprops and some turboshaft engines.
ESHP = SHP + HP from jet thrust.

erg:
Unit of energy (C.G.S.) equal to one dyne centimeter or approximately equal to the work done by a force of 1 milligram causing a movement of 1 centimeter.

etching:
Subjecting the surface of a metal to preferential chemical or electrolytic attack in order to reveal structural details.

ethylene dibromide:
A compound of bromine added to aviation gasoline to convert the lead deposits from the tetraethyl lead into lead bromides that are volatile enough to vaporize and pass out the exhaust rather than foul the spark plugs.

ethylene glycol:
A type of alcohol used as an antifreeze.

ETOPS:
Extended Twin Engine Operations

eutectic metal:
An alloy that changes directly from a solid to a liquid with no plastic or semi-liquid state.

eutectic solder:
An alloy of 63 percent tin and 37 percent lead. Melts at 361° F.

evaporator:
The component in a vapor cycle air conditioning system where the liquid refrigerant absorbs heat from the cabin to change the refrigerant into a vapor. Air blown over the evaporator loses its heat and is cooled.

EVM:
Engine Vibration Monitor

excitation voltage:
The supply voltage required to activate a circuit.

exciter:
1. An electrical device that produces the electrical field for a generator or alternator.

2. The high voltage power source for a turbine engine ignition system.

exclusive OR gate:
A logic device having two inputs. A voltage (1) on either input but not both, will produce a voltage (1) at the output.

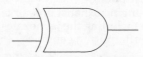

EXCLUSIVE OR GATE

exerciser jack:
A hydraulic jack placed under a landing gear to move it up and down while it is being filled and to work the air out of the system.

exfoliation:
An advanced form of intergranular corrosion that is characterized by flaking of the material.

exfoliation corrosion:
The extreme form of intergranular corrosion where flakes of metal are raised up and may be shed.

exhaust augmenter:
A length of large diameter heat- and corrosion-resistant tubing constructed with a bell mouth. The bellmouth design of the augmenter creates a venturi effect that increases the flow of air through the augmenter. This venturi effect provides a more efficient method of engine cooling.

exhaust back pressure:
Pressure produced in the exhaust system of a reciprocating engine. This pressure is a function of the diameter and length of the exhaust pipe and may be affected by muffler design. This pressure opposes the flow of exhaust gases as they are forced out of the cylinder when the exhaust valve opens.

exhaust collector ring:
See *collector ring*

exhaust cone:
Also called the *exhaust connecter*, this is a separate outer casing that houses the tail cone and is located between the turbine case and the tail pipe on some turbine engines.

exhaust duct:
The engine exhaust pipe or tail pipe including the jet nozzle of a non-afterburning engine.

exhaust gas temperature (EGT):
The average temperature of the exhaust gases as they leave the cylinder of a reciprocating engine or the turbine section of a gas turbine engine.

exhaust manifold:
A collector arrangement used to gather the exhaust products of two or more cylinders of a reciprocating engine and direct them overboard.

exhaust nozzle:
The rear opening of a turbine engine exhaust duct.

exhaust port:
A valve opening in the top of an engine cylinder for the discharge of exhaust gases.

exhaust stacks:
Short, individual pipes attached to each cylinder of a reciprocating engine. Used to direct the exhaust gases overboard.

exhaust stroke:
The final stroke of the four stroke (Otto) cycle where the byproducts of combustion are forced out of the cylinder.

EXHAUST STROKE

exhaust valve:
The valve of a reciprocating engine through which the exhaust gases are forced to exit the cylinder.

exit guide vanes:
Fixed airfoils at the discharge end of an axial flow compressor used to straighten out the swirling air prior to its entry into the combustion section.

exosphere:
The outermost layer of the atmosphere. The term is subject to different definition and understanding according to context.

expander tube brakes:
A type of non-servo brake that uses composition blocks forced out against a rotating drum by hydraulic fluid expanding a rubber tube on which they rest.

expansion turbine:
The principle component of the air cycle cooling system. Compressed air passing through the expansion turbine undergoes a pressure and temperature drop. It is this temperature drop that produces the cold air for air conditioning.

expansion valve:
Used in a vapor cycle system. The expansion valve lowers the pressure of the Freon after it leaves the condenser as a high pressure liquid. By lowering the pressure the temperature is also lowered.

experimental aircraft:
1. An aircraft built to try out an idea, or to try for certain capabilities or characteristics; an aircraft that embodies a new principal or a new application of an old principle.

2. A homebuilt aircraft.

exploded view:
This type of drawing shows the relationship of parts and can be helpful in assembling components. Exploded views are also used to illustrate parts manuals.

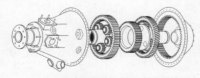

EXPLODED VIEW
(PT6 GEAR ARRANGEMENT)

explosive decompression:
A very rapid, almost instantaneous decompression, as may occur, e.g. in the rupture of an aircraft cabin at high altitude.

extended over-water operation:
1. With respect to aircraft other than helicopters: an operation over water at a horizontal distance of more than 50 nautical miles from the nearest shoreline.

2. With respect to helicopters: an operation over water at a horizontal distance of more than 50 nautical miles from the nearest shoreline and more than 50 nautical miles from an off-shore heliport structure. *(FAR 1)*

extension line:
An extension line is a thin line used to move the dimension from the surface of the object to a point where the dimension will not interfere with the other lines. Extension lines should not touch the outline of the object, but may cross object lines. They should not begin or end on object lines.

external load:
A load that is carried or extends outside of the aircraft fuselage. *(FAR 1)*

external-load attaching:
The structural components used to attach an external load to an aircraft, including external-load containers, the backup structure at the attachment points, and any quick-release device used to jettison the external load. *(FAR 1)*

externally synchronized radar:
A radar system in which timing pulses are generated by a master oscillator external to the transmitter.

external tooth washer:
A thin spring steel washer with twisted teeth around its outside

E

circumference. These teeth hold pressure between the head of a screw or bolt and the metal surface to prevent the fastener from loosening.

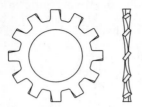

EXTERNAL TOOTH WASHER

extremely high frequency:
The band of frequencies from 30 gigahertz to 300 gigahertz.

extremely low frequency:
The band of frequencies up to 300 hertz.

extrude:
To form materials (usually metals) by forcing through a die of the desired shape.

extrusion:
1. The process or method by means of which the metals, such as aluminum, are shaped into intricate cross-sectional shapes by being forced through a die opening.

2. A part which has been formed by an extrusion process.

Ff

FAA:
Federal Aviation Administration.
(FAR 1)

FAA-PMA:
The identifying letters
required on an aircraft part or
component to signify it as being
manufactured under a Federal
Aviation Administration - Parts
Manufacturing Approval.

fabric fill face:
That side of the woven fabric
where the majority of the exposed
yarns are perpendicular to the
selvage edge.

fabric warp face:
That side of the fabric where the
majority of the exposed yarns are
parallel to the selvage edge.

face of weld:
The exposed surface of a weld,
made by an arc or gas welding
process, on the side from which
welding was done.

facsimile (fax):
A form of telegraphy for the
transmission of fixed images,
with or without half-tones, with
a view to their reproduction in a
permanent form.

FADEC:
1. Full Authority Digital
   Electronic Engine Control.

2. Full Authority Digital Engine
   Control.

3. A type of engine control that
   monitors the operation of the
   engine and constantly adjusts
   fuel and air for optimum
   performance. A fully automatic
   fuel control.

Fahrenheit (F):
A thermometer scale on which the
freezing point of water is 32°F and
the boiling point is 212°F (at sea
level atmospheric pressure).

fail-safe:
A design feature established to
transmit loads into a secondary
portion of the structure in the
event of a failure of the primary
structure.

fairing:
Streamlined covering.

fairlead:
A tube or a trough shaped piece,
through or over which a cable or
rod is passed to guide or support
it and to prevent whipping, or
chafing against another part.

false rib:
A short, semi-rib extending
from just behind the front spar
to the leading edge of a wing. It
is used to give better shape and
additional rigidity to the leading
edge of fabric covered wings.

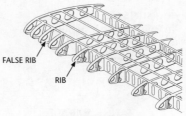

FALSE RIB

RIB

FALSE RIB

false spar:
A partial spar in an aircraft wing
used to attach the aileron hinges.

false start:
In a turbine engine, a start
during which the engine has not
accelerated, but the fuel air is
ignited. Also called a *hung start*.

fan jet:
See *turbofan engine*

FANS:
Future Air Navigation System

FAR:
Federal Aviation Regulation

91

farad:
The basic unit of capacitance. A capacitor has a capacitance of 1 farad when a voltage potential of 1 volt across it produces a charge of 1 coulomb.

fatigue corrosion:
The result of the combined action of alternating, or cycling, stresses and a corrosive environment.

fatigue crack:
Progressive cracks that develop in the surface of a part. They are caused by the repeated loading and unloading of the part, or by what is called reverse bending.

fault flag:
Any indication made on one or more avionics displays related to a complete or partial system failure.

fault isolation manual (FIM):
A part of the aircraft maintenance manuals, which contains various repair strategies for given faults.

faying surface:
An overlapping surface.

FAYING SURFACE

FCU:
1. Fuel Control Unit
2. Flight Control Unit

FDR:
Flight Data Recorder

feather edge:
A very thin, sharp edge, like the edge of a feather. This type of edge is subject to easy damage, breaking, burning, etc., depending on where it is found.

feathering propeller:
A controllable propeller that has the ability to change the pitch to an angle so that the blade angle is 90° to the apparent wind and will have no windmilling effect on an engine that has been shut down in flight. Feathering propellers must be used on multi-engine aircraft to reduce propeller drag to a minimum under engine-failure conditions.

Federal Aviation Administration (FAA):
A part of the Department of Transportation responsible for establishing and enforcing the rules for civil aviation.

feed shoes:
A narrow strip of rubber extending from the blade shank to a blade station that is approximately 75 percent of the propeller radius. Used to disperse anti-icing fluids to areas on which ice collects in large quantities on the blade leading edge.

feedthrough capacitor:
A capacitor that serves a dual purpose. In aircraft magnetos a feedthrough capacitor is used to minimize arcing at the points and to decrease radio interference caused by electrical energy radiated from ignition leads.

feeler gauge:
Also known as a *thickness gauge*. A tool consisting of precision ground steel blades of various thicknesses used to measure the clearance between parts.

female part:
A concave piece of equipment that receives a mating male (convex) part.

fence:
A fixed vane extending chordwise across the wing of an aircraft. Fences are installed to prevent air from flowing along the span of the wing.

fenestron tail rotor:
A tail rotor that is enclosed in an aerodynamic fairing.

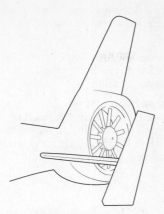

FENESTRON TAIL ROTOR

ferrite:
A solution in which alpha iron is the solvent, and which is characterized by a body-centered cubic crystal structure.

ferromagnetic material:
Materials that are strongly attracted by a magnetic field. Iron, steel, nickel, and cobalt are included in this category. Permeability is much greater than one, and is affected by the applied magnetic field.

ferrous metal:
Iron, or any alloy containing iron.

ferry permit:
Also known as a *Special Flight Permit*. This permit is issued by the FAA to allow unlicensed aircraft to be flown from one location to another. This is often done to relocate the aircraft for maintenance purposes.

fiber:
A general term used to refer to filamentary materials. Often, fiber is used synonymously with filament. It is a general term for a filament of finite length. A unit of matter, either natural or man-made, which forms the basic element of fabrics and other textile structures.

fiber content:
The amount of fiber present in a composite. This is usually expressed as a percentage volume fraction or weight fraction of the composite.

fiber locknut:
See *elastic stop nut*

fiber optics:
Conductors or optical waveguides that readily pass light.

fiberglass:
Thin glass fibers that may be woven into cloth or packed into matting. Fiberglass is used to reinforce resin matrices for aircraft structure.

fidelity:
1. The faithful reproduction of a signal.
2. The accuracy with which a system reproduces a signal at its output that faithfully maintains the essential characteristics of the input signal.

field coil:
The electromagnet that furnishes the magnetic field that interacts with the armature in motors and generators.

field effect transistor (FET):
A semiconductor device with a high input impedance. Electron flow between the source and drain is controlled by voltage applied to the gate.

field frame:
The main structural component of a motor or generator.

field maintenance:
Maintenance performed on aircraft while they are away from their home base. This is usually accomplished with minimal tools and equipment.

field strength meter:
A device for indicating the amount of magnetism in a part.

filament:
The source of electrons in a hot-cathode tube. It is usually a heated wire.

file:
A handheld cutting device made of high-carbon steel and fitted with rows of very shallow teeth extending diagonally across the width of the tool.

file card:
A small wire brush used for brushing chips from the serrations of a file.

file test:
A test for hardness in which a corner of a file is run across the piece of metal being tested. The hardness is shown by the dent the file makes.

filiform corrosion:
A thread- or filament-like corrosion that forms on aluminum skins beneath polyurethane enamel.

fill:
Yarn oriented at right angles to the warp in a woven fabric. Also called *weft* or *woof*.

filler material:
Chemically inert, finely divided material added to the elastomer to aid in processing and improve physical properties, i.e., abrasion resistance and strength, and give it varying degrees of hardness.

filler metal:
Metal to be added in making a weld.

filler neck:
The tube leading into a reservoir for replenishing fluids.

filler rod:
Metal rod used when welding to provide the necessary filler metal and to provide additional strength to the weld.

filler valve:
A readily accessible valve that provides a means to service an installed aircraft system.

fillet:
A concave junction of two surfaces which are usually perpendicular.

fillister head screw:
A machine screw, the head of which has a rounded top surface, with cylindrical sides and a flat bearing surface.

FILLISTER HEAD SCREW

fill threads:
In a woven fabric, the yarn running from selvage to selvage at right angles to the warp. Also called the *weft threads*.

film adhesive:
A synthetic resin adhesive in the form of a thin, dry film of resin.

film resistor:
A resistor manufactured by coating an insulating cylinder with a metal oxide or other thin resistive film.

film strength:
The ability of a lubricant to maintain a continuous lubricating film under mechanical pressure without breaking down.

filter:
1. A porous material on which solid particles are caught and retained when a mixture is passed through it.

2. To remove mechanically the solids or free water from a product.

fin:
A vertical attachment to the tail of an aircraft that provides

directional stability. Same as vertical stabilizer.

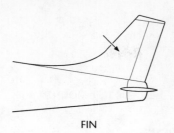

FIN

final takeoff speed:
The speed of the airplane that exists at the end of the takeoff path in the en route configuration with one engine inoperative. *(FAR 1)*

fine crack:
A discontinuity in a solid material with a very fine opening to the surface, but possessing length and depth greater than the width of this opening; usually depth is many times the width.

fine-wire spark plug:
An aircraft spark plug utilizing fine wires of platinum or iridium as electrodes. These small electrodes allow the firing end cavity to be open and provide better scavenging of the lead oxides from the plug.

finger brake:
See *box brake*

finger patch:
A type of welded patch used to repair a steel tube cluster. The fingers extend along each of the tubes in the cluster.

finger screen:
A finger-shaped filter screen used in some fuel system components to filter out contaminants.

finish:
1. Surface condition, quality or appearance of a metal.

2. Stock on a forging to be removed when finish machined.

finishing stone:
A grade of stone used to remove grinding marks and produce a smooth finish during the process of re-facing valve seats.

finite life:
A limited life. Parts or accessories with a finite life must be scrapped at the end of their predetermined life.

fire detection system:
A system installed on an aircraft to inform the pilot of a fire on-board the aircraft.

fire extinguisher:
Any device containing a fire-extinguishing agent used to cool a material below its kindling point, or to exclude oxygen from its surface.

fire point:
The temperature at which vapors given off by a substance will ignite and continue to burn when a flame is passed above the surface of the material.

fireproof:
1. With respect to materials and parts used to confine fire in a designated fire zone: the capacity to withstand at least as well as steel in dimensions appropriate for the purpose for which they are used, the heat produced when there is a severe fire of extended duration in that zone.

2. With respect to other materials and parts: the capacity to withstand the heat associated with fire at least as well as steel in dimensions appropriate for the purpose for which they are used. *(FAR 1)*

fire-resistant:
1. With respect to sheet or structural members: the capacity to withstand the heat associated with fire at least as well as aluminum alloy in dimensions appropriate for

F

the purpose for which they are used.

2. With respect to fluid-carrying lines, fluid system parts, wiring, air ducts, fittings, and powerplant controls: the capacity to perform the intended functions under the heat and other conditions likely to occur when there is a fire at the place concerned. *(FAR 1)*

firewall:
The fire resistant bulkhead installed between the engine compartment of an aircraft and the rest of the structure.

fire zone:
An area or region of an aircraft designated by the manufacturer to require fire detection and/ or fire extinguishing equipment and a high degree of inherent fire resistance.

firing order:
The sequence in which the cylinders of a reciprocating engine fire in the normal cycle of operation.

firing position:
The position of a piston in the cylinder of a reciprocating engine at which time ignition should occur. Igniting the mixture at this position allows peak cylinder pressure to occur shortly after the piston passes center.

first class lever:
Lever that has its fulcrum located between the effort and the resistance.

fir tree mount:
Manner of attaching the blades to the disk in the turbine rotor assembly. The root of the blade where it is attached to the disk is shaped like a fir tree.

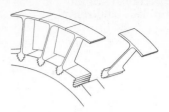

FIR TREE MOUNT

fisheyes:
Isolated areas in a painted finish that have rejected the finish, because of wax or silicone contamination on the surface.

fishmouth splice:
A welded splice in a steel tube structure where one tube telescopes over the other. The outside tube is cut into a V so that the ends resemble the mouth of a fish. This design provides additional area for the weld.

five minute rating:
An amp-hour rating associated with batteries. This is normally used when comparing high current applications such as starting.

five hour rating:
The amp-hour rating of a battery that will discharge the battery in five hours. This is the most common rating for comparing batteries.

fixed base operator (FBO):
An aviation company located on an airport to provide goods and services within the aviation community.

fixed-displacement pump:
Pump in which the volume of fluid per cycle cannot be varied. Also known as *constant displacement*.

fixed equipment:
Non-removable, attached accessories.

fixed landing gear:
A landing gear that remains fixed in position at all times. Sometimes called non-retractable landing gear.

fixed pitch propeller:
A propeller whose blade angle cannot be changed.

fixed resistor:
A resistor having a definite resistance value that cannot be adjusted.

fixed tail surfaces:
Also called the *stabilizers*, they are mounted rigidly to the fuselage. The fixed tail surfaces provide a mounting for the rudder and elevator (the movable tail surfaces).

fixed wing aircraft:
An aircraft with the wings rigidly attached. Not a helicopter or autogyro.

FIXED-WING AIRCRAFT

flag note:
Used to bring attention to a specific effectivity on a diagram or schematic

flame hardening:
A process of hardening a ferrous alloy by heating it above the transformation range by means of a high-temperature flame and then cooling as required.

flame holder:
A grid, ring, plate, or other device that provides a sheltered zone for flame stabilization in a moving stream of combustible mixture, as in an afterburner.

flameout:
The failure of a turbine engine where combustion is extinguished.

flame propagation tube:
See *crossover tube*

flame resistant:
Not susceptible to combustion to the point of propagating a flame, beyond safe limits, after the ignition source is removed. *(FAR 1)*

flammable:
With respect to a fluid or gas: susceptible to igniting readily or to exploding. *(FAR 1)*

flanged shaft:
A shaft with a flat plate formed on the end whose face is perpendicular to the shaft. Most modern aircraft engine crankshafts are fitted with a flange to mount the propeller.

flaperon:
A special type of control that serves both as an aileron and a flap. Used on swept-wing aircraft.

flap extended speed:
The highest speed permissible with wing flaps in a prescribed extended position. *(FAR 1)*

flapper valve:
A type of check valve hinged on one end. Fluid is free to flow in one direction only.

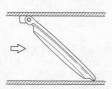

FLAPPER VALVE

flapping:
Up-and-down motion of a rotor blade.

flaps:
Hinged or pivoted airfoils forming part of the trailing edge of the wing and used to increase lift and/or drag of an aircraft.

flareless fitting:
A form of fluid line fitting used on some hydraulic lines. Instead of using a formed flare on the end of the tube, a sleeve is forced into the tube to form the sealing surface.

flaring:
A mechanical operation used to expand the end of a piece of tubing in order to produce a tight seal when coupled to another unit.

flash:
Excess material that forms at the parting line of a mold or die, or that is extruded from a closed mold.

flashback:
The burning of gases within the welding torch or beyond the torch in the hose, usually with a shrill, hissing sound.

flashing off:
Drying of a finish to touch by the evaporation of certain of the solvents. The film is not dry and hard throughout.

flashing the field:
A method of restoring the residual magnetism of a DC generator accomplished by momentarily passing a current through the field windings to induce a magnetic field.

flashover:
Condition where high voltage current is misdirected to the wrong spark plug and cylinder misfiring occurs. Condensed moisture contamination in the magneto is an excellent conductor of electricity and is usually the cause.

flash point:
The lowest temperature at which a liquid petroleum product gives off vapor in sufficient concentration to ignite (that is, flash) on application of a flame under specified conditions.

flash resistant:
Not susceptible to burning violently when ignited. *(FAR 1)*

flash tape:
A tape used in composite manufacture and repair. Flash tape is unaffected by most autoclave temperatures and pressures.

flathead pin:
This is a high-strength steel pin with a flat head on one end and a hole for a cotter pin on the other. It is often used as a hinge pin in control systems and for attaching cables to control horns. Flathead pins are designed to withstand shear loads only. Also called a *clevis pin.*

flat panel display (FPD):
A solid-state device used to display various formats of video information in modern aircraft flight displays

flat washer:
Also known as a *plain washer.* Used under the head of a bolt or nut to protect the connecting material from damage.

flexibility:
The characteristic of a material that allows it to be repeatedly bent, stretched, or twisted within its elastic limits and still return to its original condition when the deforming force is removed.

flexible control cable:
Aircraft cable consisting of seven strands of steel wire, each strand having seven separate wires. Also known as *7x7 cable.*

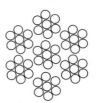

(CROSS SECTION)

FLEXIBLE CONTROL CABLE

flightcrew member:
A pilot, flight engineer, or flight navigator assigned to duty in an aircraft during flight time. *(FAR 1)*

flight data recorders (FDR):
Device that automatically records flight and control parameters, including selected instrument readings. It can record for up to 24 hours, depending on the model of the FDR.

flight deck:
The area of the aircraft occupied by the flight crew. Also known as the *cockpit*.

flight deck effects:
Any EFIS or EICAS display, or discrete annunciator used to inform the flight crew of a system fault.

flight director indicator (FDI):
A flight director is a multifunction instrument that combines attitude information from the gyro horizon with navigation information from the VOR and glideslope receivers. Some units also add airspeed and altitude warnings.

flight idle:
Lowest engine speed available in flight.

flight interphone:
The flight interphone system is used to provide communications between flight crewmembers and/or other aircraft operations personnel. The flight interphone system is typically used for communications between flight crewmembers; however, the system may be interconnected to the service and cabin interphones when needed.

flight level:
A level of constant atmospheric pressure related to a reference datum of 29.92 inches of mercury. Each is stated in three digits that represent hundreds of feet. For example, flight level 250 represents a barometric altimeter indication of 25,000 feet; flight level 255, an indication of 25,500 feet. *(FAR 1)*

flight management system (FMS):
Computer-based systems that reduce pilot workload by providing automatic radio tuning, lateral and vertical navigation, thrust management, and the display of flight plan maps.

flight manual:
Approved information that must be carried in an airplane. This includes the engine operating limits and any other information that is vital to the pilot.

flight phase:
A time period of a given flight often recorded by the CMC to help the technician determine the airplane's configuration at the time of a system fault

flight phase screening:
A software function used to help eliminate nuisance messages from entering the central maintenance system

flight plan:
Specified information, relating to the intended flight of an aircraft, that is filed orally or in writing with air traffic control. *(FAR 1)*

flight time:
1. Pilot time that commences when an aircraft moves under its own power for the purpose of flight and ends when the aircraft comes to rest after landing.
2. For a glider without self-launch capability, pilot time that commences when the glider is towed for the purpose of flight and ends when the glider comes to rest after landing. *(FAR 1)*

flight visibility:
The average forward horizontal distance, from the cockpit of an aircraft in flight, at which prominent unlighted objects may

F

99

be seen and identified by day and prominent lighted objects may be seen and identified by night. (FAR 1)

flip-flop:
A device having two stable states and two input terminals (or types of input signals), each of which corresponds with one of the two states. The circuit remains in either state until caused to change to the other state by application of a voltage pulse. A similar bistable device with an input that allows it to act as a single-stage binary counter.

float-type carburetor:
In this type of carburetor, fuel supply to jet is controlled by a float and needle valve.

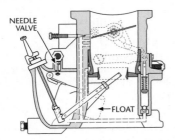

FLOAT-TYPE CARBURETOR

flock:
Pulverized wool or cotton fibers attached to screen wire used as an air filter. The flock-covered screen is lightly oiled, to hold dirt and dust preventing it from entering the engine.

flow control valve:
A valve used to control the rate of flow of fluid in a system.

flow divider:
Unit that keeps metered fuel under pressure, divides fuel to the various cylinders at all engine speeds, and shuts off the individual nozzle lines when the control is placed in idle-cutoff.

flow meter:
An instrument used to measure the velocity of flow of a liquid in a pipe; an instrument used to indicate pressure, velocity of flow, and rate of discharge of a gas or vapor.

fluid:
A substance, either gas or liquid, which flows and tends to conform to the shape of its container.

fluorescent penetrant inspection:
An inspection method utilizing a highly penetrating liquid which fluoresces when subjected to ultra-violet or black light, used to produce luminous indications of surface flaws or discontinuities.

fluoroscope:
A fluorescent screen on which appears the image of an object that has been exposed to penetrating, ionizing radiation. The results appear similar to an X-ray.

flush patch:
A type of sheet metal repair that leaves a smooth surface maintaining the aircraft's original contour. The repair is reinforced on the inside and attached with flush rivets.

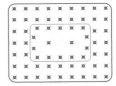

FLUSH PATCH

flush rivet:
A countersunk rivet where the manufactured head is flush with the surface of the metal when properly installed.

flute:
A groove cut into a cylindrical object.

flutter:
1. The rapid and uncontrolled oscillation of a flight control resulting from an unbalanced surface. Flutter often leads to a catastrophic failure of the structure.
2. A vibrating and oscillating movement of a wing, control surface, or the like, caused by aerodynamic forces acting upon an airfoil or surface having elastic and inertial qualities.

flux:
A cleaning agent used to dissolve oxides, release trapped gases and slag, and to cleanse metals for welding, soldering, and brazing.

flux density:
The number of magnetic flux lines per unit of area taken at right angles to the direction of magnetic field flow. This is a measure of field strength.

flux detector:
Remote sensor used in a Flux Gate Compass system

flux gate compass:
A system that employs one or more remote sensors to produce an electric signal that can be used to determine the aircraft's position relative to magnetic North

fly-by-light systems:
Aircraft control systems that are moved by electrically operated servos whose control signals are transmitted via fiber optic cables. The technology replacing fly-by-wire.

fly-by-wire systems:
Aircraft control surfaces that are moved electrically with electrical backup systems.

fly cutter:
1. A single-point cutter mounted on a bar in a fly cutter holder or a fly cutter arbor; used for special applications for which a milling cutter is not available.

2. A form milling cutter with a single tooth formed to the desired contour. Term used occasionally to describe a face milling cutter consisting of one or more inserts mounted in a steel body.

flyweights:
Rotating weights in a governor mechanism that use centrifugal force to sense changes in rotational speed and affect changes in system operation.

FM:
Fan marker. *(FAR 1)*

FMC:
Flight Management Computer

FMGS:
Flight Management Guidance System

Fn:
Net thrust produced by a turbine engine.

foaming:
The formation of froth or foam on lubricating oils or other oils as a result of aeration or release of gas dissolved in the oil.

foaming adhesive:
An adhesive film used to join honeycomb core in bonded assemblies. Contains a foaming agent that produces an expansion during cure.

FOD:
See *foreign object damage*

foil:
Metal in sheet form less than 0.006 inches in thickness.

folded fell seam:
A type of machine sewn seam recommended for use in sewing aircraft fabric.

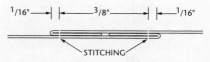

FOLDED FELL SEAM

foot pound (ft-lb):
A unit of work; one pound of force moved through a distance of one foot.

force:
A push or pull exerted on an object.

force fit:
A fitting which one part is forced or pressed into another to form a single unit. There are different classes of force fits depending on standard limits between mating parts.

forehand welding:
A gas welding technique in which the flare is directed against the base metal ahead of the completed weld.

foreign air carrier:
Any person other than a citizen of the United States, who undertakes directly, by lease or other arrangement, to engage in air transportation. *(FAR 1)*

foreign air commerce:
The carriage by aircraft of persons or property for compensation or hire, or the carriage of mail by aircraft, or the operation or navigation of aircraft in the conduct or furtherance of a business or vocation, in commerce between a place in the United States and any place outside thereof; whether such commerce moves wholly by aircraft or partly by aircraft and partly by other forms of transportation. *(FAR 1)*

foreign air transportation:
The carriage by aircraft of persons or property as a common carrier for compensation or hire, or the carriage of mail by aircraft, in commerce between a place in the United States and any place outside of the United States, whether that commerce moves wholly by aircraft or partly by aircraft and partly by other forms of transportation. *(FAR 1)*

foreign object damage (FOD):
1. Damage from any object that is ingested into a turbine engine.

2. Material left on the hangar floor or ramp that could become a source of ingestion damage.

forge welding:
The operation of joining hot metals by means of hammers or presses. Includes hand hammering, press and drop forging.

forging:
Shaping by hammering. Only the malleable metals are worked successfully. The application of heat increases plasticity.

Form 337:
FAA form used to document major repairs or alterations to aircraft, engines or appliances.

former:
A frame of light wood or metal attached to a truss fuselage to provide the required aerodynamic shape.

forming:
To shape or fashion with hand/tools or by a shape or mold.

forming block:
A hardwood block around which metal parts may be formed.

FORMING BLOCKS

forward bias:
The arrangement of voltage polarities for a transistor or a diode which allows conduction.

forward center of gravity limit:
The most forward location allowed for the center of gravity of an aircraft in its loaded condition.

F

forward fan:
A turbofan with the fan located at the front of the compressor. The fan may be a part of the compressor or a separate rotor as in the three spool engine.

forward wing:
A forward lifting surface of a canard configuration or tandem-wing configuration airplane. The surface may be a fixed, movable, or variable geometry surface, with or without control surfaces. *(FAR 1)*

Foster-Seeley discriminator:
A circuit that uses a double-tuned RF transformer to convert frequency variations in the received FM signal to amplitude variations. Also known as a *phase-shift discriminator*.

fouled spark plug:
A general term used to describe a spark plug that has been contaminated with foreign matter. This may exist in degrees up to the point where the plug is rendered inoperative.

four-cycle engine:
An engine that requires four strokes of the piston to complete a cycle of operations within the cylinder: the four strokes being the suction, or intake, stroke of combustible mixture, the compression stroke, the power stroke, and the exhaust stroke.

fowler flap:
A type of extendable trailing-edge flap that increases both the camber and wing area.

FOWLER FLAP

free electrons:
Those electrons so loosely bound in the outer shells of some atoms that they are able to move from atom to atom.

free fit:
A class of fit intended for use where accuracy is not essential, or where large temperature variations are likely to be encountered, or both conditions.

free running oscillator:
A circuit to establish a given frequency

free turbine:
A turbine wheel, not directly connected to the compressor, that drives a propeller or helicopter transmission.

free water:
Particles of entrained water that unite to form droplets.

freezing point:
The temperature at which a liquid will change into a solid.

french fell seam:
A type of machine sewn seam used to join panels of aircraft fabric.

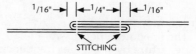

FRENCH FELL SEAM

freon:
A fluorinated hydrocarbon compound used as a fire extinguishing agent and a refrigerant for vapor cycle air conditioning systems. Most traditional freon formulas are no longer manufactured because of environmental concerns.

frequency:
1. The number of complete cycles per second existing in any form of wave motion, such as the number of cycles per second of an alternating current.

2. The rate at which the vector that generates a sine wave rotates.

frequency modulation (FM):
Angle modulation in which the modulating signal causes the carrier frequency to vary. The amplitude of the modulating signal determines how far the frequency changes, and the frequency of the modulating signal determines how fast the frequency changes.

frequency multipliers:
Special RF power amplifiers that multiply the input frequency.

frequency response:
The portion of the frequency spectrum which can be passed by a device as it produces an output within specified limits of amplitude error.

frequency synthesizer:
1. A frequency source of high accuracy.
2. A bank of oscillators in which the outputs can be mixed in various combinations to produce a wide range of frequencies.

frequency tolerance:
The maximum permissible departure by the center frequency of the frequency band occupied by an emission from the assigned frequency, or by the characteristic frequency of an emission from the reference frequency.

fretting corrosion:
Corrosion damage between close fitting parts that are allowed to rub together. The rubbing prevents the formation of protective oxide films and allows the metals to corrode.

friction horsepower:
The amount of horsepower required to overcome the friction of the moving parts in the engine and to compress the charges in the cylinders.

friction stir welding:
A process of joining metals without filler materials. The welds are created by the combined action of frictional heating and mechanical deformation due to a rotating tool. The maximum temperature reached is of the order of 0.8 of the melting temperature.

frise-type aileron:
An aileron with the nose portion projecting ahead of the hinge line. When the trailing edge of the aileron moves up, the nose projects below the wings lower surface and produces some parasite drag. This decreases the amount of adverse yaw.

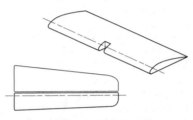

FRISE-TYPE AILERON

FSDO:
Flight Standard District Office

fuel boost pump:
A pump installed in or near the fuel tank to provide vapor free fuel with a slight head pressure to the engine driven pump. Centrifugal type pumps are often used as boost pumps.

fuel control unit (FCU):
Device that automatically and accurately regulates pump pressure and fuel delivery to the engine.

fuel dump system:
A system installed on some transport category aircraft with a takeoff weight that exceeds the landing weight. This system allows fuel to be dumped in flight to reduce the weight of the aircraft to its allowable landing weight. Also known as a *fuel jettison system*.

fuel enrichment system:
A control system on some turbine and reciprocating engines to enrich the fuel mixture for cold weather starting.

fuel heater:
A unit operates to warm the fuel and functions to protect the engine's fuel system from ice formation. However, should ice form, the heater can also be used to thaw ice on the fuel screen. The heater uses either engine bleed air or engine lubricating oil as a source of heat.

fuel injection system:
A fuel metering system used on some reciprocating powered aircraft where a constant flow of fuel is fed to injection nozzles just outside the intake valve of each cylinder.

fuel jettison system:
See *fuel dump system*

fuel metering device:
Any apparatus such as a carburetor, fuel injector, or fuel control unit that mixes fuel with intake air in the correct proportions and delivers the mixture to the engine.

fuel nozzle:
Device to inject fuel into the combustion chamber in a highly atomized and accurately shaped spray.

fuel pump:
A mechanical device that moves fuel under pressure, typically from the fuel tank towards the fuel metering device.

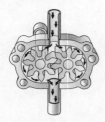

FUEL PUMP (GEAR-TYPE)

fuel shutoff valve:
A valve in the aircraft fuel system that shuts off the flow of fuel to the engine.

fuel strainer:
Unit that traps and removes dirt particles from fuel as the fuel flows through the unit.

fulcrum:
The point or support on which a lever turns.

full carrier single-sideband emission:
A single-sideband emission without suppression of the carrier.

full register position:
The position of the rotating magnet in a magneto when the poles are fully aligned with the pole shoes of the magneto frame. At this point the maximum number of lines of flux flow in the frame.

full wave rectification:
Rectified alternating current for which the rectifier is connected so that the reverse half of the cycle is turned around, and fed into the circuit flowing in the same direction as the first half of the cycle. This produces pulsating DC, but with no interval between the pulses.

fully articulated rotor:
See *articulated rotor*

fully hardened:
Applies generally to the maximum hardness obtainable. (In particular, applies to materials that are hardened by a strain and/ or age hardening process).

fungicidal paste:
Paste that is mixed with clear dope to apply as a first coat on cotton fabric. The fungicidal agent soaks into the fibers and prevents the formation of mold or fungus attack.

F

fuse:
1. To unite or blend together by melting.
2. A protective device that breaks a circuit when its current exceeds a predetermined value.

fuselage:
The main or central structure of a heavier-than-air aircraft, typically elongated and approximately streamlined, which carries the crew, passengers, or other load. The word fuselage is applied to the main central body or structure of a fixed-wing airplane, of a rotary-wing airplane, or of a glider, but it is usually not applied to a flying-boat hull.

FUSELAGE

fuselage station (FS):
Used to indicate locations longitudinally along the aircraft fuselage

fusible alloys:
A group of nonferrous alloys which melt at relatively low temperatures. They usually consist of bismuth, lead, tin, etc., in various proportions, and iron only as an impurity.

fusible plug:
A hollow plug in an aircraft wheel filled with a material having a specific melting point. If the melting temperature is reached from brake heat, the filler will melt out and deflate the tire rather than allowing the pressure to increase enough to burst the tire.

Gg

GA:
1. general aviation
2. go around

gain:
1. The ratio between the amount of energy propagated from an antenna that is directional compared to the energy from the same antenna that would be propagated if the antenna were not directional.
2. Any increase in the strength of a signal.

gain stability:
The extent to which the sensitivity of an instrument remains constant with time. The property reported in specifications should be instability.

galley:
The food preparation area on a passenger aircraft.

galling:
Fretting or pulling out chunks of a surface by sliding contact with another surface or body.

gallon (gal):
A unit of measure of volume. A U.S. gallon contains 231 cubic inches or 3.785 liters; it is 0.83268 times the imperial gallon. One U.S. gallon of water weighs 8.3374 pounds at 60°F (16°C).

galvanic corrosion:
Corrosion associated with the current of a galvanic cell consisting of two dissimilar conductors in an electrolyte solution, or two similar conductors in dissimilar electrolytes.

galvanic series of metals:
A listing of metals and alloys arranged according to their relative electrode potentials in a specified environment; indicates what metal(s) will corrode first when two or more metals are in contact.

galvanizing:
The act of coating steel with zinc in order to provide barrier and cathodic protection from corrosion.

galvanometer:
A meter used to measure small values of current by electromagnetic or electrodynamic means.

gamma rays:
The electromagnetic radiation of high frequency and short wavelength emitted by the nucleus of an atom during a nuclear reaction. Gamma rays are not affected by electric fields or magnetic fields. Although produced differently then x-rays, they are identical in nature and properties to x-rays of the same wavelength.

ganged tuning:
The process used to tune two or more circuits with a single control.

garnet paper:
An abrasive polishing paper consisting of a flexible paper backing with a layer of finely crushed garnet.

gascolator:
A type of fuel strainer located before the fuel metering device, typically mounted on the firewall of piston powered light aircraft. It contains a screen to prevent solid particles from flowing into the fuel control device, and a reservoir area where water can settle out of the fuel. Normally this unit is drained into a sample container and examined by the pilot during the preflight inspection.

G

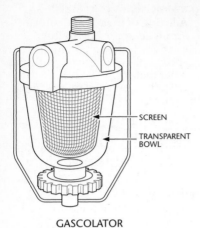

SCREEN

TRANSPARENT
BOWL

GASCOLATOR

gas generator:
The basic power-producing portion of a gas turbine engine. Generally considered to include the compressor, diffuser, combustor and turbine.

gas metal-arc welding (GMAW):
An arc welding process in which fusion is produced by heating with an electric arc between a metal electrode and the work. Shielding is obtained from an inert gas such as helium or argon. Pressure and/or filler metal may or may not be used. Sometimes called *metal inert gas (MIG) welding* or *metal active gas (MAG) welding*.

gasoline combustion heater:
An aircraft cabin heater in which gasoline from the aircraft's fuel tanks is burned to produce heat that is directed to the cabin area.

gasper:
Duct system in an air cycle system where air enters the cabin spaces through a network of ducts and diffusers and is distributed evenly throughout the spaces.

gas porosity (on radiograph):
Represented by round or elongated dark spots corresponding to minute voids, usually distributed through the entire casting.

gas tungsten-arc welding (GTAW):
An arc welding process in which fusion is produced by heating with an electric arc between a tungsten electrode and the work while an inert gas forms around the weld area to prevent oxidation. No flux is used.

gas turbine engine:
An engine in which vapor (other than steam) is directed, under pressure, against a series of turbine blades. The energy contained in the rapidly expanding vapors is converted into rotary motion.

gas welding:
A process in which the welding heat is obtained from a gas flame.

gate:
As applied to logic circuitry, one of several different types of electronic devices that will provide a particular output when specified input conditions are satisfied. Also, a circuit in which a signal switches another signal on or off.

gauge:
1. An object or instrument for the measurement of dimensions, pressures, volumes, etc.

2. An accurately dimensioned piece of metal for checking the dimensions of work.

gauge pressure:
Pressure that is measured from the existing atmospheric pressure. Oil pressure, fuel pressure and hydraulic pressure are normally expressed as gauge pressures. Gauge pressure may also be identified as p.s.i.g.

gauss:
This is the unit of flux density or induction. The strength of field induced in a ferromagnetic body is described as being so many gausses. It is usually designated by the letter B. Numerically, one

gauss is one line of flux per square centimeter of area.

gear backlash:
The measured clearance between the teeth of meshed gears.

gear type pump:
A form of constant displacement pump in which two spur-type gears mesh and rotate within a close fitting housing. Oil is picked up as the teeth come out of mesh. It is then carried around the outside of the gears and discharged from the pump when the teeth mesh.

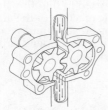

GEAR TYPE PUMP

geared engine:
A reciprocating engine utilizing a series of reduction gears to allow the engine to operate at an efficient speed while holding the propeller r.p.m. to its most efficient range.

gel coat:
A quick-setting resin used in molding processes to provide an improved surface for the composite; it is the first resin applied to the mold after the mold-release agent.

gel cell battery:
A type of lead-acid battery that has a gelling agent added to the electrolyte to make it non-spillable and to retain a high level of electrolyte in the battery.

gelling:
When a liquid phase is transformed to an irreversible solid phase without the loss of weight through evaporation, the

phenomenon is often termed gelling.

general aviation:
The segment of the aviation industry that covers all activities except military and scheduled carriers.

generator:
A machine that converts mechanical energy to electrical energy by applying the principle of magnetic induction. A machine that produces AC or DC voltage, depending on the original design.

geostationary satellite:
A geosynchronous satellite whose circular and direct orbit lies in the plane of the earth's equator and which thus remains fixed relative to the earth; by extension, a geosynchronous satellite which remains approximately fixed relative to the Earth.

geostationary satellite orbit:
The orbit in which a satellite must be placed to be a geostationary satellite.

geosynchronous satellite:
An earth satellite whose period of revolution is equal to the period of rotation of the Earth about its axis.

geometric pitch:
The theoretical distance a propeller should move forward in one revolution under perfect conditions.

germanium:
A grayish-white metallic chemical element with four valence electrons. It is used in the manufacture of semi-conductor devices such as diodes and transistors.

gerotor pump:
A form of constant displacement pump using a spur gear driven by the engine and turning inside an internal tooth gear with one more space than teeth on the drive

gear. As the pump rotates, the volume at the inlet port increases, and decreases at the outlet port, moving fluid through the pump.

GEROTOR PUMP

GHz:
Gigahertz, one billion hertz.

giga:
A metric prefix meaning billion.

gilbert:
The unit of magneto-motive force (mmf).

gill-type cowl flap:
A cowl flap used on the trailing edge of the cowling on horizontally opposed type engines.

gimbal:
The frame in which a gyro spins. The design is such that the gyro can remain upright while the base tilts. Gyros may be mounted in either a single gimbal or double gimbal depending on the application.

gland:
Cavity into which an o-ring is installed. Includes the groove and mating surface of a second part, which together confines the O-ring.

glass cloth:
Conventionally woven glass fiber material.

glass cockpit:
Flat glass panel information displays that have replaced the traditional clusters of analog gauges in newer aircraft.

glass fiber:
A fiber spun from an inorganic product of fusion that has cooled to a rigid condition. A glass filament that has been cut to a measurable length.

glass transition temperature:
The approximate midpoint of the temperature range over which the glass transition takes place.

glaze ice:
Ice formation that appears as a hard, glossy, heavy covering.

glider:
A heavier-than-air aircraft, that is supported in flight by the dynamic reaction of the air against its lifting surfaces and whose free flight does not depend principally on an engine. *(FAR 1)*

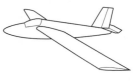

GLIDER

glideslope:
A part of the instrument landing system (ILS) that provides the pilot a radio beam to follow during descent, from the outer marker to touchdown.

glime ice:
A mixture of glaze and rime ice. Glime ice is a hard, rough mixture that can form rapidly. Formation occurs when raindrops vary in size or when liquid drops are mixed with snow or ice particles.

global positioning system (GPS):
A satellite-based radio positioning, navigation, and time-transfer system.

GLONASS:
The former Soviet Union's satellite navigation system.

GLOBALink:
The name of the ACARS service provided by ARINC Incorporated

glow plug igniter:
A form of turbine engine igniter that uses a coil of resistance wire heated to a yellow-hot temperature by high-voltage direct current.

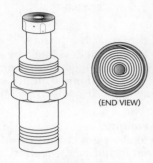

(END VIEW)

GLOW PLUG IGNITER

go-around power or thrust setting:
The maximum allowable in-flight power or thrust setting identified in the performance data. *(FAR 1)*

go/no-go gauge:
A type of measuring gauge that provides two dimensions: the minimum size and the maximum size.

goniometer antenna:
A fixed loop antenna used by automatic direction finding (ADF) equipment consisting of two coils oriented at 90° to each other. It measures the angle between a reference direction and the reference from which the radio signal is being received.

gouge:
A cut, groove, or hole that is considered to be a defect.

governor:
A device that controls or limits the speed of an engine or other component.

GPS continuity:
The probability that a GPS service will continue to be available for a period of time necessary to complete the navigation requirements of the flight

GPS integrity:
The ability of the GPS system to shut itself down when it is unsuited for navigation or to provide timely warnings to the pilot of the system failure

GPU:
See *ground power unit*

GPWS:
Ground Proximity Warning System

grade-A cotton:
Long-staple cotton fabric with 80 threads per inch in both the warp and fill directions. It is the standard material for covering aircraft structures.

grain boundary:
An interface separating two grains when the orientation of the lattices changes from that of one grain to that of another. When the orientation change is very small, the boundary is sometimes referred to as sub-boundary.

grains:
Individual crystals in metal. When metal is in molten state, the atoms have no uniform grouping. However, upon solidification they arrange themselves in a geometric pattern.

granular:
Containing or consisting of grains.

graphite:
A soft form of carbon that has a greasy feel. Graphite is used as a dry lubricant and also as the lead in a pencil.

gravity:
The force of attraction between the earth and any object on or near it. This force is proportional to the mass of the object.

G

gravity feed:
A system used on aircraft where the fuel tanks are located high enough above the carburetor so that gravity will provide enough fuel pressure to supply 150 percent of the fuel flow required for takeoff operation.

great circle:
A circle on the surface of a sphere, especially the earth, the plane of which passes through the center of the sphere and divides it into two equal parts.

great circle course:
A course plotted along a great circle. The shortest distance between two points on a sphere.

Greenwich mean time (GMT):
Also know as Zulu time. The time at the zero degree meridian at the Royal Observatory, London, England.

greige Dacron:
A synthetic polyester fiber fabric in its unshrunk or unfinished condition as it comes from the looms.

grip length:
The length of the unthreaded shank of a bolt.

grit blasting:
A process for cleaning metal in which an abrasive material, such as sand, glass beads, walnut shells, carbon dioxide, etc., is forcefully blown onto the part's surface.

grommet:
1. A metal or plastic eyelet used for reinforcing holes in aircraft fabric.

2. A small ring of rubber, plastic, or metal used as a fairlead and protector for tubing or wire going through a hole in a metal structure.

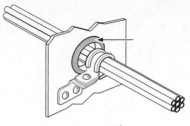

GROMMET[2]

gross thrust:
The total thrust developed by an engine, not taking into account any pressure of initial air mass momentum. Also known as *static thrust*.

gross weight:
The total weight of a fully loaded aircraft including the fuel, oil, and the cargo it is carrying.

ground adjustable propeller:
A propeller whose pitch may be adjusted and locked when the engine is not operating. It cannot be changed in flight.

ground clutter:
Unwanted echoes from surrounding land masses that appear on a radar indicator.

ground-controlled approach:
A radar system used to guide aircraft to safe landings in poor visibility conditions.

ground idle:
The minimum thrust setting for gas turbine ground operations. Usually 60 to 70 percent of the maximum r.p.m. range.

ground plane antenna:
A type of antenna that uses a ground plane as a simulated ground to produce low-angle radiation.

ground potential:
Zero potential with respect to the ground or earth.

ground power unit (GPU):
A small engine used to provide

electrical power and/or air pressure for starting aircraft engines. These units are similar to the auxiliary power units installed on some transport category aircraft.

ground range:
The distance on the surface of the earth between a radar and its target. Equal to slant range only if both radar and target are at the same altitude.

ground resonance:
A self-excited vibration of a helicopter occurring whenever the frequency of oscillation of the blades about the lead-lag axis of an articulated rotor becomes the same as the natural frequency of the fuselage.

ground speed:
The actual speed of an airplane over the ground.

ground support equipment (GSE):
Equipment separate from the airplane, but in direct support of the aircraft's operation. This can include equipment used both in the maintenance facility and on the flight line.

ground visibility:
Prevailing horizontal visibility near the earth's surface as reported by the United States National Weather Service or an accredited observer. *(FAR 1)*

growler:
Test equipment used to check generator and starter armature for shorts. The growler forms the primary of a transformer and the armature forms the secondary. Shorts show up as they cause vibration of a piece of metal, such as a hacksaw blade, held over the armature.

GS:
Glide slope. *(FAR 1)*

guide vanes:
Stationary airfoils located radially

in a turbine engine to direct the airflow from one section into the next.

gusset:
A small reinforcing member used to support the corners of a structure.

gust lock:
Devices used to prevent damage to control surfaces from wind gusts. They may be internal locking devices provided by the aircraft manufacturer, or external devices.

gyro:
Short for gyroscope. May also be used in reference to components using gyroscopic mechanisms, such as a gyro horizon.

gyrodyne:
A rotorcraft whose rotors are normally engine driven for takeoff, hovering, and landing, and for forward flight through part of its speed range, and whose means of propulsion, consisting usually of conventional propellers, is independent of the rotor system. *(FAR 1)*

gyro horizon:
An attitude gyro that indicates movement about the pitch and roll axes.

gyroplane:
A rotorcraft whose rotors are not engine-driven, except for initial starting, but are made to rotate by action of the air when the rotorcraft is moving; and whose means of propulsion, consisting usually of conventional propellers, is independent of the rotor system. *(FAR 1)*

gyroscope:
1. A device for measuring or maintaining orientation. It consists of a spinning wheel that is universally mounted and has three degrees of freedom about its center of gravity. The center of gravity is

designed to remain in a fixed position within the assembly. A gyroscope uses the principal of rigidity. This means that the gyroscope wheel's orientation will tend to remain fixed regardless of the motion of the platform around it.

2. The wheel of such a device.

3. Any other devices, such as an electronic device, having the basic properties of a common mechanical gyroscope.

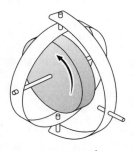

GYROSCOPE[1]

gyroscopic precession:
The characteristic of a gyroscope that causes it to react to an application of force as though the force were applied 90° in the direction of rotation.

gyrosyn compass:
A trade name for a compass incorporating a directional gyro synchronized with the earth's magnetic meridian by means of a flux gate, the flux gate detecting the direction of the lines of force of the earth's magnetic field and transmitting corresponding signals to gyro-precessing devices.

Hh

hacksaw:
A metal-cutting saw consisting of a lightweight frame and a narrow, fine-toothed blade.

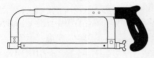

HACKSAW

half-wave dipole antenna:
An antenna, consisting of two rods ($1/4$ wavelength each) in a single line that radiates electromagnetic energy.

half-wave rectified AC:
Alternating current which passes through a rectifier in such a manner that the reversing half of the cycle (negative) is blocked out completely. It is pulsating unidirectional current. It differs from full-wave.

half-wave voltage doubler:
Two half-wave voltage rectifiers connected to double the input voltage.

Hall effect:
The phenomenon wherein a voltage is generated across the opposite edges of an electrical conductor carrying current and placed in a magnetic field. The generated voltage differential is mutually perpendicular to the direction of current flow and the applied magnetic field.

halogen:
Any of the five elements fluorine, chlorine, iodine, bromine, and astatine.

halogenated hydrocarbon agent:
Fire extinguishing compounds formed by replacement of one or more of the hydrogen atoms in the simple hydrocarbons methane and ethane by halogen atoms.

handbook:
In a general sense, any small book containing specialized information or instructions.

hand forming:
The process of forming metal using soft faced mallets or hammers to bend, shrink, stretch and form into the desire shape. The metal is usually formed over suitable forming blocks, dies or sandbags.

hand lay-up:
1. A process in which components are applied either to a mold or a working surface, and the successive plies are built up and worked by hand.

2. The process of placing successive plies of reinforcing material or resin-impregnated reinforcement in position on a mold by hand.

hangar:
A building, tent compartment or other structure or place where aircraft are housed, worked on, or tested. Often contains associated offices, shops, etc. Typically a permanent structure. Sometimes incorrectly spelled *hanger*.

HANGAR

hanging start:
An act or instance of an aircraft engine or starter sticking or hanging during an attempted start.

hardenability:
In a ferrous alloy, the property that determines the depth and distribution of hardness induced by quenching.

hardness:
1. Resistance of metal to plastic deformation, usually by indentation.

2. Stiffness or temper or resistance to scratching, abrasion or cutting.

hardness test:
An evaluation of the hardness of a material by measuring the depth of penetration of a specially shaped probe under a specified load.

hard stand:
Any paved, compacted, or otherwise specially prepared surface or area set up for parking or ground running an aircraft.

harmful interference:
Interference that endangers the functioning of a radio navigation service or of other safety services or seriously degrades, obstructs, or repeatedly interrupts a radio communication service operating in accordance with [the ITU] Radio Regulations.

harmonic:
A frequency that is a whole-number multiple of a smaller base frequency.

harness satin:
Weaving pattern producing a satin appearance.

Hartley oscillator:
A type of electronic oscillator circuit that produces feedback through a tapped inductor.

hastalloy:
A nickel-based alloy sometimes used in the fabrication of parts for turbine engines. Known for its high temperature strength.

hat channel:
An extruded structural component whose cross section resembles the shape of a hat. These pieces are used to stiffen flat sheets of metal.

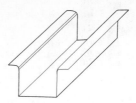

HAT CHANNEL

HAZMAT:
Hazardous Material

head pressure:
Pressure exerted by a fluid by virtue of the height of the top of the fluid column.

headshot:
A term used colloquially to designate the magnetizing current passing through a part or a central conductor while clamped between the head contacts of a stationary magnetizing unit for the purpose of circular magnetization.

heat energy:
Energy associated with molecular motion within a substance. More molecular motion equals more heat energy.

heat engine:
An engine that converts the energy of heat into mechanical or kinetic energy, such as steam and internal-combustion reciprocating and turbine engines, rocket engines, ramjet engines, etc.

heat exchanger:
Any device, such as a water radiator, oil cooler or intercooler, used to cool a liquid or gas by transferring heat to another liquid or gas.

heat of compression:
Heat generated when a gas is compressed.

heat-resistant steel:
Alloy steel designed for application at elevated temperatures.

heat shrinkable:
A material that shrinks when heat is applied. This may be seen in aircraft covering fabric and in tubing used to protect electrical wiring installations as well as other applications.

heat sink:
A device, usually copper or aluminum, that clamps on a conductor to protect a component from excessive heat. Also called a *thermal shunt*.

heat treatment of metals:
An operation, or combination of operations, involving the heating and cooling of a metal or alloy in the solid state for the purpose of obtaining certain desirable conditions or properties. Heating and cooling for the sole purpose of mechanical working are excluded from the meaning of this definition.

heliarc:
A welding process commonly associated with aircraft manufacture and repair. The process utilizes an electric arc to provide the necessary heat and provides an inert gas (helium) shield to prevent oxidation. Also called *TIG welding*.

heli-coil inserts:
Thread inserts primarily designed to be used in materials that are not suitable for threading because of their softness. The inserts are made of a diamond cross-sectioned stainless steel wire that is helically coiled and, in its finished form, is similar to a small, fully compressed spring.

helicopter:
A rotorcraft that, for its horizontal motion, depends principally on its engine-driven rotors. *(FAR 1)*

HELICOPTER

heliport:
An area of land, water, or structure used or intended to be used for the landing and takeoff of helicopters. *(FAR 1)*

henry (H):
The unit of inductance. The inductance of a circuit is 1 henry when a current variation of 1 ampere per second induces 1 volt. In electronics, smaller units are used, such as the millihenry (mH), which is one-thousandth of a henry, and the microhenry (μH) which is one-millionth of a henry.

heptane:
A liquid hydrocarbon material whose detonation characteristics are used as the low point in determining the octane rating of aviation gasoline. Iso-octane is used as the high point.

hermetically sealed:
Completely sealed so as to keep air or gas from getting in or out.

hertz (Hz):
A unit of frequency equal to one cycle per second.

hertz antenna:
A half-wave radio antenna.

hertzian waves or radio waves:
Electromagnetic waves of frequencies arbitrarily lower than 3,000 GHz propagated in space without artificial guide.

H

heterodyne:
To mix or beat together two radio frequencies to produce an intermediate frequency.

heterogeneous mixture:
Descriptive term for a material consisting of dissimilar constituents separately identifiable. A medium consisting of regions of unlike properties separated by internal boundaries. NOTE: All non-homogeneous materials are not necessarily heterogeneous.

hexadecimal system:
Pertaining to the number system with a radix of sixteen. It uses the ten digits of the decimal system and the first six letters of the English alphabet.

Hg:
Mercury

hidden line:
Hidden lines are drawing lines that indicate invisible edges or contours. Hidden lines consist of short, evenly spaced dashes and are frequently referred to as dash lines.

high aspect ratio:
An aspect ratio considered relatively high. Said of a long, narrow, airfoil.

high-bypass turbofan:
A turbofan engine with a bypass ratio of 4:1 or higher.

high-carbon steel:
Steel containing more than 0.5 percent carbon.

high frequency (HF) system:
Long-range communication system that operates in the frequency range from 3 MHz to 30 MHz.

high frequency vibration:
A vibration that has a high frequency of occurrence. Often results in metal fatigue.

high-lift device:
Any lift modifying device such as a flap, slat or slot that allows the airfoil to achieve a higher angle of attack before separation of the airflow occurs.

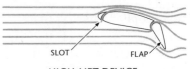

SLOT   FLAP

HIGH-LIFT DEVICE

high-pass filter:
A filter that passes a majority of the high frequencies on to the next circuit and rejects, or attenuates, the lower frequencies. Also called a *low-frequency discriminator*.

high pitch:
The pitch of a propeller blade set at a high blade angle other than feathering angle. On a controllable-pitch propeller, this term typically refers to the pitch at its maximum blade angle other than feathering angle.

high-pressure compressor:
The rear section of a dual compressor setup; the N_2 compressor. Also known as the *high-speed compressor*.

high-pressure oxygen system:
Gaseous oxygen systems utilizing cylinder pressures of 1,000 to 2,000 p.s.i.

high-pressure turbine:
The most forward of the turbine wheels on a dual spool turbine engine; the N_2 turbine. Also known as *high speed turbine*.

high-speed steel:
Steel alloys which maintain their strength at high temperatures. They are especially useful for the manufacture of metal cutting tools such as twist drills.

high-tension magneto:
A self-contained ignition source used with reciprocation aircraft engines. The magneto utilizes a rotating magnet to generate an

electrical potential, an internal transformer coil to step up the voltage and a distributor to direct the high voltage to the appropriate cylinder.

high-voltage ignition system:
A turbine engine ignition system with an output in the range of 5,000 to 30,000 volts. See also *low-voltage ignition system*.

high-wing airplane:
A monoplane with the wing mounted on top of the fuselage.

HIGH-WING AIRPLANE

Hi-Lok® fasteners:
Fastener that combines the features of a rivet and a bolt and is used for high-strength, interference-free fit of primary structures. The Hi-Lok® fastener consists of a threaded pin and threaded locking collar.

HIRL:
High-intensity runway light system. *(FAR 1)*

hi-shear rivet:
It is essentially a threadless bolt. The pin is headed at one end and grooved about the circumference at the other. A metal collar is swaged onto the grooved end, effecting a firm, tight fit. Also called a *pin rivet*.

HI-SHEAR RIVET

hits per scan:
The number of times an RF beam strikes a target per antenna revolution.

holding coil:
An auxiliary coil in an electrical relay that keeps the relay energized after the current that caused the relay to close has stopped flowing through the main coil.

hole finder:
A tool used in sheet metal work to determine the location of rivet holes when they cannot be seen.

hole flow:
In the valence band, a process of conduction in which electrons move into holes, thereby creating other holes that appear to move toward a negative potential. (The movement of holes is opposite the movement of electrons.)

holiday:
A term used to indicate a skipped area, missed unintentionally while applying a coating. Holidays can be avoided by using contrasting colors for alternating coats.

home diagram:
A diagram/schematic where the component is shown in full detail.

homogeneous:
1. In general: a material of uniform composition throughout.

2. In seals: a rubber seal without fabric or metal reinforcement.

honeycomb:
Manufactured product of resin-impregnated sheet material formed into hexagonal-shaped cells.

honeycomb core sandwich construction:
A type of construction for aircraft wings, stabilizers, or the like in which the space between the upper and lower surfaces is occupied by a strengthening material of a structure resembling a honeycomb mesh.

H

honing:

The process of finishing ground
surfaces to a high degree of
accuracy and smoothness with
abrasive blocks applied to the
surface under a light controlled
pressure and with a combination
of rotary and reciprocating
motions.

hook spanner:

A type of semi-circular spanner
wrench with the handle on one
end and a hook on the other. The
hook is used to engage a notch in
the outside of a ring-type nut.

ADJUSTABLE HOOK SPANNER

hook terminal:

A terminal with a looped end.

hopper-type oil tank:

A container within an oil tank
used to hold diluted oil for cold
weather starting. The use of a
hopper minimizes the amount of
oil that must be diluted.

horizontally opposed engine:

A reciprocating engine with
the cylinders arranged in two
horizontal rows, one on either
side of the crankshaft.

horizontal situation indicator (HSI):

Analog gauge that combines the
functions of a directional gyro
with a VHF navigation display.

horizontal stabilizer:

A stabilizer mounted more or
less horizontally on an airplane,
airship, or other aircraft, affording
longitudinal stability, and to
which the elevators, when
present, are attached.

HORIZONTAL STABILIZER

horizontal tail:

The complete horizontal
component of an aircraft's
empennage. Consists of both fixed
and movable surfaces.

horn:

A lever or other device connected
to a control surface to which an
operating cable or rod can be
connected.

horsepower (hp):

A unit of power equal to the
power necessary to raise 33,000
pounds one foot in one minute.
1 hp = 0.746 kw

horseshoe magnet:

A bar magnet, bent into the
shape of a horseshoe so that the
two poles are adjacent. Usually
the term applies to a permanent
magnet.

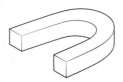

HORSESHOE MAGNET

hose:

Flexible fluid lines, which can be
used in place of rigid tubing in
areas subject to vibration or where
motion is necessary.

hose clamp:

A metal clamp used to hold a hose
onto a rigid tube.

hot dimpling:
A method of forming a dimple in metal for the installation of flush rivets or screws. The heat prevents the metal from cracking around the hole.

hot forming:
Metal working operations performed with the material heated to a plastic state. These operations may include forging, pressing, rolling, drawing, and heading.

hot-rolled steel:
Steel that is rolled to finished size while hot. Identified by a dark oxide scale left on the surface.

hot section:
The portion of a turbine engine aft of the diffuser.

hot section inspection:
Visual and dimensional check for cracks, distortions, corrosion, and evidence of excessive temperature in the combustion chamber and liners and in the turbine section, all of which are typically disassembled for this inspection.

hot spark plug:
A spark plug with a long insulator nose that creates a long heat transfer path. They are used in engines which run relatively cool in the prevention of lead fouling.

hot start:
The start of a jet engine in which the temperature of the exhaust pipe rises to an abnormally high and unsafe degree.

hot streak ignition:
An afterburner ignition system that utilizes a stream of raw fuel that continues to burn through the turbines and provides ignition for the afterburner fuel supply.

hot-tank oil system:
A type of oil system installed on some turbine engines where the oil is returned to the tank directly from the engine without being cooled. On these installations the oil cooler is installed in the pressure portion of the oil system.

hover:
To remain in a stationery position at a given altitude above the surface.

hp:
See *horsepower*

HRD system:
High Rate of Discharge. A fire extinguisher system that carries the extinguishing agent in a sealed sphere or cylinder. The entire contents of the container can be emptied in less than one second.

HUD:
Heads up display.

hull:
The frame or body of a thing built to move on or pass through water. The boat-like structure of a flying boat's fuselage.

human factors:
Awareness of the way a job is approached, the things that cause mistakes to be made, and what can be done to apply logic to the process. An attempt to reduce the maintenance error rate to the lowest level possible.

humidity:
Amount or degree of moisture in the air. If humidity increases, air density is decreased. Humidity has little effect on density, however, in comparison with temperature and pressure changes.

hung start:
Failure of a turbine engine to reach normal idling r.p.m. during starting.

hush kit:
Specialty modification that allows older, noisier aircraft to continue to operate legally (within noise regulations). Most conversions used either corrugated or lobe

type exhaust nozzles, along with soundproofing in the nacelles. Sometimes they also involve minor changes in power settings or operating methods.

hybrid:
1. A composite laminate consisting of laminae of two or more composite material systems.

2. A combination of two or more different fibers such as carbon and glass or carbon and aramid into a structure.

hydraulic:
Of or pertaining to mechanisms or devices activated by liquids forced through tubes and orifices under pressure.

hydraulic accumulator:
A reservoir for storing up hydraulic fluid under pressure.

HYDRAULIC ACCUMULATOR

hydraulic fuse:
A unit designed to stop the flow of hydraulic fluid if a leak occurs downstream of the fuse.

hydraulic lock:
Condition that occurs when oil or fuel drains into the combustion chambers of the lower cylinders of radial engines or accumulates in the lower intake pipes ready to be drawn into the cylinders when the engine starts. This liquid, being incompressible, stops piston movement as the piston

approaches top center of the compression stroke (both valves closed).

hydraulic motor:
A motor designed to turn hydraulic pressure into rotary motion.

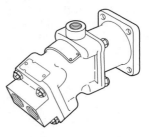

HYDRAULIC MOTOR

hydraulic pump:
An engine driven electric or hand operated pump that is used to move hydraulic fluid through the system.

hydraulic reservoir:
A container for the hydraulic fluid supply in an aircraft.

hydraulic servo:
A type of control system in which a small signal or force is used to control a much larger force.

hydraulic valve lifter:
Hydraulic units in the valve train of a reciprocating engine that automatically adjust for any change in dimension of the cylinder caused by expansion. This keeps the operating clearance between the valve and rocker at zero. Also called a *zero lash lifter*.

hydrocarbon:
An organic compound containing only carbon and hydrogen and often occurring in petroleum, natural gas, coal and bitumens.

hydrogen embrittlement:
A condition of low ductility in metals resulting from the absorption of hydrogen.

Hydromatic propeller:
Trade name for a hydraulically-operated constant speed propeller. Commonly used on large piston engined airliners. No longer in widespread use, although still found on some older aircraft.

hydromechanical fuel control:
A type of turbine engine fuel control that uses hydraulic and mechanical forces to operate the fuel scheduling mechanisms.

hydrometer:
An instrument used to determine specific gravity of liquids. It consists of a sealed, graduated tube, weighted at one end, that sinks in a fluid to a depth used as a measure of the fluid's specific gravity.

hydrophilic:
Having an affinity for, attracting, adsorbing, or absorbing water. A substance soluble in water.

hydroplaning:
A condition that can exist with some high-speed jet aircraft having small diameter, high-pressure tires. When the tire is on a water-covered runway and the brakes are applied, there is a possibility that the brake will lock up and the tire will ride on the surface of the water, much like a water-skier.

hydropneumatic:
Mechanical equipment that utilizes both hydraulic and pneumatic forces to accomplish the intended task.

hydrostatic:
A branch of physics dealing with the pressure and equilibrium of liquids, or of bodies immersed in liquids.

hydrostatic paradox:
A condition that does not at first appear to be true, in which it can be observed that the pressure exerted by a column of liquid is dependent on its height and independent of its volume.

hygrometer:
An instrument used to determine the amount of moisture in the air.

hypersonic:
Of or pertaining to the speed of objects moving at Mach 5 or greater.

hypersonic flow:
Flow at very high supersonic speeds; as arbitrarily defined, flow at a Mach number of 5 or greater.

hyperventilation:
The excessive ventilation of the lungs caused by very rapid and deep breathing that results in an excessive loss of carbon dioxide from the body.

hypotenuse:
The side of a right triangle opposite the right angle.

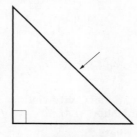

HYPOTENUSE

hypoxia:
The effects on the human body of an insufficient supply of oxygen.

hysteresis:
The time lag of the magnetic flux in a magnetic material behind the magnetizing force producing it. Caused by the molecular friction of the molecules trying to align themselves with the magnetic force applied to the material.

hysteresis loss:
The power loss in an iron-core transformer or other alternating-current device as a result of magnetic hysteresis.

IAS:
Indicated airspeed. *(FAR 1)*

I-beam:
A structural component whose cross section resembles the letter I.

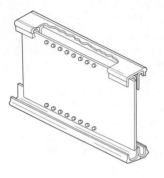

I-BEAM

IC:
Integrated Circuit

ICAO:
International Civil Aviation Organization. *(FAR 1)*

icebox rivet:
Rivets made of 2024 or 2017 aluminum alloy. These rivets must be heat treated, quenched and held at subzero temperatures (in an icebox) until they are ready to be driven. They will harden and come to their full strength after they are installed.

ice light:
A light mounted on an aircraft in such a manner that it allows the pilot to see the build-up of ice on the wing at night.

IDG:
Integrated Drive Generator

idle cutoff:
That position of the mixture control in which no fuel can flow from the metering system into the engine.

idle mixture:
A fuel mixture that at takeoff power is rich enough to supply sufficient fuel to keep the hottest cylinder cool.

idle speed:
The r.p.m. of an aircraft engine when the throttle is fully closed.

idle thrust:
The jet thrust obtained with the engine power control level set at the least thrust position at which it can be placed. *(FAR 1)*

idler gear:
A gear or gears placed between two other gears to transfer motion from one gear to the other gear without changing their speed or ratio.

IFR:
Instrument flight rules. *(FAR 1)*

IFR conditions:
Weather conditions below the minimum for flight under visual flight rules. *(FAR 1)*

IFR over-the-top:
With respect to the operation of aircraft: the operation of an aircraft over-the-top on an IFR flight plan when cleared by air traffic control to maintain VFR conditions or VFR conditions on top. *(FAR 1)*

igniter:
Part of the turbine engine ignition system that, when energized, releases a high-energy arc to ignite the atomized fuel/ air mixture in the combustion chamber.

IGNITER

ignition harness:
The system of high-tension wiring, together with any conduits or shielding, between the distributor and spark plugs of a reciprocating engine.

ignition timing:
Establishing the exact moment when the spark plug will ignite the fuel-mixture in the cylinder to produce the optimum burn.

illustrated parts list (breakdown) (IPB):
An exploded-view drawing in the service manual showing every part of a component, its proper name, part number, and number required for the assembly. This is FAA approved data and the use of parts not included in this list jeopardizes approval of the component.

ILS:
Instrument landing system. *(FAR 1)*

IM:
ILS inner marker. *(FAR 1)*

imbedded:
To make something an integral part of.

IMC:
Instrument meteorological conditions.

immiscible:
Liquids that do not mix with each other, such as oil and water.

impact ice:
Ice that forms when snow, sleet, or supercooled water droplets impinge upon aircraft surfaces, which are at or below freezing temperature.

IMPACT ICE
(ON LEADING EDGE OF WING)

impact wrench:
A power wrench, usually air driven, used to spin nuts onto bolts. Its torque forces are in a series of blows or impacts. Due to the uneven torque it produces, it should not be used for any threaded fastener where the amount of torque is critical.

impedance (Z):
The total opposition offered to the flow of an alternating current. It may consist of any combination of resistance, inductive reactance, and capacitive reactance. The symbol for impedance is Z.

impedance testing:
A term generally applied to eddy current testing that measures the overall change in impedance caused by variations in electromagnetic properties, as differentiated from phase analysis testing that measures changes in phase.

impeller:
A vaned disc where a fluid enters at the center and is accelerated outward to increase the pressure. Impellers may be found in reciprocating engine superchargers, radial flow compressors on turbine engines and in centrifugal-type fuel pumps, as well as other applications.

implode:
The reverse of explode. To burst inward.

impulse coupling:
A spring-loaded coupling between a magneto and its drive gear. When the engine is being turned over slowly, the magnet is restrained by stops, and the spring is wound. At the proper time for the starting spark to occur, the spring is released and the magnet is spun, producing a hot, late spark. When the engine starts, centrifugal force holds the coupling engaged so that it acts as a solid unit.

impulse-reaction turbine:
The most commonly used type of turbine in flight engines. The blades employed have an impulse turbine design at the base and a reaction turbine design toward the tip.

impulse turbine:
A form of turbine that is rated by the gases striking bucket-shaped turbine blades. An impulse turbine changes the direction of the airflow not a pressure change.

impurities:
Elements or compounds whose presence in a material is undesired.

inboard:
Toward the center of the aircraft.

incandescent:
Glowing because of intense heat.

incandescent lamp:
A lamp that produces light using a filament glowing white hot, encased in a glass bulb.

inches of mercury (in. Hg):
A measurement of absolute pressure. Standard atmospheric pressure at sea level with a temperature of 59°F is 29.92 in. Hg.

inches per second (IPS):
A vibration measurement used with electronic balancing equipment.

incidence board:
A device used to measure the angle of incidence of an aircraft wing.

incident wave:
1. The wave that strikes the surface of a medium.

2. The wave that travels from the sending end to the receiving end of a transmission line.

in-circuit meter:
A meter permanently installed in a circuit; used to monitor circuit operation.

inclination of an orbit (of an earth satellite):
The angle determined by the plane containing the orbit and the plane of the earth's equator measured in degrees between 0° and 180° and in counter-clockwise direction from the earth's equatorial plane at the ascending node of the orbit.

inclined plane:
A simple machine that facilitates the raising or lowering of heavy objects by the application of a small force over a relatively long distance. Some familiar examples of the inclined plane are a mountain highway and car-loading ramps.

inclinometer:
An instrument consisting of a curved glass tube housing a glass ball and filled with a liquid similar to kerosene. It may be used to indicate inclination, as a level, or to show the relationship between gravity and centrifugal force in a turn—a slip indicator.

inclusion:
A physical and mechanical discontinuity occurring within a material or part.

inclusions:
Particles of impurities, usually oxides, sulphides, silicates, and such, which are retained in the metal.

inconel:
A chromium-iron alloy similar to stainless steel.

index of refraction:
The degree of bending of an RF wave when passing from one medium to another.

indicated airspeed:
The speed of an aircraft as shown on its pitot static airspeed indicator calibrated to reflect standard atmosphere adiabatic compressible flow at sea level uncorrected for airspeed system errors. *(FAR 1)*

INDICATED AIRSPEED

indicated horsepower:
The computed total horsepower an engine develops, equal to the sum of the brake horsepower and the friction horsepower.

indicated mean effective pressure (IMEP):
The average working pressure developed within the cylinders of an engine during the power stroke. The indicated mean effective pressure is based on the indicated horsepower of the engine, and therefore is the sum of the friction mean effective pressure and the brake mean effective pressure.

induced current:
Current caused by the relative motion between a conductor and a magnetic field.

induced drag:
That part of the total drag on an aircraft induced by the airflow about the lifting surfaces.

induced voltage:
The electromotive force induced in a conductor because of the relative motion between the conductor and a magnetic field.

inductance:
A property of a circuit that opposes any change in the existing current. Inductance is present only when the current is changing. A coil is a source of inductance.

induction heating:
Heating metals by means of an alternating magnetic field.

induction manifold:
Means of distributing air, or the fuel/air mixture, to engine cylinders.

induction motor:
A simple, rugged, AC motor with desirable characteristics. The rotor is energized by transformer action (induction) from the stator. Induction motors are used more than any other type.

induction period:
A time period after catalyzed material is mixed in which the material is allowed to begin its cure before it is sprayed onto the surface.

induction vibrator:
A coil and set of contact points that produces pulsating direct current from direct current. Pulsating DC may be used in the primary winding of a magneto to produce a high voltage in the secondary winding.

inductive reactance:
The opposition to the flow of an alternating current caused by the inductance of a circuit, expressed in ohms. Identified by the symbol X_L.

inductor:
A coil of wire or other device used to introduce inductance into an electrical circuit.

inert gas:
A gas that does not normally combine chemically with other substances. Used in welding to shield the weld zone from the atmosphere to produce welds with little or no oxidation.

inert gas arc welding:
An arc welding process that utilizes an inert gas shield to prevent oxidation.

inertia:
The physical tendency of a body in motion to remain in motion and a body at rest to remain at rest

I

unless acted upon by an outside force (Newton's First Law of Motion).

inertial navigation systems (INS):
An aircraft and navigation system that does not rely on external radio signals; laser gyros and accelerometers provide three dimensional navigation capabilities

inertial reference system (IRS):
A combination of laser gyros and accelerometers used to sense the aircraft's angular rates and accelerations

inertial reference unit (IRU):
An LRU containing laser gyros and accelerometers used for aircraft navigation

inertia starter:
A type of starter associated with large radial engines that use the stored inertia of a heavy flywheel to turn the engine for starting. The flywheel was energized with either a hand crank or a removable motor driven crank.

inertia switch:
An electrical switch built into the emergency locator transmitter (ELT) that is designed to close and activate the ELT when there is a sudden change in velocity such as a crash.

inertial navigation:
A navigation system that senses changes in direction or acceleration and automatically corrects deviations from the planned course.

inerting:
The replacement of oxygen in the atmosphere with a gas to the point the atmosphere will not support combustion or explosion.

infinite:
1. Extending indefinitely, endless.

2. Boundless, having no limits.

3. An incalculable number.

infralow frequency:
The band of frequencies from 300 Hz to 3,000 Hz.

ingest:
To pull in or swallow something. Usually associated with turbine engine intakes ingesting air or foreign objects (FOD).

ingot:
A casting intended for subsequent rolling, forging, or extrusion.

inherent stability:
Stability built into an aircraft that, when disturbed, causes it to return to straight and level flight.

in hg:
Inches of mercury

inhibited sealer:
A material used to exclude moisture and air from a honeycomb repair.

inhibitive film:
A film of material on the surface of a metal that inhibits or retards the formation of corrosion. It does this by producing an ionized surface that will not allow the formation of corrosive salts on the metal.

injection pump:
A high pressure fuel pump used with one type of reciprocating engine fuel injection system. Fuel is pumped under high pressure directly into the combustion chamber where it is atomized and ignited as it leaves the injector nozzle.

inlet buzz:
A sound associated with the movement of shock waves in and out of the inlet of supersonic aircraft when design speeds are exceeded.

inlet case:
The front compressor-supporting member of a turbine engine, usually manufactured as a single casting.

inlet duct:
The portion of a turbine powered

aircraft that directs air into the engine compressor.

inlet guide vane:
Devices located in front of the first compressor rotor, to control the angle of incidence of the inlet air.

inlet screen:
A type of intake filter used on turbine-powered helicopters and stationary turbines to prevent foreign object damage.

inlet spike:
A movable device in the inlet of some supersonic aircraft to control the inlet geometry.

in-line engine:
A reciprocating engine with all of the cylinders in a single line. In-line engines were manufactured both with the cylinders located above and below the crankshaft (inverted in-line).

inner tube:
A removable airtight rubber tube installed inside a pneumatic tire to hold the air that inflates the tire.

in-phase:
A condition in an electrical circuit where the voltage and current rise and fall at the same time and in the same direction.

inrush current:
The high current flow that occurs in some electrical circuits when the switch is first closed.

inside micrometer:
A type of micrometer caliper designed to measure the inside diameter of cylindrical objects. Used to measure cylinder bores and to check for out-of-round.

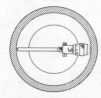

INSIDE MICROMETER

insoluble:
Not soluble; incapable or difficult to dissolve, as in liquid; as chalk is insoluble in water

inspection authorization (IA):
An authorization issued by the Federal Aviation Administration to experienced A&P Mechanics meeting certain requirements. This authorization allows them to approve aircraft for return to service following certain types of inspection and maintenance operations.

installation drawing:
A drawing that shows all of the individual components in their proper relationship for installation.

instantaneous automatic gain control (IAGC):
A circuit that can vary the gain of the radar receiver with each input pulse to maintain a nearly constant output peak amplitude.

instantaneous vertical speed indicator (IVSI):
Instrument that measures and displays rate of climb. Incorporates acceleration pumps to eliminate the limitations associated with the calibrated leak.

INSTANTANEOUS VERTICAL
SPEED INDICATOR

instrument:
A device using an internal mechanism to show visually or aurally the attitude, altitude, or operation of an aircraft or aircraft part. It includes electronic devices

for automatically controlling an aircraft in flight. *(FAR 1)*

instrument flight rules (IFR):
Flight by reference to the aircraft's instruments rather than by visual clues. The FAA establishes the conditions under which flight must be conducted according to IFR.

instrument landing system (ILS):
A precision approach and landing guidance system which normally consists of the following components: localizer, outer marker, glide slope, and approach lights.

insulation blanket:
1. Any material used to insulate against heat, cold or sound.
2. A layer of fireproof material used to keep the heat of a jet engine tail pipe from radiating into the engine compartment.

INT:
Intersection. *(FAR 1)*

intake valve:
A poppet type valve in the head of a reciprocating engine cylinder that permits the entry of the fuel/air mixture into the combustion chamber.

integer:
A whole number, either positive or negative.

integral fuel tank:
A structural configuration in which a component of the aircraft serves as a fuel container.

integrated avionics processor system (IAPS):
Provides integration functions for various avionics systems

integrated circuit (IC):
1. A circuit in which many elements are fabricated and interconnected by a single process (into a single chip), as opposed to a nonintegrated circuit in which the transistors,

diodes, resistors, and other components are fabricated separately and then assembled.
2. Elements inseparably associated and formed on or within a single substrate.

integrated display system (IDS):
A state of the art instrument system, which employs integrated display and processor circuitry

integrated engine pressure ratio (IEPR):
An engine pressure ratio calculation used on some turbofan engines that includes fan discharge total pressure and compressor inlet total pressure.

interconnector:
A small tube connecting the burner cans of a multiple can installation to allow flame propagation from one can to the next.

intercooler:
A cooler for a fluid between two stages of some process in which a fluid acquires heat, e.g., a cooler between two stages of supercharging in the induction system of an aircraft engine.

intercylinder baffles:
Sheet metal deflectors installed between and around air cooled cylinders to direct the flow of cooling air and aid in uniform cooling.

interference:
The effect of unwanted energy due to one or a combination of emissions, radiations or inductions upon reception in a radio communication system, manifested by any performance degradation, misinterpretation or loss of information that could be extracted in the absence of such unwanted energy.

interference fit:
A fit between two parts in which the part being put into a hole is larger than the hole itself. In order

to fit them together, the hole is expanded by heating, and the part is shrunk by chilling. Then, when the two parts reach the same temperature they will not separate. The area around the hole is subject to tensile stress and thus vulnerable to stress corrosion.

intergranular corrosion:
The formation of corrosion along the grain boundaries within the metal alloy.

intermittent fault:
A fault in a system that does not occur consistently.

intermittent load:
A load that is not consistently on. Something that operates for relatively short times only.

internal baffles:
Deflector plates installed inside a tank or reservoir to prevent the liquid from sloshing in flight.

internal combustion engine:
An engine in which the working substance or pressure necessary to move the engine or its parts is derived from the combustion of fuel within a chamber or chambers that are an integral part of the engine. Types of internal combustion engines include reciprocating engines where the fuel is burned within the cylinders of the engine, rocket engines, and the various types of jet engines.

internal resistance (of a battery):
The resistance of the battery itself. This resistance will cause a voltage drop proportional to the amount of current flow.

internal stresses:
Unseen forces existing within a part. These are forces that exist without the part being subjected to a working load.

internal supercharger:
A centrifugal supercharger mounted integral to the engine and driven from the crankshaft, usually through some sort of gearing.

internal thread:
Threads on the inside of a hollow cylinder.

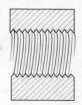

INTERNAL THREAD

internal timing:
The timing of the relationship between the E-gap position of the rotating magnet and the opening of the breaker points.

internal wrenching bolt:
A type of high-strength bolt where the head is recessed to accept a hex type allen wrench.

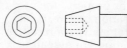

INTERNAL WRENCHING BOLT

interphone system:
Found on transport categoty aircraft to provide communications between flight crew, ground crew, flight attendants, and maintenance personnel

interplane struts:
The struts that run vertically near the wing tips between the wings of a biplane.

interpolation:
To compute intermediate values between a series of given values, such as in a table or chart.

interpole:
Field poles placed between regular generator fields. The windings around them are

in series with the armature. Interpoles are used to prevent arcing at the brushes caused by armature reaction.

interrib lacing:
Reinforcing tape run diagonally from the top of one rib to the bottom of the next throughout a truss-type wing to hold the ribs upright and in line during the covering process.

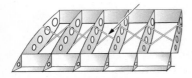

INTERRIB LACING

inter-satellite service:
A radio communication service providing links between artificial satellites.

interstate air commerce:
The carriage by aircraft of persons or property for compensation or hire, or the carriage of mail by aircraft, or the operation or navigation of aircraft in the conduct or furtherance of a business or vocation, in commerce between a place in any State of the United States, or the District of Columbia, and a place in any other State of the United States, or the District of Columbia; or between places in the same State of the United States through the airspace over any place outside thereof; or between places in the same territory or possession of the United States, or the District of Columbia. (FAR 1)

interstate air transportation:
The carriage by aircraft of persons or property as a common carrier for compensation or hire, or the carriage of mail by aircraft in commerce:

1. Between a place in a state or the District of Columbia and another place in another state or the District of Columbia

2. Between places in the same state through the airspace over any place outside that state.

3. Between places in the same possession of the United States; Whether that commerce moves wholly by aircraft of partly by aircraft and partly by other forms of transportation. (FAR 1)

inter-turbine temperature (ITT):
Temperature taken between the turbine wheels. Used on some turbine engines in place of turbine inlet temperature.

intrastate air transportation:
The carriage of persons or property as a common carrier for compensation or hire, by turbojet-powered aircraft capable of carrying thirty or more persons, wholly within the same State of the United States. (FAR 1)

invar:
A nickel-iron alloy with an extremely low temperature coefficient of expansion.

inversely:
Inverted or reversed in position or relationship.

inverted engine:
A reciprocating engine where the crankshaft is above the cylinders.

inverted gull wing:
An aircraft wing near the root that slants downward, then straightens or slants slightly upward.

inverter:
1. A device for converting DC electricity to AC electricity. May be accomplished through mechanical or solid-state means.

2. A logic function. See NOT gate.

investment casting:
Casting in a vacuum furnace or spin chamber used to produce a denser, better quality finished product.

ion:
A charged atom. That is, one with either more electrons than protons (negative ion), or more protons than electrons (positive ion).

ionization air blower:
A special air blower that will safely delete any static charge formed on nonconductors.

IPS:
Inches per second

IR Drop:
The amount of voltage drop in a given conductor due to the resistance of the conductor.

IRAN:
Inspect and repair as necessary.

iridium:
An extremely hard and brittle metallic element of the platinum group, which is used for electrodes of fine-wire spark plugs that must operate in extremely severe lead conditions.

iris exhaust nozzle:
A type of variable exhaust nozzle used with afterburner installations. The nozzle design is similar to the iris on a camera lens and is open the widest during afterburner operations.

Irish linen:
A strong fabric made from flax that was used to cover many older aircraft. It is still popular in Europe but is no longer readily available in the United States. It may be used as a direct replacement for grade-A cotton.

iron:
A heavy malleable, ductile, magnetic metallic element. It is the base metal for the production of all types of steel.

iron-core coil:
A type of inductor wound on a soft iron (usually laminated) core.

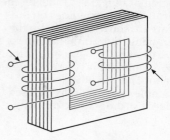

IRON-CORE COIL

iron-vane movement:
An AC measuring instrument that uses a soft iron vane or movable core operating with a coil to produce an indication of current flow.

ISO:
International Organization for Standardization. A network of national standards institutes from 140 countries working in partnership with international organizations, governments, industry, business and consumer representatives. The source of ISO 9000 family of standards and more than 13,000 international standards for business, government and society.

isobar:
A line of equal or constant barometric pressure.

isobaric metering valve:
The metering valve in a cabin pressurization system which maintains a constant cabin altitude.

isogonic lines:
Lines on charts that connect points of equal magnetic variation.

isolation mount:
Any type of rubber and metal composite mount used to prevent the transfer of vibration from one component to another.

I

isometric drawing:

A drawing where all the lines that are parallel on the part being drawn are parallel on the drawing. Vertical lines on the part are shown vertical on the drawing, but horizontal lines are drawn at a 30° angle to the horizontal. This type of drawing cannot be used to express complex parts. It may be used to clarify orthographic drawings.

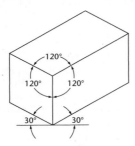

ISOMETRIC DRAWING

iso-octane symbol:

C_8H_{18}. A hydro-carbon that has a very high critical pressure and temperature. It is used as a reference for measuring the anti-detonation characteristics of a fuel.

isopropyl alcohol:

The fluid used in propeller anti-icing systems.

isothermal forging:

A hot-forging process in which a constant and uniform temperature is maintained in the workpiece during forging by heating the dies to the same temperature as the workpiece. Most commonly conducted at about 2,000°F under a controlled atmosphere or in a vacuum to prevent oxidation while forging superalloys.

isotope:

One of several nuclides having the same number of protons in their nuclei, and hence belonging to the same element, but differing in the number of neutrons, and therefore in mass number. Small quantitative differences in chemical properties exist between elements and isotopes. Isotopes may or may not be unstable. Unstable isotopes undergo transitions to other isotopes or elements with a loss of energy. Such energy is usually given off in the form of electromagnetic or particle radiation. Isotopes are used as source of radiation for radiography.

isotropic:

Having uniform properties in all directions.

isotropic laminate:

A laminate in which the strength properties are the same in all directions.

ITT:

Inter-turbine temperature.

Jj

jack:
A machine for lifting aircraft a short distance. Typically used during landing gear maintenance.

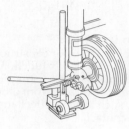

JACK

jacket:
A covering or casing of some kind.

jack pad:
A reinforced point on the lower side of an aircraft designed to handle the weight of the aircraft when jacking.

jacobs chuck:
Common term for the drill chuck used in either the headstock spindle or in the tailstock for holding straight-shank drills, taps, reamers, or small diameter workplaces.

jam nut:
A thin check nut, which may be screwed down against a regular nut as a locking device.

jet:
1. A calibrated orifice in the fuel passage of a carburetor.
2. An aircraft powered by a turbine engine.

jet assist takeoff (JATO):
A means of assisting aircraft during takeoff from short runways and with heavy loads. Small, solid fuel rockets attached to the aircraft to provide additional thrust for a few seconds at takeoff.

jet engine:
A common name for a turbine engine. See *gas turbine engine* and *turbine engine*.

jet pump:
A pump that applies Bernoulli's principle by using the flow of a fluid to produce a low pressure that can draw fuel or oil from a tank, or be used as a vapor eliminator.

Jetcal analyzer:
Device used to check the exhaust gas temperature during periodic maintenance inspections or when abnormally high or low temperatures are noted.

jeweler's rouge:
A very fine abrasive used for polishing hard metal surfaces.

jig:
A fixture or template employed to ensure exact location of one part in relation to another.

jo-bolt:
A type of internally threaded three-piece rivet.

JO-BOLT

joggle:
A small offset in sheet metal. Joggles are used to allow one part to overlap another.

johanson blocks (jo blocks):
Common term for the precision gauge blocks used and accepted

135

as dimensional standards by machinists, toolmakers and inspectors.

joule:
A unit of energy or work. A joule of energy is liberated by 1 ampere flowing for 1 second through a resistance of 1 ohm.

journal:
The part of a shaft that is in contact with, and supported by, a bearing.

junction:
1. The connection between two or more conductors.

2. The contact between two dissimilar metals or materials, as in a thermocouple.

junction box:
A box with a cover that serves the purpose of joining different runs of wire or cable and provides space for the connection and branching of the enclosed conductors.

junction diode:
A two-terminal device containing a single crystal of semiconducting material that ranges from P-type at one terminal to N-type at the other.

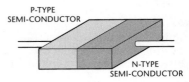

P-TYPE
SEMI-CONDUCTOR

N-TYPE
SEMI-CONDUCTOR

JUNCTION DIODE

junction transistor:
A bipolar transistor constructed from interacting PN junctions. The term is used to distinguish junction transistors from other types, such as field-effect and point-contact.

jury strut:
A small strut used to stabilize the main wing strut against vibration. The jury strut runs from approximately the mid point of the main strut to the wing spar.

Kk

K:
A constant—generally empirical; thermal conductivity; stress intensity; Kelvin—correction factor.

kalman filter:
An advanced software algorithm used in GPS receivers to process the complex position calculations necessary to determine aircraft position

K-chart:
A chart used in sheet metal fabrication to determine the setback for bends other than 90 degrees.

K monel:
A nickel, copper and aluminum alloy that exhibits high strength. It is heat treatable, corrosion resistant and non-magnetic.

keel:
The primary longitudinal member along the center bottom of a seaplane float or hull.

keeper:
A soft iron bar placed across the poles of a magnet when it is not being used. This serves to keep the magnet from losing its magnetism.

Kelvin scale:
An absolute temperature scale independent of the thermometric properties of the working substance. For convenience, the Kelvin use the degree Celsius. The freezing point of water in the Kelvin scale is 273.15°K.

KELVIN SCALE

kerf:
1. The space from which metal has been removed by a cutting process.

2. The width of cut made by a saw.

kerosene:
A refined petroleum distillate used in space heating units, in wick fed lamps, as a cleaning solvent, as a base for liquid insecticide sprays, and as the primary ingredient in jet fuel. A multiple use type is procured under Federal Specification VV K 21 1. A colorless, deodorized type is also available. The amount of gummy material present is known as its gum content, which is determined by astm methods d 381 and d 873.

Kevlar®:
DuPont company name for an aramid fiber. It has good impact resistance, low density, high strength, and low ratio frequency attenuation.

key:
One of the several types of small metal objects designed to fit mating slots in a shaft and the hub of a gear or pulley to provide a positive drive between them also. The name of the T handle wrench used on chucks.

key-click filters:
Filters used in keying systems to prevent key-click interference.

key clicks:
Interference in the form of "clicks" or "thumps" caused by

the sudden application or removal of power.

key seat:
A recessed groove (slot) machined into a shaft or a part going on the shaft (usually a wheel or gear).

keyway:
A groove machined into a shaft or its corresponding hole to accommodate some sort of key. Keys are used to prevent rotation of the shaft in the hole.

kHz:
Kilohertz

KIAS:
Knots Indicated Airspeed

kickback:
Reverse rotation of a reciprocating engine that occurs during starting. This is usually the result of premature ignition.

killed steel:
Steel deoxidized with a strong deoxidizing agent such as silicon or aluminum in order to reduce the oxygen content to such a level that no reaction occurs between carbon and oxygen during solidification.

kilo:
Metric prefix meaning one thousand. One thousand grams equals one kilogram.

kilohertz (kHz):
1,000 Hz. Abbreviation is kHz.

kilovolt amperes reactive (KVAR):
A measure of reactive power.

kilowatt:
A unit of electrical power, equal to 1,000 watts.

kilowatt hour:
Unit used in measuring amounts of electrical energy consumed. For example, if a 100-watt bulb consumes electrical energy for 20 hours, it has used 2,000 watt hours, or 2 kilowatt hours of electrical energy.

kinematic viscosity:
The ratio of the absolute viscosity to the density at the temperature of the viscosity measurement. The metric units of kinematic viscosity are the stoke and centistoke, which correspond to the poise and centipoise of absolute viscosity.

kinetic energy:
Energy possessed by an object because of motion.

kink:
A twist or curl, as in cable, wire, or tubing, caused by its doubling or bending upon itself.

Kirchoff's laws:
1. The algebraic sum of the current flowing toward any point in a circuit, and the current flowing away from it is zero.

2. The algebraic sum of the products of the current and resistance in each of the conductors in any closed path in a network is equal to the algebraic sum of the electromotive forces in the path.

kirksite:
An alloy of aluminum and zinc.

kite:
A framework, covered with paper, cloth, metal, or other material, intended to be flown at the end of a rope or cable, and having as its only support the force of the wind moving past its surfaces. *(FAR 1)*

Klincher locknut:
Fastener used to ensure a permanent and vibration proof, bolted connection that holds solidly and resists thread wear. It will withstand extremely high or low temperatures and exposure to lubricants, weather, and compounds without impairing the effectiveness of the locking element.

klystron power amplifier:
A multi-cavity, microwave

electron tube that uses velocity modulation.

knitting:
A method of constructing fabric by interlocking series of loops of one or more yarns.

knock:
Also called *ping*.

The noise associated with internal-combustion engines. After the spark ignites the charge, the charge burns smoothly until part of it is burned. Then if either the fuel or engine operating conditions are unsuitable, the remaining portions burns suddenly, which makes a knock or a ping.

knot:
A nautical mile per hour. Equals 1.1516 statute miles per hour.

knowledge, skills and abilities (ksa):
Knowledge involves the use of mental processes that enable a person to recall facts, identify concepts, apply rules or principles, solve problems and think creatively. Skills involve physical or manipulative activities and often require knowledge for their execution. Skills are actions having special requirements for speed, accuracy or coordination. Abilities are the acquired proficiency to perform. Abilities require knowledge, skills, aptitude, and/or natural talent.

knuckle pin:
The hardened steel pin that holds an articulating rod in the master rod of a radial engine.

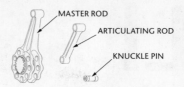

KNUCKLE PIN

knurled:
A series of small ridges or beads placed along the edge of a metal object, such as a thumbscrew, as an aid in gripping.

kraft paper:
Strong brown paper, such as the paper of which grocery sacks are made.

Krueger flap:
A type of leading edge flap hinged at the bottom side of the airfoil. When actuated, the leading edge bends downward, increasing the overall camber of the wing. This allows the wing to develop additional lift at lower airspeeds. An alternate spelling is Krüger.

KRUEGER FLAP

KVA:
Kilovolt - Ampere

KVAR:
Kilovolt amperes, reactive. A measure of reactive power.

K

labyrinth air seal:
Device for preventing leakage of gas on the gas generator shaft in a turbine. A labyrinth consists of a series of projections on the rotating element running in close contact with grooves on the stationary element.

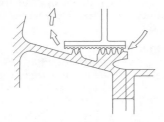

LABYRINTH AIR SEAL

lacing cord:
Strong cord used to stitch the fabric covering to the aircraft structure. The material that the cord is made of must be matched with the type of fabric being used to cover the aircraft. The type of cord to be used is generally specified in the Supplemental Type Certificate governing the covering system. Also called *rib-stitching cord*.

lacquer:
Pigments dissolved in a volatile base in which the cure is effected by the evaporation of the solvents.

lag angle:
The angle by which a rotor blade is displaced about its drag hinge, the angle being measured between the blade-span axis and a radial line taken across the rotor disc and containing the drag hinge and the axis of rotation.

lagging material:
Insulating material that is used to prevent unwanted heat transfer.

lag hinge:
See *drag hinge*

lamina:
A single ply of composite material, made up of a reinforcing element and matrix. Laminae is the plural of lamina).

laminar flow:
A smooth flow in which no cross flow of fluid particles occurs, hence a flow conceived as made up of layers.

laminate:
1. A composite metal, usually in the form of sheet or bar, composed of two or more metal layers so bonded that the composite metal forms a structural member.

2. To form a metallic product of two or more bonded layers.

laminate orientation:
The configuration of a cross-plied composite laminate, with regard to the angles of cross-plying, the number of laminae at each angle, and the exact sequence of the lamina lay-up.

laminated steel core:
The core of a coil or transformer consisting of a stack of thin, soft iron sheets, insulated from each other by an oxide film or varnish. Laminated cores minimize eddy current losses.

laminated wood:
Layers of wood glued together so that the grain in each layer runs in the same direction.

LAN:
Local Area Network

landing flaps:
A secondary control surface built into the wing of an aircraft and used to increase lift and/or drag. The net effect permits a lower

landing speed and shortens the landing roll.

landing gear:
The apparatus comprising those components of an aircraft that support and provide for the aircraft on land, water, or other surface. The landing gear consists of wheels, floats, skis, bogies and treads, or other devices, together with associated struts, bracing, shock absorbers, etc. *(FAR 1)*

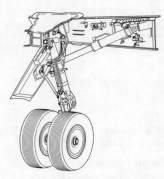

LANDING GEAR

landing gear extended speed:
The maximum speed at which an aircraft can be safely flown with the landing gear extended.

landing gear operating speed:
The maximum speed at which the landing gear can be safely extended or retracted. *(FAR 1)*

landing gear position indicating system:
A system of lights or indicators that show the pilot the position of the retractable landing gear and warn of an unsafe condition.

landing lights:
Usually one of two or more lights mounted on an aircraft and used to illuminate the surface during landing.

landing wires:
Wires attached near the inboard end of the upper wing of a biplane and extending to near

the outboard end of the lower wing. These wires brace the wings against forces opposite to the normal direction of lift.

landplane:
An airplane designed to be operated from the surface of the land, rather than water or snow.

lap joint:
A joint between two overlapping members.

lapping compound:
An abrasive paste used to polish surfaces. Often used to obtain a good seal on the intake and exhaust valves of reciprocating engine cylinders.

lapse rate:
The rate of change in value of a meteorological phenomenon, usually the rate of decrease of pressure or temperature with elevation.

large aircraft:
Aircraft of more than 12,500 pounds, maximum certificated takeoff weight. *(FAR 1)*

laser ring gyro:
Any system which senses rotation by measuring frequency shift of laser light trapped in closed circuit in a horizontal plane.

large scale integration (LSI):
An integrated circuit containing 1,000 to 2,000 logic gates or up to 64,000 bits of memory.

last chance filter:
A filter located just before the spray nozzles of a turbine engine fuel system. This filter provides the last chance to remove any impurities that might clog the spray nozzles.

latent heat:
The amount of heat required to change the state of a material without changing its temperature.

lateral axis:
The axis that extends through the

center of an airplane from wing tip to wing tip. The pitch axis. Movement of the elevators will rotate the aircraft about its lateral axis.

lateral stability:
The tendency of a body, such as an aircraft, to resist rolling, or sometimes also, to resist lateral displacement. The tendency of an aircraft to keep its wings level, either in flight or at rest.

lateral vibration:
A low frequency vibration in a helicopter that is primarily caused by an out-of-balance condition of one of the main rotor blades.

lathe:
A machine tool having a horizontal spindle that supports and rotates the work while it is being machined by a tool mounted on a cross slide. It is used primarily for turning cylindrical work.

latitude:
Measurement north or south of the equator in degrees, minutes, and seconds.

lay line:
A line used on flexible hose to visually determine if the hose has been twisted during installation.

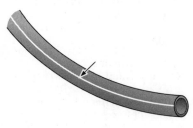

LAY LINE

lay-up:
A process of fabrication involving the assembly of successive layers of resin-impregnated material.

LC capacitor input filter:
This is the most common type of filter. It is used in a power supply where output current is low and load current is relatively constant.

LC circuit:
An electrical circuit containing both inductance and capacitance.

LCD:
Liquid crystal display. A thin, flat display panel made up of a type of liquid whose molecules can be arranged by electrical charges in such a way that polarized light cannot pass through certain areas. These areas can be shaped to resemble letters, numbers and lines. Used in cockpit displays.

LDA:
Localizer-type directional aid. *(FAR 1)*

lead (Pb):
A heavy, pliant, silvery metallic chemical element.

lead-acid battery:
A battery constructed of multiple lead-acid cells.

lead-acid cell:
A cell in an ordinary storage battery in which electrodes are grids of lead containing an active material consisting of certain lead oxides that change in composition during charging and discharging. The electrodes or plates are immersed in an electrolyte of diluted sulfuric acid.

LEAD-ACID CELL

leader line:
A solid line with one arrowhead and indicate a part or portion to which a note, number, or other reference applies.

lead fouling:
Lead oxide formed during combustion collects on combustion chamber surfaces and the electrodes of the spark plugs. These deposits are good electrical conductors at high temperatures and cause misfiring.

lead hole:
See *pilot hole*

leading edge:
The edge of an airfoil (wing, propeller, or stabilizer) that first meets or bites the air.

leading edge flap:
An auxiliary control surface attached to the leading edge of the wing, which folds downward to increase the camber of the wing. This increases both lift and drag. Leading edge flaps may be extended both for takeoff and landing. See *Krueger flap* for an illustration of one type of leading edge flap.

lead-lag hinge:
A hinge installed at the root of a helicopter rotor blade with its axis perpendicular to the plane of rotation. Also known as the *alpha, drag,* or *hunting hinge.*

leaf brake:
See *cornice brake*

lean flame out:
A condition in a turbine engine where the fire goes out because the fuel-air mixture has become so lean that it can no longer support combustion.

lean mixture:
A fuel-air mixture with an excess of air.

least common denominator (LCD):
The least common multiple of the denominators of a set of fractions. Also known as *lowest common denominator.*

left-hand thread:
A thread that when viewed axially winds in a counterclockwise and receding direction.

LEMAC:
Leading edge of the mean aerodynamic chord. A point often used as a reference for aerodynamic measurements in aircraft design and operation.

Lenz's Law:
The law of induced current. Simply stated, the current induced in a conductor will produce a magnetic field that opposes the field producing the original current.

lever:
The simplest machine, consisting of three basic parts the fulcrum, F; a force or effort, E; and a resistance. A seesaw is a familiar example of a lever in which one weight balances the other.

LFR:
Low-frequency radio range. *(FAR 1)*

life-limited part:
A part or component that has a designated number of hours or calendar time in service, after which it will be replaced and is no longer usable.

lift:
An upward force caused by the rush of air over the wings that supports the airplane in flight.

lifting body:
A wingless aircraft developed by NASA where lift is created by the shape of the craft itself.

lift-over-drag ratio:
Ratio that varies with the angle of attack but reaches a definite maximum value for a particular angle of attack. At this angle, the wing has reached its maximum efficiency.

light emitting diode (LED):
A PN-junction diode that emits visible light when it is forward biased. Depending on the material used to make the diode, the light may be red, green, amber or blue-white.

lightening hole:
Any hole cut in a part for the purpose of decreasing weight. The edges of the hole are usually flanged, making the part stronger than it was in the original condition.

light-sport aircraft:
An aircraft, other than a helicopter or powered-lift that, since its original certification, has continued to meet the following:

1. A maximum takeoff weight of not more than

   a. 660 pounds (300 kilograms) for lighter-than-air aircraft;

   b. 1,320 pounds (600 kilograms) for aircraft not intended for operation on water; or

   c. 1,430 pounds (650 kilograms) for an aircraft intended for operation on water.

2. A maximum airspeed in level flight with maximum continuous power (V_H) of not more than 120 knots CAS under standard atmospheric conditions at sea level.

3. A maximum never-exceed speed (V_{NE}) of not more than 120 knots CAS for a glider.

4. A maximum stalling speed or minimum steady flight speed without the use of lift-enhancing devices (V_{S1}) of not more than 45 knots CAS at the aircraft's maximum certificated takeoff weight and most critical center of gravity.

5. A maximum seating capacity of no more than two persons, including the pilot.

6. A single, reciprocating engine, if powered.

7. A fixed or ground-adjustable propeller if a powered aircraft other than a powered glider.

8. A fixed or autofeathering propeller system if a powered glider.

9. A fixed-pitch, semi-rigid, teetering, two-blade rotor system, if a gyroplane.

10. A nonpressurized cabin, if equipped with a cabin.

11. Fixed landing gear, except for an aircraft intended for operation on water or a glider.

12. Fixed or repositionable landing gear, or a hull, for an aircraft intended for operation on water.

13. Fixed or retractable landing gear for a glider. *(FAR 1)*

lighter-than-air aircraft:
Aircraft that can rise and remain suspended by using contained gas weighing less than the air that is displaced by the gas. *(FAR 1)*

LIGHTER-THAN-AIR AIRCRAFT
(EXAMPLE)

limit switch:
A switch designed to stop the actuator at the limit of its movement.

Lindberg fire detection system:
A type of continuous element fire detection.

linear:
Having an output that varies in direct proportion to the input.

line loss:
The voltage loss in a conductor due to its length.

line maintenance:
Inspection and repairs that are accomplished on the flight line, as opposed to those accomplished in the shop.

line of sight radio reception:
A limitation of high-frequency radio signals. This frequency range requires a clear path between the transmitting and receiving antennas.

line voltage:
The voltage of the main power line that feeds a circuit.

linear actuator:
An actuation that changes hydraulic or pneumatic pressure into linear motion.

line select keys (LSK):
Push button switches found on the control display units used to select items for display or activate functions available on the CDU

lines of flux:
Lines of magnetic force that extend between the poles of a magnet.

link rod:
See *articulating rod*

link test:
Used to test ACARS link between airborne equipment and ground based equipment.

linseed oil:
Oil obtained from flax seed and used as corrosion preventive in the treatment of steel tubing.

liquid:
One of the three states of matter. It has a definite volume but no definite form (water is a liquid).

liquid cooled:
An engine that is cooled by liquid, as opposed to air.

liquid crystal display:
See *LCD*

liquid lock:
See hydraulic lock.

liquid nitrogen:
Nitrogen that has been changed into its liquid state by cooling to −195°C or lower.

liquid oxygen (LOX):
Oxygen that has been changed into its liquid state by cooling to −113°C or lower.

liquid rain repellent:
Chemical sprayed on the windshield that causes the water to collect in larger beads that are more easily dispersed by the wipers and airflow.

liquidometer:
The commercial name for a potentiometer-type fuel gauge.

litmus paper:
An indicator paper that will change color when it comes in contact with an acid or an alkali. It turns red when wet with an acid, and blue with an alkali.

LMM:
Compass locater at middle marker. *(FAR 1)*

load bank:
A heavy duty resistor used to discharge a battery.

load cell:
A component of an electronic weighing system. The load cell contains strain gauges that are placed between the aircraft and a jack. The aircraft is raised off

of the ground and the load cell is used to measure the weight of the aircraft.

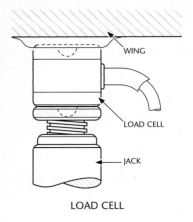

LOAD CELL

load chart:
A chart designed to aid the pilot in determining the loaded center of gravity condition.

load factor:
The ratio of a specified load to the total weight of the aircraft. The specified load is expressed in terms of any of the following: aerodynamic forces, inertia forces, or ground or water reactions. *(FAR 1)*

loadmeter:
An aircraft instrument that measures and indicates, in percentages, the output or load of a generator.

lobes:
The eccentric portion of a cam or camshaft.

LOC:
ILS localizer. *(FAR 1)*

local area augmentation system (LAAS):
A GPS upgrade designed to be used during a Category II or Category III precision approach.

localizer:
A radio beacon used in an instrument landing system to give

lateral guidance along the final approach. The localizer transmits two signal patterns overlapping along the centerline of the runway and along the projection of the centerline from both ends of the runway. Sometimes called a runway localizer.

lock-bolt:
Lock-bolts are a type of fastener designed to meet high-strength requirements. Used in many structural applications, their shear and tensile strengths equal or exceed the requirements of AN and NAS bolts. The lock-bolt consists of a pin and collar. They are available in two head styles: protruding and countersunk. Pin retention is accomplished by swaging the collar into the locking grooves on the pin. The blind lock bolt is similar to the self-plugging rivet. It features a positive mechanical lock for pin retention.

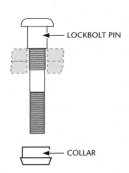

PROTRUDING HEAD LOCK BOLT

lockout debooster:
Cylinder that reduces the pressure to the brake and increases the volume of fluid flow, except, unlike a regular debooster, it does not automatically refill the (larger) cylinder. Fluid may be transferred from the high pressure to the low pressure side. The low pressure side is constantly kept filled. Not normally used on current brake debooster cylinders.

lockring:
A type of safety device consisting of a horseshoe-shaped ring, which can be expanded and installed into a grove in a shaft to prevent relative movement between the shaft and bearing.

lockstitch:
A modified seine knot used to lock the stitches when hand sewing on aircraft fabric.

lock tabs:
A type of safety device where tabs are made onto a special type of washer and are bent up after installation to prevent the nut from loosening.

lockwire:
Another name for safety wire.

lodestone:
The only naturally occurring magnet.

lofting:
The making or piecing together of full-sized drawings of a body or configuration, as of an airplane hull or fuselage or of a wing-fuselage intersection, so as to minimize error in determining dimensions and interference of components and in making patterns.

logbook:
A permanent record of the history of a particular aircraft. All of the data is recorded in chronological order, including the information concerning time-in-service, inspection status and time since last inspection. Separate logbooks are necessary for the airframe, the engine(s) and the propellers installed on the aircraft.

logic circuit:
The primary control information processor in digital equipment; made up of electronic gates and so named because their operation is described by simple equations of a specialized logic algebra.

logic element:
The smallest building blocks that can be represented by operators in an appropriate system of symbolic logic. Typical logic elements are the AND-gate and the flip flop, which can be represented as operators in a suitable symbolic logic. Also a device that performs the logic function.

logic flow chart:
A graphic way to show the flow of information through a computer program.

logic operation:
A NO arithmetical operation in a computer, such as comparing, selecting, making references, matching, sorting, and merging, where the logical YES or NO quantities are involved.

logo lights:
Two lights, one on each wing tip, that shine on the aft section of the fuselage and light up the vertical surfaces that carry the N numbers and company logo. Typically used on larger corporate and commercial airline equipment. This makes the aircraft easier to see when taxiing and during landing and takeoff, as well as advertising the airline.

LOM:
Compass locater at outer marker. *(FAR 1)*

longeron:
A principle longitudinal member in a fuselage, nacelle or the like; heavier than a stringer.

longitude:
Measurement east or west of the prime meridian in degrees, minutes, and seconds.

longitudinal axis:
An axis going from nose to tail of an aircraft, rocket, etc., usually a fore-and-aft body axis passing through the center of gravity.

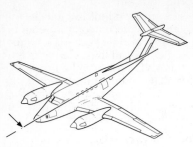

LONGITUDINAL AXIS

longitudinal stability:
The stability of an aircraft with respect to pitching motions, or, sometimes also, with respect to vertical displacement and fore-and-aft motion.

Long-range communication system (LRCS):
A system that uses satellite relay, data link, high frequency, or another approved communication system that extends beyond line of sight. *(FAR 1)*

long range navigation (LORAN):
An electronic navigational system by which lines of position are determined by measuring the difference in the time of reception of synchronized pulse signals from fixed transmitters. *(FAR 1)*

loop antenna:
A highly directional receiving antenna formed by winding wire in a large coil. The loop can be used to find the direction between the loop and the station that is transmitting.

LORAN:
Long range navigation.

low by-pass turbofan:
An engine with a bypass ratio less than two-to-one (2:1).

lowest common denominator:
See *least common denominator*

low frequency:
The band of frequencies from 30 khz to 300 khz.

low lead 100-octane avgas:
100 octane aviation gasoline that contains a maximum of two milliliters of tetraethyl lead per gallon. Normal 100 octane avgas is allowed to contain 4.6 milliliters per gallon.

low pass filter:
1. A filter that passes a majority of the low frequencies on to the next circuit and rejects, or attenuates, the higher frequencies.

2. A filter that transmits alternating current below a given cut-off frequency and substantially attenuates all other currents. Also called a *high-frequency discriminator*.

low pitch:
The pitch of a propeller set at a low blade angle. On a controllable-pitch propeller, the pitch at its minimum blade angle.

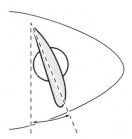

LOW PITCH ANGLE

low-pitch stop:
Device that prevents the propeller from entering the reverse range unless desired. Consists of a beta valve that shuts off the governor oil to the propeller when the pitch reaches the low position. This valve is actuated by a linkage to the piston.

low pressure compressor:
The front section of a dual compressor turbine engine. The N_1 compressor.

low pressure turbine:
The rear turbine wheels on a dual spool turbine engine. The N_1 turbine.

low tension magneto:
A magneto system designed for aircraft that fly at high altitudes. The magneto coil contains only the primary winding. A second coil with both a primary and secondary winding is used to generate the high voltage at each spark plug.

low voltage ignition system:
A turbine engine ignition system with an output voltage in the range of 1,000 to 5,000 volts. See also *high-voltage ignition system*

low-wing airplane:
An airplane with one wing installed below the fuselage.

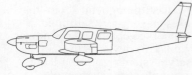

LOW-WING AIRPLANE

LOX:
See *liquid oxygen*

lubber line:
1. A line on any direction-indicating instrument or device, such as a compass or directional gyro, representing the longitudinal axis of the aircraft or vessel, and hence indicating heading.

2. Loosely, a reference line on any instrument, such as a horizontal line on an attitude gyro.

lubricant:
A substance, especially oil, grease, and graphite, which may be interposed between moving surfaces to reduce friction and wear.

Lucite:
A transparent acrylic thermoplastic resin manufactured by DuPont, which is used for windshields and side windows of small aircraft.

lumen:
A unit of luminous flux equal to the light emitted in a unit solid angle by a uniform point source of one candle.

lumped impedance tuning:
The insertion of an inductor or capacitor in series with an antenna to electrically lengthen or shorten the antenna.

L

M:
Mach number. *(FAR 1)*

MAA:
Maximum authorized IFR altitude. *(FAR 1)*

MAC:
Mean Aerodynamic Chord

mach:
Speed of sound. Mach 1 = 1,116 feet per second at sea level.

mach meter:
A special airspeed indicator that measures speed relative to the speed of sound, and indicates the speed that the particular airplane using the mach meter cannot exceed without encountering damage due to compressibility or mach effects.

mach number:
The ratio of true airspeed to the speed of sound. *(FAR 1)*

machineability:
The ease and speed with which a metal may be cut (with free chip removal) to produce a reasonably smooth surface.

machine screw:
A screw-type fastener with uniform threads that can be screwed into a tapped hole or a nut. Machine screws are manufactured with a variety of head styles.

ROUND HEAD MACHINE SCREW

macroporosity:
Voids or gas pockets in metals that are large enough to be seen at magnification of less than 10X.

magnesium:
A lightweight, ductile metal similar to, but lighter than, aluminum.

magnesyn system:
A remote indicating system. A permanent magnet is used as the rotor and a saturable-core toroidal-wound coil as the stator. The system is excited with low-voltage AC.

magnet:
A device or a material that has the property of attracting or repelling magnetic materials. Lines of magnetic flux link its external poles, and a conductor cutting across the flux will have a voltage induced in it.

magnetic amplifier:
An electromagnetic device that uses one or more saturable reactors to obtain a large power gain. This device is used in servosystems requiring large amounts of power to move heavy loads.

magnetic brake:
A type of brake installed on an electric motor to prevent rotation when current stops flowing through the winding of the motor.

magnetic compass:
Any compass in which the sensing element, as a magnetic needle or compass card, aligns itself with the direction of the horizontal component of the earth's magnetic field at any given place.

magnetic drain plug:
A drain plug employing small permanent magnets to attract and hold any ferrous metal particles that may be present in the oil.

magnetic field:
1. The region in which the magnetic forces created by

a permanent magnet or by a current-carrying conductor or coil can be detected.

2. The field that is produced when current flows through a conductor or antenna.

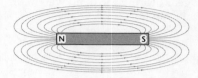

MAGNETIC FIELD

magnetic microphone:
A microphone in which the sound waves vibrate a moving armature. The armature consists of a coil wound on the armature and located between the pole pieces of a permanent magnet. The armature is mechanically linked to the diaphragm.

magnetic particle inspection (Magnaflux®):
A method for detecting discontinuities, on or near, the surface in suitably magnetized materials, which employ finely divided magnetic particles that tend to concentrate in regions of the magnetic nonuniformity; i.e., along cracks, over inclusions, voids, etc.

magnetic permeability:
A term indicating the ease with which a magnetic field can be established in a material. It is determined by the ratio of the resultant magnetic force to the applied magnetic force.

magnetic poles:
The section of a magnet where the flux lines are concentrated; also where they enter and leave the magnet.

magneto:
A self-contained, permanent-magnet AC generator with a set of current interrupter contacts and a step-up transformer. It is used to

supply the high voltage required for ignition in an aircraft engine.

magneto, booster:
A small, high-voltage magneto, usually turned by hand, used to produce a hot spark for starting reciprocating engines. The output for the booster magneto is fed into a trailing finger on the distributor that fires the cylinder following the one in position for normal ignition.

magneto, dual:
Actually a single magneto housing that holds one rotating permanent magnet and one cam, with two sets of breaker points, two condensers, two coils, and two distributors. For all practical purposes, this constitutes two ignition systems.

magneto, high-tension:
A magneto that consists of a rotating magnet, cam, breaker points, condenser, and a coil with a primary and a secondary winding. The output of the secondary winding goes to a distributor, then to the spark plugs.

magneto, low-tension:
A magneto consisting of a rotating magnet, a cam, breaker points, condenser, a coil with only the primary winding, and a carbon-brush-type distributor. The primary current is directed through the distributor to a coil for each individual spark plug. These coils have a primary and a secondary winding. The high voltage is generated at the spark plug.

magneto, Scintilla:
The trade name of a Swiss designed and built magneto. The forerunner of the Bendix magnetos.

magnetomotive force (MMF):
The magnetizing force in a magnetic field. Measured in gilberts.

M

magnet wire:
Wire coated with an enamel insulation and used in coils, relays, transformers, motor windings, and so forth.

main bus:
The common tie point for electrical circuits to obtain their voltage.

main rotor:
Main system of rotating airfoils on a helicopter; distinguished from tail rotor. *(FAR 1)*

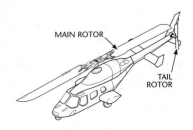

MAIN ROTOR

maintenance:
Inspection, overhaul, repair, preservation, and the replacement of parts, but excludes preventive maintenance. *(FAR 1)*

maintenance control display unit (MCDU):
Used on some Boeing aircraft to monitor and test the flight control computers, flight management computers, and the thrust management computers

maintenance manual:
Documentation that provides understanding of a specific system and the design specifications for each component within that particular system.

maintenance release:
A return to service approval in the appropriate maintenance record.

maintenance resource management:
Organizational method that provides maintenance organizations with the vehicle to accomplish competence in team skills and competence in technical skills.

main wheel:
One of the wheels of the landing gear bearing the main weight of the aircraft.

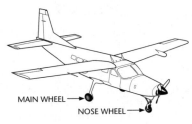

MAIN WHEEL

major alteration:
An alteration not listed in the aircraft, aircraft engine, or propeller specifications:

1. That might appreciably affect weight, balance, structural strength, performance, powerplant operation, flight characteristics, or other qualities affecting airworthiness.

2. That is not done according to accepted practices or cannot be done by elementary operations. *(FAR 1)*

major overhaul:
The complete disassembly, cleaning, inspection, repair, and reassembly of an aircraft, engine or other component. This overhaul must be accomplished in accordance with the applicable manufacturer's specifications and with the appropriate replacement of required parts.

major repair:
1. A repair that if improperly done, might appreciably affect weight, balance, structural strength, performance, powerplant operation, flight characteristics, or

other qualities affecting airworthiness.

2. A repair that is not done according to accepted practices or cannot be done by elementary operations. *(FAR 1)*

malleable:
Capable of being extended or shaped by hammering or rolling.

MALS:
Medium intensity approach light system. *(FAR 1)*

MALSR:
Medium intensity approach light system with runway alignment indicator lights. *(FAR 1)*

Manchester II Code:
Often simply referred to as Manchester

A serial digital data format that incorporates a voltage change in each data bit

mandrel:
A form fixture or male mold used for the base in the production of a part by lay-up, filament winding or braiding.

maneuvering speed (V$_a$):
The maximum speed at which full and abrupt control movements will not overstress the airplane.

manganese:
A grayish-white, usually hard and brittle metallic element found in steel that resembles iron but is not magnetic.

manifold:
A chamber having several ports through which a liquid or gas is gathered or distributed.

manifold pressure:
The absolute pressure measured at the appropriate point in the induction system of an aircraft engine, and usually expressed in inches of mercury. *(FAR 1)*

manometer:
An instrument consisting of a glass tube filled with a liquid and used for measuring the pressure of gases or vapors above or below atmospheric pressure.

manual depressurization valve:
A valve that permits manual control of the outflow valve of an aircraft cabin pressurization system.

manufactured rivet head:
The pre-formed head of a rivet.

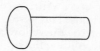

MANUFACTURED RIVET HEAD

Marconi antenna:
A quarter-wave antenna that is operated with one end grounded and is positioned perpendicular to the earth.

marker beacon:
An electronic navigation device used as a part of the instrument landing system (ILS) to indicate a specific location along the landing path. This signal illuminates an indicator light and produces an audible tone when the aircraft is directly above the marker.

MARKER BEACON ANTENNA

martensite:
A microconstituent or structure in quenched steel characterized by an acicular or needle-like pattern on the surface of polish. It has the maximum hardness of any of the structures resulting from the decomposition products of austenite.

Marvel balancer:
The proprietary name of a type of balancing equipment widely used in helicopter operations.

mass:
A measure of the amount of material or matter contained in a body.

massive-electrode spark plug:
Spark plugs using two, three or four large ground electrodes.

mass-type flowmeter:
A type of fuel flow measuring system seen on turbine engine installations. This system indicates the mass flow rather than the volume flow.

master cylinder:
A form of brake system in which a pilot-controlled pump forces fluid into the brake cylinder. The amount of pressure delivered to the brake is determined by the amount of force the pilot applies to the master cylinder.

master oscillator:
In a transmitter, the oscillator that establishes the carrier frequency of the output.

master rod:
The only connecting rod in a radial engine whose big end passes around the crankshaft. All of the other rods connect to the master rod and oscillate back and forth rather than encircling the crankshaft.

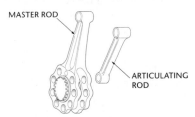

MASTER ROD

ARTICULATING ROD

MASTER ROD

master switch:
A single switch designed to control electrical power to all circuits in the aircraft.

mat:
A fibrous material consisting of randomly oriented chopped or swirled filaments loosely held together with a binder.

mating surfaces:
Two surfaces that come together to form a seal.

matrix:
The essentially homogeneous material in which the fibers of a composite are embedded and supported. Usually a resin or polymer material.

maximum except takeoff power (METO):
The maximum continuous power an engine is allowed to develop without any time restrictions.

maximum landing weight:
The maximum authorized weight of the aircraft at landing.

maximum power:
The greatest amount of engine power available to a given aircraft for use in emergency operation by control of the power settings and the use of certain augmentation devices, such as the afterburner for jet engines or water injection. May only be used, without damaging the engine, for a limited amount of time on some aircraft.

maximum speed for stability characteristics, V_{FC}/M_{FC}:
A speed that may not be less than a speed midway between maximum operating limit speed (V_{MO}/M_{MO}) and demonstrated flight diving speed (V_{DF}/M_{DF}), except that, for altitudes where the Mach number is the limiting factor, M_{FC} need not exceed the Mach number at which effective speed warning occurs. *(FAR 1)*

maximum takeoff weight:
The maximum design weight of the aircraft on takeoff without exceeding design factors.

maximum weight:
The maximum certificated weight of an aircraft.

Maxwell:
The unit of magnetic flux. One magnetic line of flux.

mayday:
International radio distress signal. When repeated three times, it indicates imminent and grave danger and that immediate assistance is requested.

MCA:
Minimum crossing altitude. *(FAR 1)*

MDA:
Minimum descent altitude. *(FAR 1)*

MEA:
Minimum en route IFR altitude. *(FAR 1)*

mean aerodynamic chord (MAC):
The chord of an imaginary rectangular airfoil having the same pitching moments throughout the flight range as that of the actual wing.

mean power (of a radio transmitter):
The average power supplied to the antenna transmission line by a transmitter during an interval of time sufficiently long compared with the lowest frequency encountered in the modulation taken under normal operating conditions.

mean sea level (MSL):
The average height of the surface of the sea for all stages of tide; used as a reference for elevations throughout the U.S.

measling:
Damage to a substrate caused by excessive heat.

mechanical advantage:
The increase in force or speed that is gained by the use of simple machines, such as levers or pulleys.

mechanical blockage thrust reverser:
A thrust reverser system generally employing a post-exit (clamshell) type design that is used to reverse the exhaust stream of a turbine engine to help slow the aircraft after landing.

mechanical bond:
Joining two or more parts by mechanical methods such as bolts, screws, or rivets.

mechanical efficiency:
The ratio of brake horsepower to indicated horsepower of an engine.

mechanical mixture:
A mixture where two or more elements or compounds are mixed, but still can be identified by microscopic examination.

mechanical properties:
The properties of a material that are associated with elastic and inelastic reaction when force is applied, or the properties involving the relationship between stress and strain.

media reclamation:
Most blasting processes have a media reclamation process that reclaims, or at least collects, the used media and the material it removes.

medical certificate:
Acceptable evidence of physical fitness on a form prescribed by the Administrator. *(FAR 1)*

medical oxygen:
Although pure, medical oxygen contains water that can freeze in the cold temperatures found at the altitudes where in-flight oxygen is necessary. It must not be used in aircraft systems. Only aviator's breathing oxygen can be used in aircraft systems.

medium bypass turbofan:
Turbo-fan engine with bypass ratios between 2:1 and 3:1.

M

mega:
Metric prefix meaning million.

megger:
Short for megohmmeter. A meter that measures very large values of resistance; usually used to check for insulation breakdown in wires.

meniscus:
The curved surface of a column of liquid in a narrow tube; the curve is concave when the containing walls are wet with the liquid and convex when they are not wet.

mercerizing:
The process of dipping cotton yarn or fabric into a hot solution of caustic soda. It gives the material greater strength and luster.

mercury:
A heavy, silver-colored, toxic, liquid, metallic chemical element that remains liquid under standard conditions of temperature and pressure. Mercury is approximately 13 times heavier than water.

mesh rating:
A U.S. sieve number and filtration rating common to fuel filters. A U.S. sieve number of 200 has 200 meshes per inch and is the equivalent of a 74 micron filter.

metal fatigue:
A form of work hardening of metal which results from vibration or flexing in service. This can increase the brittleness of the material and result in failure.

metal foil:
A very thin sheet of metal, such as aluminum foil.

metallic rectifier:
Also known as a *dry-disc rectifier*. A metal-to-semiconductor, large-area, contact device in which a semiconductor is sandwiched between two metal plates. This asymmetrical construction permits current to flow more readily in one direction than the other.

metallic ring test:
A test for delamination of bonded structure. A coin or similar object is used to tap on the surface of the structure. A metallic ringing sound will be heard if the structure is sound. If delamination has occurred, a dull thud will be heard.

metalizing:
A technique of coating metal with molten zinc by atomized spraying or vacuum deposition. Applying an electrically conductive metallic layer to the surface of another material. Also called *spray metalizing*.

metal spinning:
A metal forming process where a metal sheet is clamped into a lathe-like machine and forced over a male die while being spun.

metal spraying:
A method of initial coating or repairing parts by spraying with metal that has been heated to a liquid state.

metering jet:
A calibrated orifice in a fluid flow system.

metering pin:
A flow control device whose shape determines the amount of fluid that can flow from one chamber into the other. This is commonly seen on oleo struts.

metering valve:
A valve used to control the flow of a fluid.

meter sensitivity:
The tolerance of a meter used for measuring pressure, voltage or amperage.

meter shunt:
A resistor placed in parallel with the meter terminals to provide increased range capability.

methyl-ethyl-ketone (MEK):
A highly volatile solvent commonly used to prepare surfaces for painting and as a paint stripper for certain types of finishes.

mho:
The unit of electrical conductance.

mica:
A transparent silicate mineral. It has been used as an electrical insulator in capacitors and other applications.

micro:
A metric prefix meaning one-millionth.

microballoons:
Microscopic sized phenolic or glass spheres used to add body without adding weight to a resin. Used to make a filler or potting compound. Also called *microspheres*.

microbes:
Microscopic forms of animal and plant life. They exist in water and feed on hydrocarbon aircraft fuel. Microbes form a water-entrapping scum on the bottom of jet aircraft fuel tanks.

microbiological growths:
These growths are a problem in jet fuel. There are a number of varieties of microorganisms that can live in the free water in jet fuel. Some variations of these organisms are airborne, others live in the soil. The aircraft fuel system becomes susceptible to the introduction of these organisms each time the aircraft is fueled. The most favorable conditions for the growth of micro-organisms in the fuel are warm temperatures and the presence of iron oxide and mineral salts in the water. The best way to prevent microbial growth is to keep to fuel dry.

microburst:
A small downburst with outbursts of damaging winds extending 2.5 miles or less. In spite of its small horizontal scale, an intense microburst could induce wind speeds as high as 150 knots.

microfiche:
A method of storing microfilmed information on single 4 x 6 inch sheets of photographic film. The information is retrieved using a microfiche reader or reader/printer which enlarges the image to a readable size.

microfilm:
A fine-grained strip of film containing very small photographic images of a book, newspaper, manual or other printed matter.

micrometer caliper:
A caliper having a spindle moved by a finely threaded screw for making precise measurements.

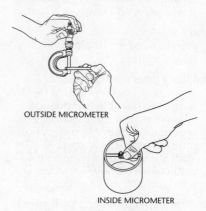

OUTSIDE MICROMETER

INSIDE MICROMETER

MICROMETER CALIPERS

micron:
One millionth of a meter. It is normally used to denote the effectiveness of a filter.

micronic filter:
The trade name of a filter having a porous paper element.

microphone:
An energy converter that changes sound energy into electrical energy.

microspheres:
Very small glass beads that are mixed with resins to make a slurry that is easier to handle and shape after curing. Also called *microballoons*.

midwing airplane:
A monoplane having its wings set approximately halfway between the top and bottom of the fuselage.

MIDWING AIRPLANE

mil:
A metric term meaning $1/1,000$ of an inch. In painting, it usually refers to the thickness of a film.

mild steel:
A term used for low-carbon, machine steel.

military operations area:
A military operations area (MOA) is airspace established outside Class A airspace to separate or segregate certain nonhazardous military activities from IFR Traffic and to identify for VFR traffic where theses activities are conducted. *(FAR 1)*

military specifications (mil-spec):
Technical requirements and standards adopted by the Department of Defense that must be met by vendors selling materials to DOD.

milli:
A metric prefix meaning one-thousandth.

mils:
The circular mil is the standard unit of wire cross-sectional area used in American and English wire tables. Therefore, the diameter of a wire that is 0.025

inch may be more conveniently expressed as 25 mils.

mineral oil:
Conventional oil produced from crude oil distillation. When used for engine break-in, these oils have few if any additives.

minimum descent altitude:
The lowest altitude, expressed in feet above mean sea level, to which descent is authorized on final approach or during circle-to-land maneuvering in execution of a standard instrument approach procedure, where no electronic glide slope is provided. *(FAR 1)*

minimum fuel:
The amount of fuel for one half hour of operation at the rated maximum continuous power setting for the engine.

minor alteration:
An alteration other than a major alteration. *(FAR 1)*

minority current:
A very small current that passes through the base-to-collector junction when this junction is reverse biased.

minor repair:
A repair other than a major repair. *(FAR 1)*

mixed exhaust:
A turbofan-type engine where the primary and secondary airstreams are mixed prior to leaving the engine. This may be accomplished to achieve a reduction in noise.

mixer:
In radar, a circuit that combines the received RF signal with a local-oscillator signal to effectively convert the received signal to a lower IF frequency signal.

mixture control:
The primary control on a carburetor for adjusting the fuel/air mixture. The usual limits are full-rich to idle cutoff.

MM:
ILS middle marker. *(FAR 1)*

mmHg:
Millimeters of mercury. In
vacuum work, this is a measure
of absolute pressure, being the
height of a column of mercury
that the air or other gas will
support. Standard atmospheric
pressure will support a mercury
column 760 mm high (760
mmHg). Any value less than
this represents some degree of
vacuum.

MOA:
Memorandum Of Agreement

mobile earth station:
An earth station in the mobile-
satellite service intended to be
used while in motion or during
halts at unspecified points.

MOCA:
Minimum obstruction clearance
altitude. *(FAR 1)*

Mode S:
Type of secondary surveillance
radar (SSR) equipment which
provides Mode A and Mode C
interrogations, discrete address
(Mode S) interrogations from the
ground or air, and a data link
capability

modular maintenance:
A maintenance scheme that
allows the replacement of major
assemblies, called modules, with
a minimum of down time. The
modules are then returned to the
repair facility to be tested and
repaired as necessary.

modulated anti-skid system:
A type of anti-skid system that
senses the rate of deceleration of
the wheels to maintain a pressure
in the brakes that will hold the
unit in the slip area, yet not
allow a skid to develop. This is
accomplished by modulating, or
continually changing, the pressure
in the brake.

modulation:
The process of impressing
intelligence upon a transmission
medium, such as radio waves.

modulus:
A measure of the ratio of the
applied load to the resultant
deformation of the material. The
stiffness of a material.

modulus of elasticity:
The ratio of the stress applied
to the strain of deformation
produced in a material that is
elastically deformed.

moisture-separator:
A device used in pneumatic
systems to separate moisture from
the air.

molecule:
The smallest particle of an
element or compound that is
capable of retaining the chemical
identity of the substance.

molybdenum:
A chemical element similar to
chromium and used as an alloying
agent in many aircraft steels.

moment:
The product of the weight of
an object in pounds, and the
distance from the center of
gravity of the object to the datum
or fulcrum in inches. Moment
is used in weight and balance
computations and is expressed in
pound-inches.

monel:
The leading high-nickel alloy,
consists of 68 percent nickel,
29 percent copper, 0.2 percent
iron, 1 percent manganese, and
1.8 percent of other elements.
Characteristics of this metal are
a combination of high strength
and excellent corrosion resistance.
It cannot be hardened by heat-
treatment.

M

monocoque:
A stressed skin type construction. The stiffness of the skin provides a large measure of the strength of the structure.

monoplane:
An airplane having one set of wings.

MONOPLANE

monopulse radar:
A radar that gets the range, bearing, and elevation position data of a target from a single pulse.

Morse taper:
A self-holding standard taper largely used on small cutting tools such as drills, end mills, and reamers, and, on some machines' spindles in which these tools are used.

MOSFET:
Metal oxide silicon field effect transistor. A semiconductor device that contains diffused source and drain regions on either side of a P- or N-channel area. Also contains a gate insulated from the channel area by silicon-oxide. Operates in either the depletion or the enhancement mode.

motor over:
The process of rotating the engine with the starter for reasons other than starting.

mounting pad:
Provisions made on the accessory section of the engine for the attachment of accessories such as generators, alternators, pumps, etc.

moving-vane meter movement:
A meter movement that uses the magnetic repulsion of the like poles created in two iron vanes by current through a coil of wire. It is the most commonly used movement for AC meters.

MRA:
Minimum reception altitude. *(FAR 1)*

MSDS:
Material Safety Data Sheet. Documents relating to hazardous materials that contain information for safe handling and use and for health professionals in case of an accident.

MSL:
Mean sea level. *(FAR 1)*

muff:
A shroud placed around a section of the exhaust pipe and used as a heat exchanger. Air heated by passing through this arrangement may be used for carburetor deicing or for cabin heat.

muffler:
A mechanical device designed to reduce exhaust noise. The mufflers used in reciprocating engines are normally a large diameter section of heat- and corrosion-resistant steel with baffles attached to the inside.

mule:
An auxiliary hydraulic power supply used to supply pressure to the hydraulic system when the engine is not running. A mule is normally used during maintenance operations to test the various systems.

multiconductor:
More than one conductor, as in a cable.

multi-engine:
An aircraft with more than one engine.

MULTI-ENGINE

multifunction display (MFD):
An EFIS display used to display weather radar data, course and flight plan information, system checklist, and provide back-up functions in the event of a partial system failure

multifunction processor unit (MPU):
A processor used with the Collins EFIS 85/86 that provides signal processing and switching to the multifunction display

multigrade oil:
A multi-viscosity oil that acts as a high-viscosity oil in high temperatures but as a low-viscosity oil in low temperatures.

multimeter:
An electrical meter designed to measure several parameters, usually including voltage, current and resistance. Generally, multimeters are capable of measuring these values in either AC or DC circuits.

multiplexer (MUX):
Converts parallel data into serial data

multiplexing:
A method for simultaneous transmission of two or more signals over a common carrier wave.

multipurpose control and display unit (MCDU):
LRU containing an alpha numeric keyboard and CRT display found on Airbus aircraft used to input data to the CMCS and the CFDS

multi-satellite link:
1. A radio link between a transmitting earth station and a receiving earth station through two or more satellites, without any intermediate earth station.

2. A multi-satellite link comprises one up-link, one or more satellite-to-satellite links and one down-link.

multistage compressor:
1. A central compressor that utilizes two or more impellers acting successively upon the flow of air or other fluid so as to increase pressure energy.

2. An axial-flow compressor having two or more rows of rotor and stator blades, one behind the other.

multivibrator modulator:
An astable multivibrator used to provide frequency modulation. The modulating AF voltage is inserted in series with the base return of the multivibrator transistors to produce the frequency modulation.

multi-viscosity:
Type of oil that has polymers added to the base stock for the purpose of modifying the oil's viscosity by its temperature. A 20W oil that will not thin more than a 50W oil when hot is an example.

music wire:
A high-quality steel wire used for making springs. Also called *piano wire*.

mutual inductance:
The inductance of a voltage into one coil due the field produced by an adjacent coil.

M

N₁:
1. Low Pressure Shaft Speed.

2. R.p.m. of a low pressure compressor.

3. Speed or a low pressure compressor.

N₁ tachometer:
A tachometer that indicates the speed of the low pressure compressor in a dual spool turbine engine.

N₂ tachometer:
A tachometer that indicates the speed of the high pressure compressor in a dual spool turbine engine.

NACA:
National Advisory Committee for Aeronautics. The precursor of NASA.

NACA cowling:
A type of radial engine cowling developed by NACA. A ring-shaped cowling that provides for low-drag flow cooling around the engine.

nacelle:
An enclosed shelter (cowling) on an aircraft for a powerplant.

NACELLE

nacelle station (NS) or elevator station (ES):
Used on larger aircraft to help technicians find components in specific areas of the aircraft

NAND gate:
A logic function of A and B that is true if either A or B is false.

NAND GATE

nano:
Metric prefix meaning one billionth.

nap:
The short fiber ends that protrude from the surface of a fabric. When the fabric is doped these fibers become stiff and must be sanded off. This is called "laying the nap."

naptha:
A volatile and flammable hydrocarbon liquid used chiefly as a solvent or cleaning agent.

NAS:
1. National Aircraft Standards

2. National Airspace System.

NASA:
National Aeronautics and Space Administration. The U.S. Government agency established to direct and aid research and development in civil aeronautics and aerospace technology.

National Telecommunications and Information Administration (NTIA):
An agency of the United States Department of Commerce that serves as the President's principal advisor on telecommunications and information policy issues. NTIA manages Federal use of the radio spectrum and coordinates Federal use with the FCC.

natural aging:
Solution treated aluminum alloy that has been heat treated and allowed to harden over time, at room temperature.

natural frequency:

The frequency at which an undamped system with a single degree of freedom will oscillate upon momentary displacement from rest position by a transient force.

naturally aspirated:

See *normally aspirated*

nautical mile:

A measure of distance equal to approximately 6,080 feet (or 1,853.2 meters). One nautical mile equals one minute of a great circle. Because the earth is not a perfect sphere, this measure may vary from one location to another. Defined by the U.S. Government as 6,076.115 feet. Used to measure distances in nautical and aerial navigation.

NAVAID:

Short for navigational aid.

NAVCOMM:

A term for a radio that has both a navigation receiver and a communication transceiver.

navigable airspace:

Airspace at and above the minimum flight altitudes prescribed by the federal aviation regulations, including airspace needed for safe takeoff and landing. *(FAR 1)*

navigation lights:

Lights required by the FAA for aircraft operating during the hours of darkness. They consist of a red light on the left wing tip, a green light on the right wing tip and a white light on the tail. Also called *position lights*.

NAVSTAR GPS:

The formal name for the global positioning system in the United States

NDB(ADF):

Nondirectional beacon (automatic direction finder). *(FAR 1)*

NDI:

Nondestructive Inspection

necessary bandwidth:

For a given class of emission, the width of the frequency band that is just sufficient to ensure the transmission of information at the rate and with the quality required under specified conditions.

needle valve:

A valve offering fine adjustment of fluid flow via linear translation of tapering pointed rod centered in an orifice.

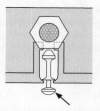

NEEDLE VALVE

negative alternation:

That part of a sine wave that is below the reference level.

negative dihedral:

A downward angle formed by the wings and the lateral axis of the aircraft.

negative ion:

An atom that has more electrons that protons.

negative logic:

The form of logic in which the more positive voltage level represents a logic 0, FALSE, or LOW and the more negative voltage represents a logic 1, true or high.

negative stagger:

The placement of the wings of a biplane so that the leading edge of the lower wing is ahead of the leading edge of the upper wing.

negative static stability:

Condition that exists when the disturbed object tends to continue in the direction of disturbance.

negative torque sensor:
A system that senses the torque of an engine; in the event of engine failure it will feather the propeller to prevent windmilling and excess drag.

neoprene:
An oil resistant synthetic rubber used in seals, etc.

nested laminate:
The placing of plies of fabric so that the yarns of one ply lie in the valleys between the yarns of the adjacent ply. Also called *nested cloth*.

net thrust (FN):
The effective thrust developed by a jet engine during flight. This takes into consideration the initial momentum of the air mass prior to entering the engine.

neutral flame:
A gas flame in which the oxygen and acetylene volumes are balanced and both gases are completely burned.

neutralize:
To cancel the effect of. Typically used in context with acids. Acids must be neutralized to prevent continuing attack to the surface.

neutral plane:
An imaginary line drawn perpendicular to the resultant flux in a generator. For arcless commutation, the neutral plane should lie directly over the plane of the brushes.

neutral position:
The position of the rotating magnet of a magneto between the pole shoes. In the neutral position no lines of flux flow in the magneto frame.

neutral static stability:
Condition that exists when the disturbed object has neither the tendency to return nor continue in the direction of displacement, but remains in equilibrium in the direction of disturbance.

neutron:
An uncharged particle in the nucleus of an atom. The mass of a neutron is approximately the same as the mass of a proton.

Newton's first law:
An object at rest will remain at rest and an object in motion will remain in motion unless it is acted on by an outside force.

Newton's second law:
The amount of acceleration imparted to an object is directly proportional to the amount of force acting on it and inversely proportional to the mass of the object.

$$F = ma$$

NEWTON'S SECOND LAW

Newton's third law:
For every action there is an equal and opposite reaction.

Ng:
Speed, gas producer turbine.

nibbler:
A sheet metal cutting tool that cuts the metal by taking a series of small bites, or nibbles.

nichrome:
An alloy of nickel and chromium.

nickel:
An alloying element that increases the strength, toughness, and wear and corrosion resistance of steels.

nickel-cadmium battery:
A battery made of alkaline secondary cells. The positive plates are nickel hydroxide, the negative plates are cadmium hydroxide, and potassium hydroxide is used as the electrolyte.

NICKEL-CADMIUM CELL

nicopress process:
Method of swaging cable that uses copper sleeves that are strong enough to allow the cable to be used at full rated cable strength, provided a thimble is used.

night:
The time between the end of evening civil twilight and the beginning of morning civil twilight, as published in the American Air Almanac, converted to local time. *(FAR 1)*

nitrate dope:
A finish for aircraft fabric consisting of a film base of cellulose fibers dissolved with the necessary plasticizers and thinners.

nitriding:
A form of case hardening in which the steel part is heated in an atmosphere of ammonia. The ammonia breaks down and its nitrogen combines with aluminum in the steel to form an extremely hard, abrasive-resistant aluminum-nitride surface. Cylinder walls and crankshaft journals are nitrided.

nitrile (buna-N):
The most commonly used elastomer for O-rings because of its resistance to petroleum fluids, good physical properties, and useful temperature range.

nitrogen:
A colorless, tasteless, odorless, gaseous element forming nearly 80 percent of the earth's atmosphere.

noble gas:
See *inert gas*

no break power transfer (NBPT):
An automated system that allows the aircraft to switch AC power supplies without a momentary interruption of electrical power

node:
A point in a standing wave where some characteristic of the wave field has essentially zero amplitude.

noise suppressor:
A device installed in the tailpipe of a turbojet engine to slow the mixing of exhaust gases with the surrounding air and decrease the intensity of the sound.

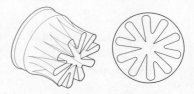

NOISE SUPPRESSOR

nomex:
Aramid fiber or paper. The paper form is used to make honeycomb.

nominal value:
A value assigned for the purpose of a convenient designation. A nominal value exists in name only.

nomogram:
A chart representing numerical relationships.

nondestructive testing:
Using nondestructive methods to investigate the quality, integrity, properties and dimensions of materials and components without damaging or impairing their serviceability. This is done primarily by using liquid penetrant, magnetic particle, eddy current, ultrasonic and radiographic methods.

N

nondirectional beacon:
See *NDB*

nonferrous metal:
Metals or alloys that contain no appreciable quantity of iron. This term applies to such metals as aluminum, copper, magnesium, and their alloys.

nonflammable:
Not flammable.

nonflexible control cable:
Cable made of 7 or 19 strands of solid wire preformed into a helical or spiral shape.

(1 x 7)   (1 x 19)

NONFLEXIBLE CONTROL CABLE

nonporous:
Any material that does not allow a liquid to pass through it.

nonprecision approach procedure:
A standard instrument approach procedure in which no electronic glide slope is provided. *(FAR 1)*

non-return to zero (NRZ):
A self-clocking data bus format that does not return to zero at the end of each data bit

nonstandard parts:
Parts that have been improperly repaired, were produced for automotive or other non-aviation use, or counterfeit parts that are low in quality but made to look serviceable.

nontautening dope:
A special formulation of aircraft dope to use on heat-shrunk polyester fabric. It provides the necessary fill for the fabric but has minimum shrinking characteristics.

non-trip-free circuit breaker:
A circuit breaker that can be held in the ON position during an overcurrent condition.

NOPT:
No procedure turn required. *(FAR 1)*

NOR gate:
A logic function of A and B that is true if both A and B are false.

NOR GATE

normal heptane (C_7H_{16}):
A hydrocarbon that has a very low critical pressure and temperature. It is used as the low reference for measuring anti-detonation characteristics of a fuel.

normalizing:
Heating steel to above its critical range, as in annealing, and then cooling it in still air at ordinary room temperature.

normal lapse rate:
The average rate of decrease in temperature with rise in altitude. The normal lapse rate is 3.3°F decrease per 1,000 feet of altitude.

normally aspirated:
A reciprocating engine that uses atmospheric pressure to force the mixture of fuel and air into the cylinders. Also naturally aspirated.

normal rated power:
The maximum power or thrust specified for an engine by the manufacturer as allowable for continuous operation under specified conditions.

normal shock wave:
A shock wave perpendicular, or substantially so, to the direction of flow.

nose:
1. The forward point or section of an aircraft. See also *bow*.
2. The leading edge of an airfoil.

nose dock:
A special framework or scaffolding used during large aircraft maintenance to enable personnel to work on the forward part of the airplane. May be fixed or movable.

nose gear:
The landing gear unit located at the nose of an aircraft equipped with tricycle landing gear.

nose rib:
See *false rib*

nose wheel:
The landing wheel on a nose gear.

note:
Found in various service manuals, used to draw your attention to a particular procedure, that will make the task easier to perform

NOT gate:
A NOT gate reverses, or inverts, the input signal. The output is always the opposite of the input.

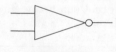

NOT GATE

notch filter:
An arrangement of electronic components designed to attenuate or reject a specific frequency band with sharp cut-off at either end.

nozzle:
A duct through which liquid or gas is directed. It is designed to increase the velocity of the liquid or gas.

nozzle diaphragm:
A ring of stationary vanes in a turbine engine just ahead of the turbine and used to direct the flow of gases onto the turbine at the most efficient angle.

nozzle screen:
A filter screen installed immediately upstream of a fuel nozzle in a gas turbine engine.

NPN transistor:
A three layer semiconductor device made up of a layer of P-type material between two pieces of N-type material.

N-strut:
The struts on a biplane near the wing tips that are shaped in the form of the letter N.

N-type silicon:
Silicon that has been doped with an impurity having five valence electrons.

nuisance message:
Any FDE or CMC message that is not caused by an actual fault

numerator:
The part of a fraction above the line.

nutplate:
A special form of nut that may be riveted to the inside of a structure.

N

Oo

OAT:
Outside air temperature

oblique:
An angle other than 90° or a multiple of 90°.

oblique drawing:
Representation of an object shown as its true size and shape with horizontal lines drawn at 30°, 45°, or 60° angles to the horizontal. The oblique sides are drawn to any scale to give a realistic depth.

oblique shock wave:
A shock wave attached to the bow and tail of an aircraft flying at speeds greater than Mach 1. The sides of the oblique shock wave form the Mach cone.

occupied bandwidth:
1. The width of a frequency band such that, below the lower and above the upper frequency limits, the mean powers emitted are each equal to a specified percentage Beta/2 of the total mean power of a given emission.

2. Unless otherwise specified by the CCIR for the appropriate class of emission, the value of Beta/2 should be taken as 0.5%.

octal number system:
A number system based on powers of eight. This system is used extensively in computer work.

octane number:
See *octane rating*

octane rating:
A method used to express the anti-detonation characteristics of aviation gasoline.

OEI:
One engine inoperative. *(FAR 1)*

oersted (H):
A unit of field strength that produces magnetic induction. The oersted is numerically equal in air or in a vacuum. Oersted (H) refers to the magnetizing force tending to magnetize an unmagnetized body, and gauss refers to the field (B) so induced in the body.

OFCC:
Optical Fiber Cable Component

ohm:
The unit of electrical resistance. That value of electrical resistance through which a constant potential difference of 1 volt across the resistance will maintain a current flow of 1 ampere through the resistance.

Ohm's law:
The current in an electrical circuit is directly proportional to the electromotive force in the circuit. The most common form of the law is $E = IR$, where E is the electromotive force, or voltage, across the circuit, I is the current flowing in the circuit, and R is the resistance of the circuit.

ohmmeter:
A meter used to measure resistance. Usually one function of a multimeter.

OHMMETER

oil canning:
The unwanted wrinkling of sheet metal, particularly thin sheets, that can occur if over-driving occurs when installing rivets in close patterns.

oil control ring:
The piston ring below the compression rings used to control the amount of oil between the piston and the cylinder wall. It is usually a multi-piece ring and normally fits into a groove with holes to drain part of the oil back to the inside of the piston.

oil cooler:
A radiator for dissipating heat from lubricating oil. A type of heat exchanger. Also called an *oil radiator*.

oil hardening:
The process of quenching in oil when heat treating alloy steel to bring out certain qualities.

oil pressure-relief valve:
Valve used to limit the engine's oil pressure to a predetermined value.

oil pump:
A pump that maintains the pressure of the oil and circulates it in the lubrication system of an aircraft's powerplant.

oil scraper (wiper) ring:
A piston ring located at the bottom, or skirt end, of a piston used to wipe the oil either toward or away from the oil control ring, depending on the design of the engine.

OIL SCRAPER RING

oil slinger:
A rotating device used as a centrifugal impeller to direct oil flow, usually away from a bearing sump and towards a scavenge pump.

oilstones:
Molded abrasives in various shapes used to hand-sharpen cutting tools.

oil sump:
A container built into the lower part of an aircraft engine that holds the supply of lubricating oil.

oil tank:
A reservoir or tank for oil in the lubrication system of an aircraft's powerplant.

oil temperature regulator:
A control device that maintains oil temperature within the desired limits by either passing it through the oil cooler or bypassing it around the cooler.

Oilite bushing:
A special type of bushing made of a bronze material impregnated with oil. The friction of parts moving in the bushing generates enough heat to bring the oil to the surface and provide adequate lubrication.

oleo:
Short for oleo strut.

oleo strut:
An aircraft landing gear shock strut that absorbs the initial impact of landing by the transfer of oil from one chamber to another through a restricting orifice. Taxi shocks are absorbed by compressed air or spring pressure.

OM:
ILS outer marker. *(FAR 1)*

omnidirectional antenna:
An antenna that radiates and receives equally in all directions (nondirectional).

on condition:
A method used in determining the airworthiness of parts. Parts are repaired or replaced when their condition is such that they are no longer airworthy. Differs from life-limited in that no preset repair

or replacement times have been established.

online test equipment:
Continuously monitors the performance of electronic systems.

on-speed condition:
1. The condition in which the actual engine speed is equal to the desired engine speed established by the pilot.

2. The condition in a governor when the speeder spring and flyweights are balanced.

open center selector valve:
A type of hydraulic selector valve used with an open center hydraulic system that allows fluid to flow from the pump to the reservoir when the selector valve is placed in the neutral position.

open circuit:
1. The condition of an electrical circuit caused by the breaking of continuity of one or more conductors of the circuit; usually an undesired condition.

2. A circuit that does not provide a complete path for the flow of current.

open circuit voltage welder:
The voltage between the terminals of the welding source when no current is flowing in the welding circuit.

open end wrench:
A non-adjustable wrench with open parallel jaws on one or both ends.

OPEN END WRENCH

operate:
With respect to aircraft: use, cause to use or authorize to use aircraft, for the purpose (except as provided in §91.13 of the Federal aviation regulations) of air

navigation including the piloting of aircraft, with or without the right of legal control (as owner, lessee, or otherwise). *(FAR 1)*

operating pressure:
The hydraulic or pneumatic pressure to which a system is normally subjected.

operating weight:
The basic weight of an aircraft plus the weight of oil, trapped fuel, the crew and their baggage, and emergency and extra equipment. Does not include fuel and payload.

operational amplifier (op amp):
An amplifier designed to perform computing or transfer operations and that has the following characteristics:

1. Very high gain

2. Very high input impedance

3. Very low output impedance

operational checks:
Checks made to a unit to determine if it is operating properly and within the specifications established by the manufacturer.

operational control:
With respect to a flight, means the exercise of authority over initiating, conducting or terminating a flight. *(FAR 1)*

operations manual:
A manual that contains all the information necessary to operate an organization relating to aircraft.

opposed engine:
An internal-combustion, reciprocating aircraft engine having one or more cylinders located on each side of the crankshaft with the piston strokes on each side working in a direction opposite to the direction of the strokes on the other side.

optical coupler:
A coupler composed of an LED and a photodiode and contained in a light- conducting medium. Suitable for frequencies in the low-megahertz range.

optoelectronic devices:
Devices that either produce or use light in their operation.

OR gate:
A logic device that will have a voltage (1) on its output any time a voltage appears at any one of its inputs (1).

OR GATE

orange peel:
Pebble-effect appearance caused by too high air pressure during spraying, or occurring when the spray gun is held too close to the surface, or when a quick-drying thinner is used that prevents the normal flow of lacquer solids.

orbit:
The path, relative to a specified frame of reference, described by the center of mass of a satellite or other object in space subjected primarily to natural forces, mainly the force of gravity.

organic:
Natural or biological as opposed to synthetic or man-made.

organic brake linings:
Organic materials reinforced with brass wool and attached to solid metal backings.

orifice:
A small hole of a specific size to meter or control the flow of a fluid.

orifice check valve:
A component in a hydraulic or pneumatic system that allows unrestricted flow in one direction

and restricts flow in the opposite direction.

O-ring:
A torus; a circle of material with a round cross section which effects a seal through squeeze and pressure.

oronasal oxygen mask:
An oxygen mask covering only the mouth and nose of the wearer.

orthographic projection:
A form of mechanical drawing that is capable of yielding six possible views of an object as if the object is encased in a transparent cube and viewed from each face of the cube.

oscillator:
An electronic device that produces alternating current with frequencies determined by the inductance and capacitance in the circuit.

oscilloscope:
An electronic device for detecting and displaying visually the changes occurring in an electric voltage or current.

OSHA:
Occupational Safety and Health Administration. The federal agency that is charged with the enforcement of health and safety regulations.

OSI:
Open System Interconnection (ISO defined communications architecture used in data link to permit heterogeneous data communication systems to be interconnected in order to allow the reliable exchange of messages without regard to the implementation of the networks and physical media through which the messages pass.)

Otto cycle:
A constant volume cycle, with four distinct operations performed intermittently. Reciprocating engines operate on this cycle.

O

171

outflow valve:
The principle control of the cabin pressurization system. It maintains the desired cabin pressure by controlling the amount of air flowing out of the cabin.

out-of-circuit meter:
A meter that is not permanently installed in a circuit. Usually portable and self-contained, these meters are used to check the operation of a circuit or to isolate troubles within a circuit.

out-of-phase:
A condition of cyclic values in which two waves, such as voltage and current, do not pass through the same point at the same time.

out-of-rig:
A condition of flight control rigging that prevents the aircraft from being flown hands off because the controls are not properly rigged.

out-of-round:
Eccentrically shaped because of wear.

OUT-OF-ROUND

out-of-trim:
A condition where hands-off flight is not possible because of an improperly adjusted trim device.

output end:
The end of a transmission line that is opposite the source; the receiving end.

output impedance:
The impedance that is presented to the load by the transmission line and its source.

outrigger:
A frame, boom or similar structure projecting away from the central body of an aircraft, to which a component, such as a stabilizer or engine, is attached.

outside air temperature (OAT):
The ambient temperature outside of a flying aircraft.

overboost:
A condition in which a supercharged reciprocating engine has exceeded the maximum manifold pressure allowed by the manufacturer.

overhaul:
The complete disassembly, cleaning, inspection, repair, and reassembly of an engine or other component of an aircraft.

overheat warning system:
A type of fire warning system that warns the pilot of an overheat condition that could result in a fire.

overload:
An amount of power flowing in an electrical device or circuit over and above that for which the device or circuit was designed.

overprime:
To introduce an excess of fuel into an engine during the process of priming.

overrunning clutch:
Generally a pawl and ratchet arrangement that will allow the starter to turn the engine, but not allow the engine to turn the starter.

overseas air commerce:
The carriage, by aircraft, of persons or property for compensation or hire, or the carriage of mail by aircraft, or the operation or navigation of aircraft in the conduct or furtherance of a business or vocation, in commerce:

1. Between a place in any State of the United States, or the District of Columbia, and

any place in a territory or possession of the United States.

2. Between a place in a territory or possession of the United States, and a place in any other territory or possession of the United States. *(FAR 1)*

overseas air transportation:
The carriage by aircraft of persons or property as a common carrier for compensation or hire, or the carriage of mail by aircraft, in commerce:

1. Between a place in a state or the District of Columbia and a place in a possession of the United States.

2. Between a place in a possession of the United States and a place in another possession of the United States; whether that commerce moves wholly by aircraft or partly by aircraft and partly by other forms of transportation. *(FAR 1)*

oversized stud:
A stud having a greater diameter than standard, but with the same number of threads and same pitch as the standard. Used to replace loose studs.

over-speed condition:
A condition in a propeller system where the propeller is operating above the r.p.m. for which the governor has been set.

over-the-top:
Above the layer of clouds or other obscuring phenomena forming the ceiling. *(FAR 1)*

over-voltage protector:
A protective device used to prevent damage from voltage surges. If the voltage exceeds the design limits the over-voltage protector opens the circuit.

oxidation:
A chemical action in which a metallic element is united with oxygen. Electrons are removed from the metal in this process.

oxide film:
A layer or coating of metallic oxide on the surface of a material.

oxidizing flame:
An oxyacetylene flame in which there is an excess of oxygen. An oxidizing flame can be detected by a sharp-pointed inner cone and a hissing noise being made by the torch.

oxyacetylene welding:
A welding process in which the required temperature is attained by flames obtained from the combustion of acetylene with oxygen.

oxygen cell corrosion:
A form of corrosion where a solution that is in contact with a surface contains dissolved oxygen. An oxygen cell can develop at any point where the oxygen in the air is not allowed to diffuse into the solution, thereby creating a difference in oxygen concentration between the two points. The area of low oxygen concentration is anodic, and corrosion starts there.

oxygen generator:
A source of oxygen produced by a chemical generator. This unit consists of a chemical compound that when ignited by a percussion cap, burns and releases pure oxygen gas. It is used on airline equipment as an emergency oxygen supply. Because an oxygen generator is classified as a pyrotechnic device, it has special handling requirements. Also known as an *oxygen candle*.

ozone:
Form of oxygen formed from an electrical charge.

O

pack carburizing:
Case hardening process in which carbon is added to the surface of low carbon steel parts after they have been packed in a container with charcoal, or some other material rich in carbon, sealed with fire clay, heated to approximately 1,700°F and soaked at that temperature for several hours. As a result of the temperature increase, carbon monoxide gas forms inside the container and, being unable to escape, combines with the gamma iron on the surface of the steel. The depth to which the carbon penetrates depends on the length of the soaking period.

packing:
A type of seal used to provide a leakproof connection between two parts of a unit that move in relation to each other.

packing ring:
An O-ring used to confine liquids or gases and prevent them from passing between a fixed body and movable shaft.

pad bits:
Fill in any portion of the data field not used for the transmission of data.

page block:
Used to categorize a given chapter-section-subject of the maintenance manual.

pal nut:
Type of nut used in addition to a traditional nut that forces the nut thread against the bolt or screw thread when tightened. These nuts should never be reused and should be replaced with new ones when removed.

PAMA:
Professional Aviation Maintenance Association

pan-head screw:
A sheet metal or machine screw with a slightly domed head.

PAR:
Precision approach radar. *(FAR 1)*

parachute:
A device used or intended to be used to retard the fall of a body or object through the air. *(FAR 1)*

par-al-ketone:
A heavy, wax like grease that is often used to protect control cables from corrosion. It may also be found protecting other types of hardware fittings on seaplanes.

parallel circuits:
An electrical circuit having more than one path for electron flow from one side of the electrical source to the other.

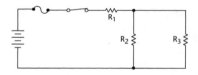

PARALLEL CIRCUIT

parallel limiter:
A resistor and diode connected in series with the input signal in which the output is taken across (parallel to) the diode.

parallel-resonant circuit:
A resonant circuit in which the source voltage is connected across a parallel circuit (formed by a capacitor and an inductor) to furnish a high impedance to the frequency at which the circuit is resonant. Often referred to as a tank circuit.

paralleling generators:
Controlling the output of more than one generator so that they will equally share the load.

paramagnetic:
A material whose permeability is greater than a vacuum but less than that of a ferromagnetic material.

parasitic drag:
That part of total drag created by the form or shape of airplane parts.

parasitic element:
The passive element of an antenna array that is connected to neither the transmission line nor the driven element.

parasol wing aircraft:
An airplane having one main supporting surface (i.e.,wing) mounted above the fuselage on cabane struts.

PARASOL WING AIRCRAFT

parity bit:
A binary bit set by the transmitter that permits error checks by each receiver connected to the bus.

parkerizing:
A surface corrosion preventive treatment where parts are immersed into a solution of phosphoric acid and manganese dioxide.

Parker-Kalon screws (PK screws):
A particular type of self-tapping sheet metal screws. These screws are made of hardened steel, have a sharp point, and course threads.

parting agent:
A material used to cover a mold to prevent the resin from adhering to it during the manufacture of a part.

part power trim check:
A routine check for some types of turbine engines where the engine is operated with a trim stop or pin

in place and the EPR or N_1 speed recorded. This reading is then corrected for standard conditions. If the correct value is not present, adjustment of the fuel control (i.e., trimming) is required.

parts manufacturing approval (PMA):
An approval to produce a part for sale for installation on a type-certificate aircraft. Applicable to both replacement parts and parts for aircraft modifications. One of the methods of obtaining FAA approval to manufacture aftermarket parts.

Pascal's law:
A basic law of fluid power that states that pressure in an enclosed container is transmitted equally and undiminished to all points of the container and acts at right angles to the enclosing walls.

passenger address system (PAS):
System for transmitting audio through a series of cabin speakers to announce messages

passive matrix LCD:
Employs a grid of conductors with pixels located at each intersection of the grid.

passive satellite:
A satellite that reflects radio signals back to earth.

pasty range:
The condition of solder between the solid and liquid state; the soft, mushy, pasty condition where liquid and solid crystals exist together.

pawl:
A pivoted stop in a mechanical device that will allow motion in one direction only. Commonly seen in a ratchet mechanism.

payload:
In commercial aircraft, the part of the load carried that produces revenue, i.e., the passengers with their baggage, the air cargo, or both.

P-band radar:
Radar frequency between 225 and 390 MHz.

peak envelope power (of a radio transmitter):
The average power supplied to the antenna transmission line by a transmitter during one radio frequency cycle at the crest of the modulation envelope taken under normal operating conditions.

peak-to-peak:
The measure of absolute magnitude of an ac waveform, measured from the greatest positive alternation to the greatest negative alternation.

peak value:
The maximum instantaneous value of a varying current, voltage, or power. It is equal to 1.414 times the effective value of a sine wave.

peak voltage:
The maximum value present in a varying or alternating voltage. This value may be positive or negative.

peel ply:
A layer of open-weave material applied directly to the surface of a prepreg lay-up. The peel ply is removed from the cured laminate immediately before bonding operations.

peen:
To strike repeatedly with a hammer.

penetrating oil:
A thin, nonviscous oil used to loosen rusted or frozen metal parts such as nuts, screws, bolts, or pins. Penetrating oil is not intended for use as a lubricant. It is produced to specification VV-P-216.FM 10-67-2

performance number:
The anti-detonation rating of a fuel that has a higher critical pressure and temperature than iso-octane (100). Iso-octane treated with varying amounts of tetraethyl lead is used as the reference.

period:
The time required for a complete oscillation or for a single cycle of events. The reciprocal of frequency.

period (of a satellite):
The time elapsing between two consecutive passages of a satellite through a characteristic point on its orbit.

periodic inspection:
Any inspection that is repeated at a regular interval. This term is often used when referring to the annual inspection of an aircraft.

perimeter:
1. The whole outer edge of something, as of a building, parcel of land or geometric figure.
2. A place near the outer edge of something.

perlite:
Perlite is the lamellar aggregate of ferrite and iron carbide resulting from the direct transformation of austenite at the lower critical point.

permalloy:
An alloy of iron and nickel used to manufacture permanent magnets.

permamold crankcase:
An engine crankcase that has been manufactured using a process involving pressure molding into a permanent mold. This results in a product that is thinner and denser than a crankcase made by the traditional sand casting method.

permanent magnet:
A body that possesses the ability to retain or hold a large amount of the applied magnet field after the active power of the field is removed.

permeability:
1. The measure of the ability of a material to act as a path for magnetic lines of force.
2. The extent to which a material will allow a liquid or gas to pass through it.

Permold Crankcase:
Trade name for permamold crankcases manufactured by Teledyne Continental Motors.

person:
An individual, firm, partnership, corporation, company, association, joint-stock association, or governmental entity. It includes a trustee, receiver, assignee, or similar representative of any of them. *(FAR 1)*

perspective drawing:
A view of an object in which parallel lines do not appear parallel, but converge at a vanishing point outside the drawing.

petrol:
A British term for gasoline.

pH:
A term used to indicate acidity or alkalinity. The pH scale runs from 0 to 14; pH 7 is neutral, less than 7 is acid, 7 to 14 is alkaline. The further the rating is from seven, the greater the acidity or alkalinity.

phantom line:
Phantom lines indicate the alternate position of parts of the object or the relative position of a missing part. Phantom lines are composed of one long and two short evenly spaced dashes.

phase:
In a periodic function or wave, the fraction of the period that has elapsed measured from some fixed origin, if the time for one period is represented as 360° along a time axis, the phase position is called the phase angle.

phase angle:
1. The number of electrical degrees of lead or lag between the voltage and current waveforms in an AC circuit.
2. The angle between two vectors representing two simple periodic quantities that vary sinusoidally and that have the same frequency.
3. A notation for phase position when the period is designated by 360°.

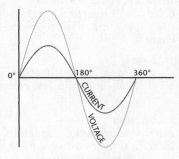

PHASE ANGLE

phase modulation (PM):
Digital modulation of the carrier for GPS and satellite

phase shift:
A change in the phase relationship between two periodic functions. See *phase*.

phase splitter:
A device that provides two output signals from a single input signal. The two output signals differ from each other in phase (usually by 180°).

phenolic plastic:
A thermosetting phenolic-formaldehyde resin material, reinforced with cloth or paper.

phillips head screw:
A type of recessed head screw designed to be driven using a special cross-pointed screw driver whose point has two distinct tapers.

P

phonetic:
Representing vocal sounds.

phonetic alphabet:
An alphabet code utilizing individual words to represent letters.

phosphate ester base hydraulic fluid:
A synthetic, fire-resistant, hydraulic fluid used in the high-pressure hydraulic systems of jet aircraft. See *Skydrol*.

phosphate rust proofing:
Corrosion protection that involves the application of a phosphate coating.

photo cell:
An electronic device that becomes conductive or produces a voltage when struck by light.

photodiode:
A light-controlled PN junction. Current flow increases when the PN junction is exposed to an external light source.

piano hinge:
A continuous metal hinge consisting of hinge bodies attached to both the fixed and movable surfaces. A hard steel wire connects the two bodies and serves as the hinge pin.

piano wire:
The hard steel wire in a piano hinge. See also *music wire*.

pickling:
Removing surface oxides from metals by immersion in ambient temperature, dilute hydrochloric acid or hot sulfuric acid (180°F or 82°C).

pico:
A prefix adopted by the National Bureau of Standards meaning 10-12.

pictorial diagram:
A drawing which shows the object as it appears, as in a photograph.

PICTORIAL DIAGRAM
(FUEL QUANTITY GAUGE)

pierced terminal:
Having a hole or opening.

piezoelectric effect:
The effect of producing a voltage by placing a stress, either by compression, expansion, or twisting, on a crystal and, conversely, producing a stress in a crystal by applying a voltage to it.

pig iron:
A cast slab of primary metal that must be remelted before use.

pilotage:
Navigation by visual reference to landmarks. *(FAR 1)*

pilot hole:
A starting hole for large drills to serve as a guide, reduce the resistance, and aid in maintaining the accuracy of the larger hole. Also called a *lead hole*.

pilot in command:
1. The person who has final authority and responsibility for the operation and safety of the flight.

2. The person who has been designated as pilot in command before or during the flight.

3. The person who holds the appropriate category, class, and type rating, if appropriate, for the conduct of the flight. *(FAR 1)*

pilot valve:
Valve used to control the operation of another valve; the spool in a selector valve.

pinion gear:
A small gear with teeth that fit into those of a larger gear or rack. See *rack and pinion*.

pinking shears:
A special type of scissors that cut the fabric in a series of small V's to prevent raveling.

pin programming:
Also known as *configuration strapping*.

Specific electrical connections used to determine various display, input/output signal formats and other system parameters

pin punch:
A long punch with a uniform diameter, which is often used to remove bolts or rivets.

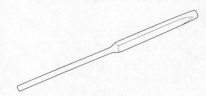

PIN PUNCH

pin rivet:
See *hi-shear rivet*.

pip (blip):
On a CRT display, a spot of light or a baseline irregularity representing the radar echo.

pipe threads:
Tapered threads which are capable of providing a seal.

piston:
A sliding plug in an actuating cylinder used to convert pressure into force and then into work.

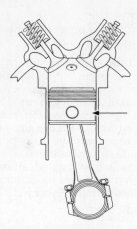

PISTON

piston engine:
See *reciprocating engine*

pitch:
1. The cant or slant of a chosen chord of a propeller blade, rotor blade, or other blade with respect to a plane perpendicular to the axis of rotation of the blade (i.e., blade angle).

2. The rotational or oscillatory movement of an aircraft, rocket missile, etc., about a lateral axis or pitch axis (i.e., pitching).

3. The distance between centers of adjacent rivets in a row.

pitch control:
1. A mechanism for controlling the pitch of a propeller or rotor.

2. A lever for working a pitch control.

pitch setting:
The propeller blade setting as determined by the blade angle measured in a manner, and at a radius, specified by the instruction manual for the propeller. *(FAR 1)*

pitot head:
See *pitot tube*

P

pitot pressure:
The absolute pressure of the air that enters the pitot tube.

pitot-static system:
The system providing reference points for the operation of several critical flight instruments. The pitot tube measures impact air at whatever speed the aircraft is traveling and the static port provides a zero reference. Normally the airspeed, altimeter and vertical speed indicators are connected to this system.

pitot tube:
A device that funnels impact air pressure into the airspeed indicator. Also called *pitot static tube*.

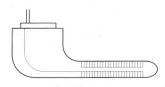

PITOT TUBE

pitting corrosion:
The formation of pockets of corrosion products on the surface of a metal.

plain bearing:
A simple form of bearing that is designed only to take loads that are perpendicular to its face. The crankshaft and camshaft bearings of most reciprocating engines are plain bearings.

plain flap:
The elemental flap, non-extensible, non-slotted, and non-split, hinged to a wing and forming part of a trailing edge. Also called a *simple flap*.

plain weave:
A weaving pattern in which the warp and fill fibers alternate. Both faces of a plain weave are identical.

Planck's constant:
A fundamental physical constant; the ratio of the energy of a photon to its frequency.

planform:
A term used to refer to a wing's shape when viewed from above.

PLANK:
Formula used to determine reciprocating engine power. P = indicated mean effective pressure, in p.s.i., L = length of the stroke in feet or in fractions of a foot, A = area of the piston head or cross-sectional area of the cylinder, in square inches, N = number of power strokes per minute, (r.p.m. divided by 2), K = number of cylinders.

plasma coating:
A process used to extend the life of turbine engine parts. A thin coat of highly wear-resistant material is applied and fused at very high temperatures.

plate:
1. One of the electrodes in a storage battery.

2. One of the electrodes in a capacitor.

3. The principal electrode to which the electron stream is attracted in an electron tube.

plating:
Forming an adherent layer of metal upon an object.

play:
A commonly used term that describes the relative movement between two parts.

P-lead:
The commonly used term for the primary lead from a magneto to the ignition switch.

plenum chamber:
An air chamber opening into the compressor chamber on certain turbine engines, and in which air is collected for the compressor.

Plexiglas®:
Transparent thermoplastic material commonly used for aircraft windshields and side windows. Sometimes incorrectly spelled *plexiglass*.

plumb bob:
A heavy pointed weight normally suspended on a string to establish a location directly below its attach point. Used in aircraft leveling and rigging.

ply:
1. In general, fabrics or felts consisting of one or more layers.

2. The layers that make up a stack.

3. A single layer of prepreg.

ply orientation:
The filament orientation of material with respect to the tool or part reference axis.

ply rating:
The number of reinforcing plies on a tire.

plywood:
Layers of wood glued so that the grain in each layer is 45° or 90° to the previous layer.

PMA:
Parts manufacturing approval.

pneudraulic:
Of or pertaining to mechanisms or devices that work by both pneumatic and hydraulic action.

pneumatic:
Of or pertaining to mechanisms or devices worked by compressed air or other gas.

pneumatic servo:
Vacuum actuated autopilot component used to move control surfaces; typically found on light aircraft.

P-N junction:
The point, or junction, where the two materials, commonly germanium and silicon, are in contact in a semiconductor device.

PNP transistor:
A three-layer semiconductor device made up of one piece of N-type silicon or germanium sandwiched between two pieces of P-type material.

pod nacelle:
An engine nacelle slung beneath a wing.

POD NACELLE

point-contact diode:
A diode in which the end of a fine wire is pressed against a semiconductor. Used as a detector or mixer over the microwave region.

polarization:
1. *Physics* - The act or process of affecting light waves or electromagnetic waves so that they are made to vibrate in a certain given direction.

2. *Electricity* - The formation or accumulation of gas or some of the substance on the electrodes of an electric cell as a result of the passage of current; the condition arising from such formation or accumulation.

pole piece:
1. A piece of ferromagnetic material used to control the distribution of magnetic lines of force; that is, it concentrates the lines of force in a particular place or evenly distributes the lines of force over a wide area.

2. The shaped magnetic material upon which the stator windings of motors and generators are mounted or wound.

polyester fiber:
A type of synthetic fiber known for its mechanical strength, chemical stability and long life. Polyester may be used to make woven fabric for aircraft covering.

polyethylene:
A lightweight, thermoplastic resin material with good chemical resistance.

poly-fiber®:
A registered trade name for a fabric woven from polyester fibers.

polystyrene:
A transparent plastic used to make cell casings for some nickel-cadmium batteries.

polyurethane enamel:
A hard, chemically resistant finish whose long flow-out time and even cure throughout give a flat surface and a glossy wet look. Especially suitable for seaplanes and agricultural planes because of its resistance to chemical action and abrasion.

polyvinyl chloride:
A thermoplastic resin used in the manufacture of transparent tubing for electrical insulation and fluid lines that are subject to low pressures.

poppet valve:
A circular head, t-shaped valve with many uses. This is the type of valve used for both intake and exhaust on reciprocating engines.

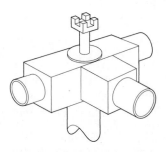

POPPET VALVE

porous chrome plating:
A plating of hard chromium on bearing surfaces. The surface of the plating consists of tiny cracks in which lubricant can adhere to reduce sliding friction.

port side:
Left side, looking forward.

position lights:
See *navigation lights*

positive control:
Control of all air traffic, within designated airspace, by air traffic control. *(FAR 1)*

positive displacement pump:
A type of fluid pump that moves a specific amount of fluid each time it rotates. Gear pumps, gerotor pumps and vane pumps are all positive displacement pumps.

positive ion:
An atom with fewer electrons that protons.

positive static stability:
The condition of stability that causes an aircraft, when disturbed from straight and level flight, to tend to return to straight and level flight.

positron:
A fundamental particle of nature having a mass equal to that of the electron and possessing a positive charge equal to the negative charge of the electron. The mass of the positron is therefore 9.107×10^{-28} gm; the electrical charge carried by the positron is equal to 4.802×10^{-10} stat coulomb (electrostatic unit of charge).

pot life:
The period of time during which a reacting thermosetting composition remains suitable for its intended processing after mixing with a reaction initiating agent.

potential difference:
The principle that causes the electrons to move, when a proper

path is available, from a point of excess electrons to one deficient in electrons.

potential energy:
The energy of an object derived from position with respect to a specified datum and equal to that object weight multiplied by its height above said datum.

potentiometer:
A variable resistor, used as a position sensor in servo systems, having a terminal connected to each end of a resistive element and a third terminal connected to a wiper contact. The output is a voltage that is variable depending upon the position of the wiper contact. The potentiometer is commonly referred to as a variable voltage divider. It, in effect, converts mechanical information into an electrical signal.

potting compound:
A substance, usually a two-part epoxy, that sets to a ceramic-like hardness and is used to bond two or more objects. May be used to fill small indentations is some types of bonded structures.

pour point:
The lowest temperature at which an oil can be poured (ASTM Method D 97).

powder metallurgy:
A process where metal powders are forced into a mold under pressure. The resulting part is then heated to bind the particles (i.e., sintering).

power-amplifier (chain) transmitter:
Transmitter that uses a series of power amplifiers to create a high level of power.

power distribution system:
One or more electrical distribution points used to connect the main power supply for the aircraft

powered-lift:
A heavier-than-air aircraft capable of vertical takeoff, vertical landing, and low speed flight that depends principally on engine-driven lift devices or engine thrust for lift during these flight regimes and on nonrotating airfoils for lift during horizontal flight. *(FAR 1)*

powered parachute:
A powered aircraft comprised of a flexible or semi-rigid wing connected to a fuselage so that the wing is not in position for flight until the aircraft is in motion. The fuselage of a powered parachute contains the aircraft engine, a seat for each occupant and is attached to the aircraft's landing gear. *(FAR 1)*

power enrichment system:
Power compensator that increases the richness of a fuel air mixture during high power operation of the carburetor system. Sometimes called an economizer.

power factor:
The ratio of the actual power of an alternating or pulsating current, as measured by a wattmeter, to the apparent power, as indicated by ammeter and voltmeter readings. The power factor of an inductor, capacitor, or insulator is an expression of their losses.

power gain:
In an antenna, the ratio of its radiated power to that of a reference.

power lever:
The cockpit lever that connects to the fuel control unit of a turbine engine to schedule changes in fuel flow.

power loading:
The ratio of the maximum gross weight of an aircraft to the brake horsepower produced by the engines.

powerplant:
The complete engine or engines in an aircraft, together with propeller or propellers (if any), accessories, fuel and oil tanks and lines, etc.

power pump:
An engine or electric driven pump used to produce pressure in the hydraulic system, as opposed to a hand pump.

power recovery turbine (PRT):
A device used with the Wright R-3350 engine to extract additional horsepower from the exhaust gases. The power recovery turbines extract some energy from the exhaust and transfer it back to the crankshaft through a series of gears and fluid drive couplings.

power section:
1. That portion of a radial engine crankcase where the cylinders are mounted.
2. That portion of a turbine engine containing the power turbines.

power stroke:
The stroke of the four-stroke cycle where work is done. Following ignition, the piston is forced downward on the power stroke by the expanding gases and this energy is transmitted to the crankshaft to accomplish work.

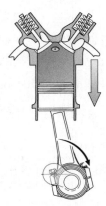

POWER STROKE

power turbine:
Also referred to as a free turbine. This is a turbine installed in a turboprop or turboshaft installation that is not connected to the gas generator section. Its only function is to drive the propeller or shaft.

Pratt truss:
A truss used in certain fuselages or airfoils with tensioned cross-bracing rods, wires, or cables between uprights or side-by-side members.

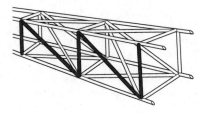

PRATT TRUSS

preamplifier (preamp):
An amplifier that raises the output of a low-level source for further processing without appreciable degradation of the signal-to-noise ratio.

precipitation heat treatment:
Artificial aging in which a constituent precipitates from a supersaturated solid solution.

precision approach procedure:
A standard instrument approach procedure in which an electronic glide slope is provided, such as ILS and PAR. (FAR 1)

pre-exit thrust reverser:
A thrust reverser installed forward of the exhaust nozzle.

pre-ignition:
Ignition occurring in the cylinder before the time of normal ignition. It is often caused by a local hot spot in the combustion chamber igniting the fuel-air mixture.

pre-oiling:
The act of forcing lubrication through the oil passages of an engine prior to startup. This is often done after overhaul before the engine is run for the first time, after de-preservation, or after a long period of not operating.

prepreg:
1. Ready to mold or cure material in sheet form which may be tow, tape, cloth, or mat impregnated with resin. It may be stored before use.

2. Ready-to-mold material in sheet form or ready-to-wind material in roving form, which may be cloth, mat, unidirectional fiber, or paper impregnated with resin and stored for use.

presetting:
To adjust or set a predetermined point prior to installation.

press fit:
An interference fit between parts that requires one part be pressed into the other. This is sometimes aided by heating one part and cooling the other prior to assembly.

pressure altitude:
Height above the standard pressure level of 29.92 in. Hg. Obtained by setting 29.92 in the barometric pressure window and reading the altimeter.

pressure carburetor:
A type of fuel metering device that requires fuel supplied under pressure and senses the relationship between impact air pressure and venturi pressure to provide proper fuel metering.

pressure demand oxygen regulator:
A type of oxygen regulator that is capable of furnishing 100 percent oxygen under pressure to force oxygen into the lungs of the wearer.

pressure plate:
A heavy, stationary disc in a multi-disc brake assembly that receives the force from the pistons and transmits it to the disc stack.

pressure pot:
A container holding material, usually paint, to be sprayed. It often employs a manual or air-driven agitator.

pressure ratio:
A ratio between two pressures, such as the ratio between the inlet and outlet pressure in a compressor or between chamber pressure and nozzle pressure in a rocket.

pressure regulator:
A device used with a constant displacement pump to maintain a constant output by bypassing a portion of the fluid back to the inlet side of the pump.

pressure relief valve:
A pressure control valve that bypasses fluid back to the reservoir if the pressure rises above the preset value.

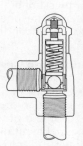

PRESSURE RELIEF VALVE

pressure switch:
A switch activated by a given ambient pressure, as with a barometric switch.

pressurization:
The process or action of pressurizing.

P

pressurization safety valve:
Valve that prevents over-pressurization and the subsequent destruction of the airplane. It operates similarly to an outflow valve, except that it is preset to a maximum cabin pressure differential. Should the outflow valve malfunction, the safety valve will not allow the cabin pressure to exceed the safe limit.

pressurize:
1. To produce and maintain in a cockpit, cabin, or compartment of an aircraft, an air pressure higher than the ambient atmospheric pressure, in order to compensate for the lowered pressure at high altitudes; to create a higher pressure in the air within a cockpit, cabin, etc., by the introduction of additional air.

2. To subject a transmission line, piece of equipment, or the like to a pressure higher than the ambient pressure.

pressurized:
Subjected to pressurization; containing air pressure higher than the ambient atmospheric pressure; done under conditions of pressurization.

pressurizing and dump valve (P&D):
Device to prevent flow of fuel to the nozzle until enough pressure is built up in the fuel control. It also drains the fuel manifold at engine shutdown and traps fuel in the upper portion of the system to keep the fuel control primed for faster starts.

preventive maintenance:
Simple or minor preservative operations and the replacement of small standard parts not involving complex assembly operation as listed in Appendix A of 14 CFR Part 43. (FAR 1)

primary cell:
The unit in a battery that converts chemical energy into electrical energy. Primary cells are not rechargeable.

primary coil:
The input coil or winding of a transformer.

primary flight controls:
The flight surfaces that control movement around or about the aircraft axis. These are: rudder elevator and aileron. Does not include flaps, slats, trim tabs, spoilers or other devices not related to the primary control of the airplane.

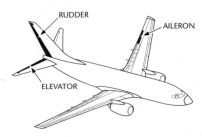

PRIMARY FLIGHT CONTROLS

primary fuel:
On turbine engines with duplex nozzles, primary fuel is that which initially flows on starting, usually from the center orifice. Also called *pilot fuel*.

primary glider:
A ruggedly built glider, typically having an open-framework fuselage, for the elementary training of glider pilots. The craft is designed chiefly for gliding, rather than soaring.

primary heat exchanger:
Device that removes heat from a source and expels it to a secondary circuit or into the atmosphere.

primary radar:
A radio determination system based on the comparison of reference signals with radio signals reflected from the position to be determined.

primary structure:
Those portions of an aircraft whose failure would seriously endanger the safety of the craft. This would include wings, controls, engine mounts, etc.

primary winding:
The winding of a transformer where the applied voltage flows. In a magneto this is the portion of the coil through which the voltage induced by the rotating magnet flows.

prime:
To introduce fuel into the induction system of an engine preparatory to starting the engine.

primer:
A coating applied directly to the basic metal and upon which a subsequent topcoat is to be applied.

primer line:
A line of tubing in an aircraft's fuel system that carries fuel to prime the engine.

primer pump:
A manually operated or electrically driven pump for pumping fuel to prime the engine. Sometimes called a primer.

printed circuit board:
The general term for completely processed printed circuit or printed wiring configurations. It includes single and double sided, multilayer, flexible, and flexible multilayer boards.

priority valve:
Valve used to route fluid to those components requiring immediate completion of action when a reduction in normal system flow and pressure occurs.

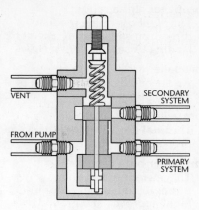

VENT
SECONDARY SYSTEM
FROM PUMP
PRIMARY SYSTEM

PRIORITY VALVE

progressive inspection:
A procedure in which a maintenance mechanic can split an annual inspection into small portions that are performed at shorter intervals.

prohibited area:
A prohibited area is airspace designated under FAR part 73 within which no person may operate an aircraft without the permission of the using agency. *(FAR 1)*

prony brake:
Device that measures the usable power output of an engine on a test stand.

prop:
Propeller. Used as a common noun.

propeller:
A device for propelling an aircraft that has blades on an engine-driven shaft and that, when rotated, produces by its action on the air, a thrust approximately perpendicular to its plane of rotation. It includes control components normally supplied by its manufacturer, but does not include main and auxiliary rotors or rotating airfoils of engines. *(FAR 1)*

P

propeller alpha range:
The flight operating mode for a turboprop engine from takeoff to landing. Also called *alpha mode*.

propeller arc:
An arc of the circle described by a rotating propeller.

propeller area:
The total propeller blade area of a propeller.

propeller beta range:
The operating range of a turboprop engine used for in-flight approach and ground handling of the aircraft and engine. Also called *beta mode*.

propeller blade:
Any one of the arms of an aircraft propeller; specifically, that part of the arm which serves to bite the air, i.e., the part from the shank outward.

propeller blade angle:
The acute angle between the chord of a propeller blade and the plane of rotation.

propeller brake:
Device designed to prevent the propeller from windmilling when it is feathered in flight and to decrease the time for the propeller to come to a complete stop after engine shutdown.

propeller critical range:
An operational range for a particular engine-propeller combination that is subject to the formation of harmonic vibration in the propeller. Engines are usually placarded against operation in this range.

propeller cuff:
A streamlined fairing fitted around the shank of a propeller.

propeller diameter:
The diameter of the circle described by a rotating propeller.

propeller disc:
The space occupied or covered by a rotating propeller.

propeller-driven:
Aircraft driven by an engine-propeller combination.

propeller efficiency:
The ratio of thrust horsepower to brake horsepower.

propeller governor:
A governor that regulates the pitch of a constant-speed propeller.

propeller ground clearance:
The distance between the ground and the propeller disc of an airplane in a level attitude on the ground.

propeller hub:
The center portion of a propeller to which the blades attach, and by which the propeller is attached to the engine.

propeller pitch:
The acute angle between the chord of a propeller and a plane perpendicular to the axis of rotation.

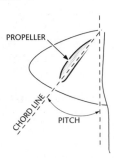

PROPELLER PITCH

propeller protractor:
A tool that can be used to measure aileron, elevator, or wing flap travel. Although the design is over fifty years old, they are still available today, and they are infinitely adjustable. Also called *universal protractor*.

propeller radius:
The radius of a propeller disk, i.e., the distance of a propeller tip from the axis of rotation. Also called *tip radius*.

propeller section:
A blade section of a propeller blade.

propeller slip:
The difference between geometric pitch and effective pitch.

propeller synchronization:
System that provides a means of controlling and synchronizing engine r.p.m. Synchronization reduces vibration and eliminates the unpleasant beat produced by unsynchronized propeller operation.

propeller thrust:
The component of total air force on the propeller that is parallel to the direction of advance of the aircraft.

propeller tip:
The outermost end of a propeller blade.

propeller tipping:
Thin sheet brass or stainless steel installed on the leading edge and around the tip of a wooden propeller to protect the blade from erosion.

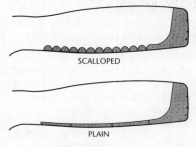

SCALLOPED

PLAIN

PROPELLER TIPPING

propjet:
See *turboprop engine*

proton:
An elementary particle with a single positive electrical charge and a mass approximately 1847 times that of the electron. The atomic number of an atom is equal to the number of protons in its nucleus.

protruding head rivet:
Any aircraft rivet whose head protrudes above the surface of the metal. Not countersunk.

Prussian blue:
A compound used as an indicator when checking valve seating in reciprocating engines and cone seating on propellers.

P-type silicon:
Silicon doped with an impurity having three valence electrons.

puck:
A colloquial term used for the spot-type lining for single-disc brakes.

pull test:
A test used with aircraft fabric where a one-inch wide sample is pulled until it breaks. The strength of the fabric is determined by the force it took to break the sample.

pulsating direct current:
A direct current signal that repeatedly pulses from zero to its maximum value. This may be created by an electronic circuit or by mechanical means (i.e., a vibrator). Pulsating DC can then be used in transformers and other circuitry that is normally associated with alternating current.

pulse-amplitude modulation (pam):
Pulse modulation in which the amplitude of the pulses is varied by the modulating signal.

pulse-code modulation (PCM):
A modulation system in which the standard values of a quantized wave are indicated by a series of coded pulses.

P

pulse-duration modulation (PDM):

Pulse modulation in which the time duration of the pulses is changed by the modulating signal.

pulse-echo:

An inspection method in which the presence and position of a discontinuity is indicated by the echo amplitude and time position; also designates a method of inspecting bonded honeycomb structures by monitoring the echoes from the far side of the core.

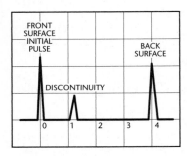

PULSE-ECHO ON CRT DISPLAY

pulse length:

The pulse duration of an electromagnetic wave.

pulse modulation:

The frequency modulation or amplitude modulation of a carrier wave so as to produce signal pulses.

pulse oscillator:

A sine-wave oscillator that is turned on and off at specific times. Also known as a *ringing oscillator*.

pumice:

An extremely fine natural abrasive powder used for polishing metal surfaces.

pulsejet engine:

A type of jet engine without a compressor in which combustion takes place intermittently, producing thrust by a series of explosions, commonly occurring at the approximate resonance frequency of the engine.

punch press:

A machine tool for piercing, blanking, forming, coining, drawing and performing other operations on parts made from sheet metal.

punch test:

A test of the strength of aircraft fabric while on the airplane. A pointed, spring-loaded plunger is pushed into the fabric, and the amount of force required to penetrate indicates the strength of the fabric.

purge:

A process which removes flammable or combustible fluids and vapors from a confined area.

purple K:

Potassium Bicarbonate. A dry chemical used in the fire extinguishers that puts out fires by smothering them.

push-button switch:

A type of momentary single-pole single-throw switch. Consists of a spring-loaded contact that must be pushed to close the circuit.

pusher:

Short for pusher airplane or pusher propeller.

pusher airplane:

An airplane propelled by a pusher propeller or pusher propellers.

pusher propeller:

An airplane propeller so mounted as to push the airplane through the air; a propeller mounted aft of its engine. Seaplanes and amphibious aircraft use a greater percentage of pusher propellers than other kinds of aircraft.

push fit:

A type of interference fit where the parts may be assembled by pushing them together by hand. They are not expected to require pressing or driving.

push-pull amplifier:
An amplifier that uses two transistors whose output signals are in phase opposition.

push rod:
A hollow, tubular-shaped component in a reciprocating engine that transmits the force of the valve tappet to the rocker arm.

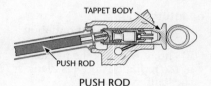

PUSH ROD

push to test lights:
A type of indicator light that can be pushed to test the integrity of the light bulb.

push-pull rod:
A rigid type of linkage used to move a control by pushing or pulling it.

pylon:
1. Structure that links aircraft to loads and engines.

2. A rotor mast.

pyrometer:
Any device used for determining temperatures over a wide range, including extremely high temperatures.

P

Qq

Q:

1. Figure of merit of efficiency of a circuit or coil.

2. Ratio of inductive reactance to resistance in servos.

3. Relationship between stored energy (capacitance) and rate of dissipation in certain types of electric elements, structures, or materials.

QEC:
Quick Engine Change

qt:
Quart

Q-tip® propeller blades:
Blade formed by bending the tip section of the blade 90° toward the face side. Aerodynamic improvements include a reduced diameter and decreased tip speeds. This results in quieter operation and reduced tip vortices. The 90° bend reduces the vortices that, on traditional blades, pick up debris that can contact the blades and cause nicks, gouges and scratches. In essence, it works like a winglet.

Q-TIP PROPELLER BLADE

QTY:
Quantity

quality (of sound):
The factor that distinguishes tones of pitch and loudness.

quality assurance:
The function of evaluating product quality and the procedures taken to ensure that the final product conforms to the specification requirements.

quantum (RT):
A discrete amount of radiation energy. The quantum energy is $E = hu$, where u is the frequency of the radiation and h is Plank's constant.

quantum-mechanical tunneling:
The action of an electron crossing a PN junction because of tunnel effect.

quarter-sawn wood:
Wood which has been sawn from the tree in such a manner that the edges of the grain are visible in the wide part of the plank. Also called *quarter-sawed*.

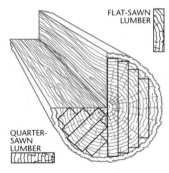

QUARTER-SAWN WOOD

quarter turn fastener:
Any of a number of cowling fasteners that are secured by turning 90 degrees.

quarter wave antenna:
Same as the Marconi antenna.

quartz:
A very hard mineral composed of silica. Pure quartz crystals are transparent and colorless.

quartz lamp:
A durable lamp constructed of quartz rather than glass.

quasi-isotropic laminate:
A laminate laid up symmetrically with an equal number of plies.

quench aging:
Aging induced by rapid cooling after Solution Heat Treatment.

quench annealing:
Annealing an austenitic ferrous alloy by Solution Heat Treatment.

quench hardening:
Hardening a ferrous alloy by austenitizing and then cooling rapidly enough so that some or all of the austenite transforms to martensite.

quenching:
To rapidly cool heated metal in water, oil brine, or air in the process of heat treating.

quick engine change assembly (QECA):
A pre-assembled, ready to mount engine. This generally includes the engine, engine mount, all accessories, cowling, and propeller (if used). These units are pre-assembled to minimize downtime when an engine change is required. Sometimes referred to as a *QEC*.

quick-disconnect coupling:
A type of fluid coupling designed for easy connect and disconnect. A check valve is built in each half to prevent spillage when the unit is separated.

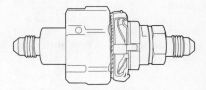

QUICK DISCONNECT COUPLING

quicksilver:
A common name for mercury. See *mercury*.

quiescence:
1. The state of an amplifier with no signal applied.

2. The operating conditions that exist in a circuit when no input signal is applied to the circuit.

quill shaft:
A hardened steel shaft with round cross section and splines on each end. Torsional flexing of the shaft is used to absorb torsional vibrations.

quotient:
The number resulting from the division of one number by another.

Q

rabbet:
A groove cut into the edge of a piece of wood in such a way that another board can be fit into it to form a joint.

race:
A hardened, polished steel surface on which a bearing is supported.

rack:
A bar having gear teeth cut on the face so that as it meshes with a gear, rotary motion is converted to reciprocating motion or vice versa.

rack and pinion:
A set of gears arranged in such a way that the rotary motion of the pinion is changed into linear motion of the rack.

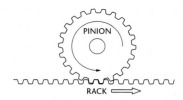

RACK AND PINION

radar:
A term derived from radio detection and ranging. It is an electronic system where a pulse of electromagnetic energy is transmitted, travels to the target, bounces off and returns to the transmitter. The display interprets this information to determine the direction and distance to the target. Ground- based and airborne systems are in common use today.

radar altimeter:
Airborne radar that measures the distance of the aircraft above the ground.

radar beacon transponder:
Device used in conjunction with a ground-based surveillance radar to provide positive aircraft identification directly on the controller's radar scope. See also *transponder*.

radar beam:
The space in front of a radar antenna where a target can be effectively detected or tracked. Defined by areas that contain half or more of the maximum power transmitted.

radar contact:
Term used by ATC to advise a pilot that the aircraft is identified on radar.

radar mile:
Time interval (12.36 microseconds) for RF energy to travel out from a radar to a target and back to the radar; radar nautical mile.

radial:
A navigational signal generated by a vor or vortac, measured as a magnetic bearing from the station.

radial engine:
An internal-combustion reciprocating engine having its cylinders arranged radially around the crankshaft.

radial outflow compressor:
See *centrifugal compressor*

radial-ply tire:
Tire with plies that are laid roughly 90° to the circumference of the tire.

radian:
A unit of angular measurement equal to the angle between two radii, separated by an arc equal to the length of the radius. Radians are used in the measurement of angular velocity.

radiant energy:
Any form of energy that is radiating from electromagnetic waves.

radiation:
The outward flow of energy from any source in the form of radio waves.

radiation hazard (RT):
A situation or condition that represents potential danger to health as the result of exposure to ionizing radiation.

radiation pattern:
A plot of the radiated energy from an antenna.

radical sign:
The mathematical sign placed before a quantity to show its root to be extracted; the square root sign.

radio:
A general term applied to the use of radio waves.

radio altimeter:
An absolute altimeter that measures altitude by measuring the lapsed time between the transmission of radio waves from an aircraft and the reception of the waves reflected from the earth's surface.

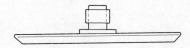

RADIO ALTIMETER ANTENNA

radio beacon station:
A station in the radio navigation service whose emissions are intended to enable a mobile station to determine its bearing or direction in relation to radio beacon station.

radio communication:
Telecommunication by means of radio waves.

radio direction-finding:
Radio determination using the reception of radio waves for the purpose of determining the direction of a station or object.

radio frequency (RF):
Frequencies of alternating current that produce electromagnetic waves that radiate from the conductor. It is above the audible frequency range and below the frequency range of heat and light.

radio location:
Radio determination used for purposes other than those of radio navigation.

radiography:
1. A nondestructive testing method wherein a source of X-rays or gamma rays is utilized to indicate the subsurface condition of opaque materials.

2. A specially prepared film on which a permanent record of the soundness characteristics is generally made.

radio horizon:
The boundary beyond the natural horizon in which radio waves cannot be propagated over the earth's surface.

radio-isotope:
An unstable isotope of an element that decays or disintegrates spontaneously, emitting radiation. More than 1,300 natural and artificial radioisotopes have been identified.

Radio Magnetic Indicator (RMI):
A radio-navigation instrument coupled with a gyrosyn compass, or the like, that indicates magnetic heading and bearing with respect to a transmitting station.

radio navigation:
Radio determination used for the purposes of navigation, including obstruction warning.

radiosonde:
An automatic radio transmitter in the meteorological aids service usually carried on an aircraft, free balloon, kite or parachute, and which transmits meteorological data.

R

radio waves or hertzian waves:
Electromagnetic waves of frequencies arbitrarily lower than 3,000 GHz propagated in space without artificial guide.

radium:
A radioactive element with the atomic number 88 and an atomic weight of 226. In nature, radium is found associated with uranium, which decays to radium by a series of alpha and beta emissions. Radium is used as a radiation source.

radius:
1. The maximum distance out from its point of departure that an aircraft can fly without landing and return to its departure point under the given or specified conditions.

2. The distance from the center of a circle, or in the case of an arc, its theoretical center if it were a circle, to the outside edge. A means of measuring the curvature of a blade or leading edge.

radius bar:
The part of a cornice brake top leaf that has an accurately ground radius at its edge for bending sheet metal to obtain a specific bend radius.

rag wing:
A common slang term used to refer to a fabric-covered airplane.

RAIL:
Runway alignment indicator light system. *(FAR 1)*

RAM:
Random access memory

ram:
1. An increase in pressure in a tube duct or inlet as a result of forward speed.

2. Movable portion of a hydraulic press.

ram air intake:
Intake opening located so that the air is forced into the induction system, giving a ram effect.

ram air pressure:
Free stream air pressure, provided by the forward motion of the engine.

ram air temperature rise:
Inlet temperature rise due to inlet ram pressure rise.

ram air turbine (RAT):
A propeller driven system which is deployed from the fuselage to provide emergency power in the event of a catastrophic hydraulic or electrical system failure

ram drag:
Gross thrust minus net thrust.

ramjet:
1. A jet engine that has no internal components. Compression is due entirely to ram air pressure. Inefficient at speeds below mach 3 and cannot be started from a resting state.

2. Engine system that produces thrust by passing the hot exhaust from combustion of a fuel through a nozzle. The nozzle accelerates the flow, and the reaction to this acceleration produces thrust. To maintain the flow through the nozzle, the combustion must occur at a pressure that is higher than the pressure at the nozzle exit.

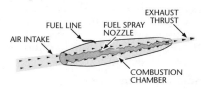

RAM JET[2]

ramp:
Area outside of airport buildings where airplanes are parked to be serviced or to pick up and discharge passengers and cargo.

ramp maintenance manual (RMM):
An abbreviated maintenance manual designed specifically for line maintenance and minor troubleshooting

ram pressure rise:
Pressure rise in the inlet due to the forward speed of the aircraft.

ramp weight:
The total weight of the aircraft while on the ramp. It differs from takeoff weight by the weight of the fuel that will be consumed in taxiing to the point of takeoff.

ram ratio:
The ratio of ram pressure to ambient pressure in a jet engine.

ram recovery:
The ability of an engine's air inlet duct to take advantage of ram pressure.

ram temperature rise:
See *ram air temperature rise*

rankine temperature scale (°R):
A temperature scale with the degree-interval of the Fahrenheit temperature scale and the zero point at absolute zero. The ice point is thus 491.69° Rankine and the boiling point of water is 671.69° Rankine.

rapid decompression:
Almost instantaneous loss of cabin pressure in aircraft with pressurized cabins.

rarefied air:
Thin air such as that found at higher altitudes.

rasp:
A type of rough file used for rough forming soft materials such as wood or plastic.

ratchet:
A mechanism consisting of a toothed wheel and pawl, which allows the wheel to turn in one direction only.

rated 2-minute OEI power:
With respect to rotorcraft turbine engines: the approved brake horsepower developed under static conditions at specified altitudes and temperatures within the operating limitations established for the engine under part 33 of the Federal Aviation Regulations, for continued one-flight operation after the failure of one engine in multi-engine rotorcraft, limited to three periods of use no longer than 2 minutes each in any one flight, and followed by mandatory inspection and prescribed maintenance action. *(FAR 1)*

rated 2 1/2-minute OEI power:
With respect to rotorcraft turbine engines: the approved brake horsepower developed under static conditions at specified altitudes and temperatures within the operating limitations established for the engine under Part 33 of the Federal Aviation Regulations, and limited in use to a period of not more than 2 1/2 minutes after the failure of one engine of a multi-engine rotorcraft. *(FAR 1)*

rated 30-minute OEI power:
With respect to rotorcraft turbine engines: the approved brake horsepower developed under static conditions at specified altitudes and temperatures within the operating limitations established for the engine under Part 33 of the Federal Aviation Regulations, and limited in use to a period of not more than 30 minutes after the failure of one engine of a multi-engine rotorcraft. *(FAR 1)*

rated 30-second OEI power:
With respect to rotorcraft turbine engines: the approved brake horsepower developed under static conditions at specified altitudes and temperatures within the operating limitations established for the engine under

R

part 33 of the Federal Aviation Regulations, for continued one-flight operation after the failure of one engine in multi-engine rotorcraft, limited to three periods of use no longer than 30 seconds each in any one flight, and followed by mandatory inspection and prescribed maintenance action. *(FAR 1)*

rated continuous OEI power:
With respect to rotorcraft turbine engines: the approved brake horsepower developed under static conditions at specified altitudes and temperatures within the operating limitations established for the engine under Part 33 of the Federal Aviation Regulations, and limited in use to the time required to complete the flight after the failure of one engine of a multi-engine rotorcraft. *(FAR 1)*

rated horsepower:
The maximum horsepower an engine is approved to produce under a given set of circumstances.

rated maximum continuous augmented thrust:
With respect to turbojet engine type certification: the approved jet thrust that is developed statically or in flight, in standard atmosphere at a specified altitude, with fluid injection or with the burning of fuel in a separate combustion chamber, within the engine operating limitations established under Part 33 of the Federal Aviation Regulations, and approved for unrestricted periods of use. *(FAR 1)*

rated maximum continuous power:
With respect to reciprocating, turbopropeller, and turboshaft engines: the approved brake horsepower that is developed statically or in flight, in standard atmosphere at a specified altitude, within the engine operating

limitations established under Part 33, and approved for unrestricted periods of use. *(FAR 1)*

rated maximum continuous thrust:
With respect to turbojet engine type certification: the approved jet thrust that is developed statically or in flight, in standard atmosphere at a specified altitude, without fluid injection and without the burning of fuel in a separate combustion chamber, within the engine operating limitations established under Part 33 of the Federal Aviation Regulations, and approved for unrestricted periods of use. *(FAR 1)*

rated takeoff augmented thrust:
With respect to turbojet engine type certification: the approved jet thrust that is developed statically under standard sea level conditions, with fluid injection or with the burning of fuel in a separate combustion chamber, within the engine operating limitations established under Part 33 of the Federal Aviation Regulations, and limited in use to periods of not over 5 minutes for takeoff operation. *(FAR 1)*

rated takeoff power:
With respect to reciprocating, turbopropeller, and turboshaft engine type certification: the approved brake horsepower that is developed statically under standard sea level conditions, within the engine operating limitations established under Part 33, and limited in use to periods of not over 5 minutes for takeoff operation. *(FAR 1)*

rated takeoff thrust:
With respect to turbojet engine type certification: the approved jet thrust that is developed statically under standard sea level conditions, without fluid injection and without the burning of fuel in a separate combustion chamber, within the engine operating

limitations established under
Part 33 of the Federal Aviation
Regulations, and limited in use to
periods of not over 5 minutes for
takeoff operation. *(FAR 1)*

rated thrust:
The manufacturer's rated
thrust, as specified on the Type
Certificate Data Sheet.

rate gyro:
A gyroscopic instrument that is
not affected by roll or pitch. A rate
gyro measures the rotation about
the vertical axis.

rate of climb indicator:
An instrument that measures
the rate at which the aircraft is
climbing or descending. Also
called the *vertical speed indicator*.

RATE OF CLIMB INDICATOR

rating:
A statement that, as a part of
a certificate, sets forth special
conditions, privileges, or
limitations. *(FAR 1)*

ratio:
The value obtained when one
number is divided by another.
This value indicates the relative
proportions of the two numbers.

ratiometer:
A type of remote indicating
system where pointer movement
is determined by the ratio
of current flow between two
resistors or portions of a special
variable resistor.

rat-tail file:
A type of long, round, tapered file.

rawhide mallet:
A soft faced mallet made from
rawhide wound into a tight
cylinder. Used in hand forming
sheet metal.

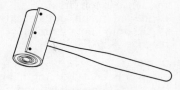

RAWHIDE MALLET

RBN:
Radio beacon. *(FAR 1)*

RC circuit:
An electrical circuit containing
both resistance and capacitance.

rc constant:
Time constant of a resistor-
capacitor circuit; equal in seconds
to the resistance value in ohms
multiplied by the capacitance
value in farads.

RCLM:
Runway centerline marking.
(FAR 1)

RCLS:
Runway centerline light system.
(FAR 1)

rc oscillator:
An oscillator in which the
frequency is determined by
resistive and capacitive elements.

reach (of a spark plug):
The length of the threaded portion
of a spark plug. For 18mm plugs,
long reach plugs are threaded for
$^{13}/_{16}$ and short reach plugs are
threaded for $^{1}/_{2}$.

reactance:
The opposition to the flow of
electricity resulting from the
presence of an inductor or
capacitor in the circuit.

reactive current:
Current in an AC circuit that is
not in phase with the voltage.

R

reactive power:
1. Kilovolt amperes reactive (KVAR).

2. The power consumed in the inductive and capacitive reactance in the circuit, expressed in volt-amps reactive (VAR) or in kilovolt-amps reactive (KVAR).

real power:
The power in an AC circuit that is the product of the voltage and the current in phase with the voltage. It equals voltage times current times power factor.

reamer:
A specially designed cutting tool used for enlarging or tapering drilled holes in preparation for an assembly with close tolerances.

REAMER

rebreather oxygen mask:
A type of oxygen mask employing a bag that allows oxygen delivered at a fixed rate to become mixed with a portion of the expired air.

rebuilt engine:
An engine that has been overhauled using new and used parts to new limits by the manufacturer or a facility approved by the manufacturer. The engine's previous operating history is expunged and it is returned to service with zero hours total time in service.

receiver sensitivity:
1. The degree to which a receiver can usefully detect a weak signal.

2. The lower limit of useful signal input to the receiver.

receiving antenna:
The device used to pick up the RF signal from space.

reciprocal (of a quantity):
The value obtained by dividing the number one by that quantity.

reciprocating engine:
An internal combustion engine, in which a piston or pistons moving back and forth work upon a crankshaft or other device to create a rotational movement.

reciprocity:
The property of interchangeability of the same antenna for transmitting and receiving.

recirculating fan:
A fan in the aircraft's cabin comfort system that circulates the air without taking in any outside air.

reclaimed oil:
Used lubricating oil that has been processed to remove impurities, restored to a useful condition and sold for reuse.

rectifier:
A device used to convert AC to pulsating DC.

rectifier bridge:
A type of rectifier utilizing four diodes arranged in a bridge circuit.

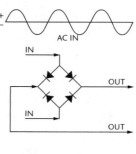

RECTIFIER BRIDGE

recurring AD:
An airworthiness directive that requires compliance at regular hourly or calendar time periods.

redline:
The mark on the instrument indicating the maximum allowable operating limit.

reducing agent:
An agent that removes the oxygen molecules from a substance.

reducing flame:
See *carburizing flame*

reduction gears:
Gear assembly between a powered shaft and another shaft by which the latter shaft is driven at lower r.p.m. than the powered shaft.

Reed and Prince screws:
A form of recessed-head, cross-point screw that is driven by a special cross-point screwdriver whose tip has a single taper. This is different from that used for Phillips head screws.

reed valve:
Thin, leaf-type valves located on the valve plate of a reciprocating type air conditioning compressor to control the inlet and outlet of the refrigerant.

reface:
To resurface an object, specifically to grind the valves on a reciprocating engine to remove evidence of wear.

reference datum:
See *datum*

reference junction:
One of two junctions in a thermocouple system that is held at a constant or stable temperature to serve as the reference for the measuring junction; the cold junction.

reference landing speed:
The speed of the airplane, in a specified landing configuration, at the point where it descends through the 50 foot height in the determination of the landing distance. *(FAR 1)*

refining:
The process by which crude oil is broken down into all of its different parts.

reflected wave:
1. The wave that reflects back from a medium.

2. The wave moving back to the source from the termination of a transmission line after reflection has occurred.

reflector:
The parasitic element of an antenna array that causes maximum energy radiation in a direction toward the driven element.

refrigerant:
The fluid used in an air conditioning system to absorb heat and carry it to where it can be transferred to the outside air.

registration certificate:
The document carried in an aircraft which contains the name and address of the person to whom the aircraft is registered.

regulator section:
In a pressure carburetor or fuel injection system: the part that consists of a fuel diaphragm that opposes the air metering force. Fuel inlet pressure is applied to one side of the fuel diaphragm and metered fuel pressure is applied to the other side. The differential pressure across the fuel diaphragm is a fuel-metering force

reid vapor pressure:
The measure of pressure exerted by a product on the interior of a special container due to its tendency to vaporize.

REIL:
Runway end identification lights. *(FAR 1)*

reinforced shell construction:
A modification of monocoque construction where the skin is reinforced by a complete framework.

R

reinforcing tape:
A narrow woven cotton or polyester tape used over the fabric to reinforce it at the stitching attachments.

rejuvenator:
A finishing material consisting of potent solvents and plasticizers, used to restore resilience to weathered and cracked dope film.

relative humidity:
The ratio of the quantity of water vapor actually present in the atmosphere to the greatest amount possible at the given temperature.

relative movement:
The movement of one object relative to another.

relative wind:
Air in motion with respect to a body in it; the velocity or direction of air in motion with respect to a body, usually of the air outside the region affected by the body (i.e., the free stream).

relay:
A type of electrically operated switch.

release fabric/film:
Is used in direct contact with the resin/adhesive or where control of resin flow is desired. Non-porous release film/fabric is often referred to as a separator, in that resin/adhesive contact can be made on one side, but it does not pass through. Porous or perforated release films/fabrics allow resin and air to pass through, yet it is easily removed from the part after the cure.

relief hole:
A hole drilled in a flat, sheet metal part at the point where two bends will intersect. The relief hole will prevent the metal from buckling.

relief tube:
An installed urinal that drains overboard. The discharge area

around these tubes is an area highly susceptible to corrosion.

relief valve:
It is installed in any system containing a confined liquid subject to pressure. Releases pressure at a preset value.

reluctance:
Opposition to magnetic flux. Reluctance is the opposite of permeability.

remanufactured:
A term often used to describe repairs made to aircraft engines and accessories but not defined by the FAA.

repairman certificate:
Documentation for personnel who do not hold a technician's certificate, but are otherwise competent in one or more specialty areas.

reporting point:
A geographical location in relation to which the position of an aircraft is reported. *(FAR 1)*

reservoir:
The tank in which a fluid is stored for an aircraft system.

residual fuel or oil:
The fuel or oil that remains trapped in the system after it has been drained by normal means. Residual fuel and oil is considered to be part of the aircraft's empty weight.

residual magnetism:
The magnetic field that remains when the magnetizing force has been reduced to zero or the magnetizing current is shut off.

residual voltage:
The voltage produced by a generator as a result of the residual magnetism in the field frame. This is the voltage that excites the generator circuit.

resin:
Any of various solid or semisolid

organic substances exuded from various plants and trees, or comparable materials prepared synthetically.

resin content:
The amount of matrix present in a composite either by percent weight or percent volume.

resin core solder:
Wire solder that has its center filled with resin.

resistance:
The opposition to the flow of an electrical current through a conductor or circuit that does not include inductive or capacitive elements. It can be expressed as the ratio of the applied voltage to the current.

resistor spark plug:
A spark plug that has a carbon resistor installed in the barrel to reduce the burning and erosion of the electrodes on engines using shielded ignition harnesses.

resolution:
The smallest unit of data that can be measured or transmitted by a given system

resonance:
1. The condition in a circuit containing inductance and capacitance in which the inductive reactance is equal and opposite to the capacitive reactance. This condition occurs at only one frequency and the circuit in that condition is said to be in resonance.

2. reinforcing and prolonging of motion by reflection or by vibration of other objects. See also *ground resonance*.

respirator:
A device worn over the nose and mouth to prevent or reduce the inhalation of dangerous substances.

restricted area:
A restricted area is airspace

designated under Part 73 within which the flight of aircraft, while not wholly prohibited, is subject to restriction. *(FAR 1)*

retard breaker points:
An auxiliary set of breaker points in a magneto equipped with the Shower of Sparks® starting system. These points are operative only during the starting cycle and open later than the run, or normal, points. This provides a late, or retarded, spark.

retarder:
A slow-drying solvent used to prevent blushing of aircraft dope or other coatings, or to provide a more glossy finish by allowing the material a longer flow-out time.

retentivity:
The ability of a material to retain magnetism after the current has been removed.

retirement schedule:
A list of components installed on an aircraft or engine that have a finite (limited) life. The list will include the name of the part, serial number, date and time installed, and retirement date or time.

retractable landing gear:
Portion of the aircraft that makes landing safely possible and is capable of being withdrawn into the aircraft so that it does not protrude or protrudes only partially.

R

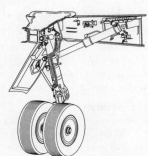

RETRACTABLE LANDING GEAR

retread:
A process by which tires may be reconditioned by the application of new treads.

retreating blade:
Any helicopter blade that is located in the semicircular part of the rotor disc where the blade direction is opposite to the direction of flight.

RETREATING BLADE

return current path:
The path through which the current in an electric cell returns to the source

return to service:
The completion of all applicable maintenance records and forms after maintenance has been performed on an aircraft that will allow the aircraft to be legally flown.

return to zero (RZ):
A self-clocking data bus format that returns to zero during the second part of each bit

reverse bias:
The arrangement of voltage polarities to a transistor or a diode that does not allow conduction.

reverse polarity:
The arrangement of direct current arc welding leads in which the work is the negative pole and the electrode is the positive pole of the welding arc.

reverse-current cutout:
A relay incorporated into the generator circuit to disconnect the generator from the battery when the battery voltage is greater than the generator voltage. This prevents the battery from attempting to motor the generator.

reverse-flow annual combustor:
A turbine engine combustor which forms an S-shaped path from the diffuser to the turbine. This design allows for a shorter engine.

reversible pitch propeller:
A propeller whose pitch may be changed to a negative angle so as to give reverse thrust, used for braking action.

revision block:
That portion of a drawing where a record of all revisions is made.

rheostat:
A variable resistor used for the purpose of adjusting the current in a circuit.

rhombic antenna:
A diamond-shaped antenna used widely for long-distance, high-frequency transmission and reception.

rib:
The structural member of a wing that gives it the desired aerodynamic shape.

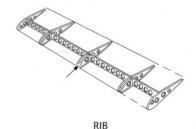

RIB

ribbon direction:
In honeycomb, the direction of the node bonds.

rib stitching:
A method used to attach fabric covering to the wing structure.

rich flameout:
A turbine engine failure that occurs because there is too much fuel for the amount of air present.

rich mixture:
A charge that contains more fuel than required.

rigid rotor:
A type of helicopter rotor system that does not permit the blades to flap or drag, only to change pitch.

rime ice:
An opaque white ice of granular structure less dense than glaze.

ring cowl:
A type of streamlined cowling that covers only the cylinders of a radial engine.

ring gear:
The central gear in planetary gearing, within which the planetary gear and sun gear rotate. The ring gear is fixed to the engine case. Also called *stationary gear*.

ring laser gyro (RLG):
A device that measures the rotation of a laser on a turntable with a phase detector to calculate yaw, pitch and roll.

ringworms:
A circular pattern of cracks in a brittle dope finish that results when a blunt object presses against the fabric.

rivet gauge:
The transverse pitch, or distance, between rows of rivets.

rivet gun:
A hand-held pneumatic device used for the installation of rivets. This is accomplished by hammering them against a heavy bucking bar.

rivet pitch:
The distance between the center of the rivet holes in adjacent rows.

rivet squeezer:
A heavy, tong-like, clamping device used to squeeze the ends of rivets to form the upset head.

rivnut:
A hollow rivet made of 6063 aluminum alloy that is counter-bored and threaded on the inside. They are manufactured in flat and countersunk head styles and in two shank designs: open and closed ends.

RIVNUT

R-NAV or RNAV:
Area Navigation (generic acronym for any device capable of aircraft guidance between pilot-defined waypoints)

rocker arm:
A lever that transmits the lifting force from the cam to the valves. It is actuated by the push rod to open the valve at the appropriate time.

rocker arm boss:
Area of a cylinder head that supports the rocker arm shaft.

rocket:
An aircraft propelled by ejected expanding gases generated in the engine from self-contained propellants and not dependent on the intake of outside substances. It includes any part which becomes separated during the operation. (*FAR 1*)

Rockwell hardness test:
A test for determining the hardness of a material based upon the depth of penetration of a specified penetrator into the specimen.

R

roll:
Motion of an aircraft about
the longitudinal axis. Roll is
controlled by the ailerons.

ROLL

roller bearings:
Straight or tapered surface that
is supported by, or supports
another surface in such a way that
it allows for freedom of motion
with little or no accumulation
of friction. Takes radial and/or
thrust loads.

roll pin:
A spring-steel pin that is press fit
into a hole.

ROM:
Read only memory.

root mean square (RMS):
The equivalent heating value of
an alternating current or voltage,
as compared to a direct current or
voltage. It is 0.707 times the peak
value of a sine wave.

roots blower:
A positive displacement air pump
that uses two intermeshing figure-
eight-shaped rotors to move the
air. Often used as a source of
cabin pressure, typically in aircraft
equipped with reciprocating
engines. Acting much like a gear
pump, it takes a predetermined
volume of air, compresses it
and then delivers it to the cabin
duct. It is also called a *positive
displacement supercharger*.

rosette weld:
A weld made through a small hole
in a piece of steel tubing to weld
the inner tube to the outer tube
and prevent relative movement.

rosin core solder:
A soft solder manufactured as a
hollow tube and filled with rosin
as a flux. During the soldering
process the rosin melts along with
the solder.

rotary radial engine:
A type of early aircraft engine
where the propeller was bolted
to the crankcase and the pistons
were attached to an offset cam
mounted on the airframe. When
the engine was running, the
cylinders, crankcase and propeller
were all spinning.

rotary wing aircraft:
See *rotorcraft*

rotating beacon:
A rotating lamp located on the top
or bottom of an aircraft to make it
more visible.

rotor brake:
A device used to stop the
rotor blades of a helicopter on
shutdown.

rotor disc:
The area within the tip plane of a
helicopter rotor.

rotorcraft:
A heavier-than-air aircraft
that depends principally for
its support in flight on the lift
generated by one or more rotors.
(FAR 1)

rotorcraft-load combination:
The combination of a rotorcraft
and an external-load, including
the external-load attaching means.
Rotorcraft-load combinations are
designated as class A, class B,
class C, and class D, as follows:

a. Class A rotorcraft-load
combination means one
in which the external load
cannot move freely, cannot be
jettisoned, and does not extend
below the landing gear.

b. Class B rotorcraft-load
combination means one in
which the external load is

jettisonable and is lifted free of land or water during the rotorcraft operation.

c. Class C rotorcraft-load combination means one in which the external load is jettisonable and remains in contact with land or water during the rotorcraft operation.

d. Class D rotorcraft-load combination means one in which the external-load is other than a class A, B, or C and has been specifically approved by the Administrator for that operation. *(FAR 1)*

route segment:
A portion of a route bounded on each end by a fix or navigation aid (NAVAID). *(FAR 1)*

roving:
A slightly twisted roll of fibers used to reinforce resins when making molded parts.

RR:
Low or medium frequency radio range station. *(FAR 1)*

rudder:
A control surface attached to the trailing edge of the vertical stabilizer and can be used to deflect the airflow to the left or right, causing the airplane to change direction.

ruddervator:
A control surface, set at a pronounced dihedral, that serves both as a rudder and as an elevator. Also called an *elerudder.*

run-in:
The period of time an aircraft engine is operated to seat the rings and other moving parts after overhaul.

runway:
A surface or area on the airport designated for airplanes to take-off and land.

runway localizer:
A radio beacon used in an instrument landing system to give lateral guidance along the final approach. The localizer transmits two signal patterns overlapping along the centerline of the runway and along the projection of the center line from both ends of the runway.

rust:
Corrosion product consisting of hydrated iron oxides; this term is applicable only to ferrous (iron-containing) alloys

rust preventive:
A preservative oil used to provide a waterproof film over iron or steel surfaces exposed to oxidation.

RVR:
Runway visual range as measured in the touchdown zone area. *(FAR 1)*

R

Ss

sacrificial corrosion:
A method of corrosion protection in which a surface is plated with a metal less noble than itself. Any corrosion will attack the plating rather than the base metal.

SAE:
Society of Automotive Engineers

SAE rating:
A rating system for oils from the Society of Automotive Engineers that divides oils into seven groups according to viscosity at either 130°F or 210°F.

safety gap:
In a magneto, the space between the electrode on the high-tension brush holder and the ground electrode. It relieves the voltage in the secondary winding of the magneto should a spark not be generated in the spark plug. The gap between the two electrodes is greater than the gap between the distributor finger and the contacts in the cap.

safety switch:
See *squat switch*

safety wire:
A wire set into a component to lock movable parts into a safe, secure position.

SAFETY WIRE

sailplane:
A high performance glider.

SALS:
Short approach light system. *(FAR 1)*

salts:
Produced by the reaction of an acid and an alkali such as sodium chloride (table salt), magnesium sulfate (epsom salt), calcium chloride, and copper sulfate.

sandbag bumping:
Sheet metal forming operation that employs a smooth faced mallet and a sandbag for free-forming and contouring of metal.

sandblasting:
A process of blowing sand through a hose using compressed air with considerable force to engrave, clean or cut an object.

sand casting:
Reproduction process that employs sand molds bonded together using either synthetic compounds or clay and water. The molds contain the shape of a part being reproduced and contain the sprues and risers to accommodate flow of molten metal. These molds have the advantage of being filled by gravity without the need for any pressure differentials or mechanical action. However, sand castings have the greatest susceptibility to defects and impurities in the resulting metal form and the molds cannot be reused.

sanding:
Use of an abrasive material to remove rough edges or severe tool marks.

sanding coat:
A coat of surfacer or heavy-bodied material which is applied and sanded off to fill small surface imperfections and thus provide a smooth surface for subsequent coats.

sandwich construction:
A bonded structure where the core of one material is bonded between two face sheets of metal or composite material.

SANDWICH CONSTRUCTION

SATCOM:
Satellite Communications

satellite:
A body which revolves around another body of preponderant mass and has a motion primarily and permanently determined by the force of attraction of that other body.

satellite eclipse:
An eclipse where the rays of the sun do not reach the satellite. This prevents recharging of the satellite's solar cells and decreases the power to the transmitter.

satellite link:
A radio link between a transmitting earth station and a receiving earth station through one satellite. A satellite link comprises one up-link and one down-link.

satellite network:
A satellite system or a part of a satellite system, consisting of only one satellite and the cooperating earth stations.

satellite sun conjunction:
A period when the satellite and sun are close together and the noise from the sun prevents or hampers communications.

satellite system:
A space system using one or more artificial earth satellites.

saturable-core reactor:
A coil in which the reactance is controlled by changing the permeability of the core.

saturation:
The condition that prevails when further increase in input signal produces no corresponding increase in output—particularly:

a. Where the input is magnetizing current and the output is the resulting flux density within a core material

b. Where further increase in anode potential produces no corresponding increase in anode current.

Saybolt universal second (SUS):
The measure of viscosity of lubricating oils. It represents the number of seconds that it takes for 60cc of oil to flow through a calibrated orifice at a specific temperature.

S-band radar:
Radar frequency range between 1,550 and 5,200 MHz.

scale:
A formation of oxide in a flaky film or in thin layers.

scalene triangle:
A triangle where all sides and angles are unequal.

scarf joint:
A joint in which the ends of the material are cut in such a way as to overlap.

SCAT:
Flexible ducting temperature-rated from −80°F to 450°F. It is made of a single ply of red-silicone rubber-impregnated fiberglass. It also has a copper-coated steel spiral inside and a fiberglass cord wrapped around the outside.

scat code:
A four-digit, subcategory code used to identify the functional measurement parameters that can be satisfied by any one of many pieces of test equipment.

scavenger pump:
A pump that drains oil from the sumps at various parts of the engine, returns it through the oil cooler, and back to the oil tank.

S

SCEET:
Flexible ducting temperature-rated from -80°F to 500°F. It is made of two plies of red silicone rubber with wire spiral between the plies and fiberglass cord around the outside.

schematic drawing:
Diagram that indicates the electrical connection and function of electrical or electronic circuits. This type of diagram aids in the tracing, function, and troubleshooting of the circuit without regard to size, shape, or physical location of the components.

Schraeder valve:
A high pressure air valve used on accumulators and struts.

scimitar blade:
A propeller design that sweeps back the blades from leading edge to trailing edge. This decreases the tip disturbances and induced drag.

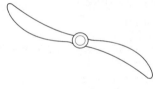

SCIMITAR BLADE

scoop:
An air inlet that projects above the immediate surface of the aircraft structure.

score:
A deep, scratch mark or line made across a piece of material.

scoring:
1. Multiple scratches, usually parallel and resulting from the same cause.

2. Marring or scratching of any formed part by metal pickup on the punch or die.

3. Reducing the thickness of a material along a line to weaken it purposely along that line.

Scramjet:
A variant of a ramjet, where combustion takes place in supersonic airflow. Ramjets decelerate the air to subsonic velocities before combustion. Airflow in a scramjet is supersonic throughout the entire engine. This allows the scramjet to efficiently operate at extremely high speeds. It is predicted that scramjets may be operations up to speeds between Mach 12 and Mach 24.

scraper:
A hardened steel hand tool used to scrape surfaces very smooth by removing minute amounts of metal.

scraper ring:
The bottom ring on a piston whose function is to scrape the lubricating oil away from the cylinder wall to prevent the oil from getting into the combustion chamber.

scratch:
A shallow mark or injury produced by abrasion.

screech liner:
A perforated liner within an afterburner, designed to combat destructive vibrations, which can cause metal fatigue and noise emissions (screech).

screen-type filter:
Compact unit that strains oil through an internal mesh area.

screw pitch gauge:
A gauge used to check the number of threads of a screw or bolt.

scribe:
A hardened steel or carbide tipped tool used to scratch lines on metal.

scrim:
A low cost reinforcing fabric made from continuous filament yarn in an open-mesh construction.

scrubbing:
Excessive abrasive wear to a piston caused by detonation.

scupper:
A recess around the filler neck of a fuel tank to collect spilled fuel and drain it overboard rather than allowing it to enter the aircraft's structure.

sea level boosting:
A reciprocating engine that has had its sea level horsepower boosted by supercharging.

sea level engine:
A reciprocating aircraft engine having a rated takeoff power that is producible only at sea level. *(FAR 1)*

seal:
Any device used to prevent the passage of a fluid (gas or liquid).

seam welding:
See also *spot welding*

1. A method of electrical resistance welding that forms a continuous line of weld instead of individual spots.

2. Welding a lengthwise seam in sheet metal either by abutting or overlapping joints.

seaplane:
An airplane that operates from water.

SEAPLANE

secondary air:
Large surplus of air that cools the hot sections of a gas turbine engine to lower temperatures.

secondary cell:
A cell that can be recharged by a current being passed through the cell in a direction opposite to the discharge current.

secondary control surfaces:
Control surfaces such as trim tabs that reduce the force required to actuate the primary control surfaces.

secondary current:
The current flowing in the secondary winding of a transformer.

secondary fuel:
In a turbine engine, the fuel that flows in a duplex nozzle at higher power settings then exits the secondary orifice. Also called the *main fuel*.

second class lever:
A simple machine with the fulcrum at one end and the effort applied at the other end. The resistance is somewhere between these two points. A wheelbarrow is an example of a second class lever.

second detector (demodulator):
The part of the receiver that separates the audio or video component from the modulated intermediate frequency.

second in command:
A pilot who is designated to be second in command of an aircraft during flight time. *(FAR 1)*

sectional drawing:
A detailed view of an object that shows the inside of the object.

sectional view:
A detail view in an aircraft drawing that shows the inside of a part. A cutting plane line is used to indicate at what point a surface is cut. The portion that is cut is indicated by the use of section lines. A viewing plane line is used to indicate what surface is being viewed and the direction from which it will be viewed.

S

section line • semi-monocoque

section line:
A section line is generally thin, and is sometimes referred to as cross-hatching. Section lines serve two purposes: they indicate the surface of an object that has been cut to make it stand out from the rest of the object; and they indicate the type of material from which the object is made.

SECTION LINES

sediment:
Foreign matter other than water that settles to the bottom of a container.

SELCAL:
Selective calling. A radio system that allows an airline operator to communicate with any of the airline's airplanes while they are in the air.

selective plating:
A process of electroplating only a section of a metal part.

selectivity:
The ability of a receiver to select the desired signal and reject unwanted signals.

selector switch:
A multi-pole switch used to connect a single conductor to several conductors.

selector valve:
A valve used to direct the flow of a fluid to a particular mechanism, as in a hydraulic system; a valve by means of which fluid is drawn from a particular tank.

self accelerating:
The ability of a turbine engine to produce enough power to accelerate.

self-induction:
1. The production of a counter-electromotive force in a conductor when its own magnetic field collapses or expands with a change in current in the conductor.
2. The phenomenon caused by the expanding and collapsing fields of an electron that encircle other electrons and retard the movement of the encircled electrons.

self-locking nut:
A nut utilizing a built in locking device to prevent the nut from loosening during service.

self-sealing fastener:
A fastener that provides a fuel tight seal without the application of sealant.

self-sealing fuel cell:
A cell designed to automatically seal itself when punctured.

self-tapping screw:
A type of wood or metal screw that cuts its own threads as it is installed.

selsyn system:
A DC-type synchro remote indicating system.

selvage:
The woven-edge portion of a fabric parallel to the warp, finished off so as to prevent the yarns from unraveling. Selvage is always cut off.

semiconductor:
A device or material that will conduct under some conditions and act as an insulator under others.

semi-duplex operation:
A method which is simplex operation on one end of the circuit and duplex operation at the other.

semi-monocoque:
1. A type of construction, as of a fuselage or nacelle, in which longitudinal members, as well as formers, reinforce the skin and help carry the stresses.
2. Something incorporating such construction, such as a wing.

212

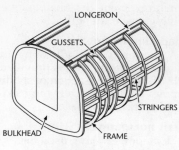

LONGERON

GUSSETS

STRINGERS

BULKHEAD

FRAME

SEMI-MONOCOQUE

semi-rigid rotor:
1. A type of helicopter rotor that allows the blades to be rotated about their feather axis. The entire rotor is free to rock back and forth about the mast.

2. A helicopter rotor system that is able to both change pitch (feather) and flap.

sensible heat:
The heat that is added to a substance that causes a change in the temperature without changing the physical condition.

sensitive altimeter:
A pneumatic altimeter where the pointer makes one complete revolution for each 1,000 feet, and has an adjustable barometric scale that can be adjusted to the existing barometric pressure.

sensitive wires:
Considered critical to flight safety and must not be modified without specific manufacturer approval

sequence valve:
An automatic valve in a fluid power system that causes operations to occur in a definite order.

serial:
Transmission of data one binary digit or bit at a time

serial interface module (SIM):
An ARINC 629 subsystem that changes the Manchester current signal from the LRU into an analog voltage doublet signal

series circuit:
An electrical circuit arrangement where electrical devices are connected so that the total current must flow through all the devices; electrons have one path to travel from the negative terminal to the positive terminal.

series motor:
An electric motor that has the field coils connected in series with the armature. Used where high torque is needed.

series-parallel circuit:
A combination of series and parallel circuits. Also called a *complex circuit.*

series wound generator or motor:
Machines in which the armature and field windings are connected in series with each other.

serviceable:
Equipment or parts that are in a condition that allows them to be returned to operational status.

service bulletins:
Information issued by the manufacturer of an aircraft, engine or component that details maintenance procedures that will enhance safety or improve performance of the product.

service ceiling:
The maximum height above mean sea level, under normal conditions, at which a given airplane is able to maintain a rate of climb of 100 feet per minute.

service life:
The expected length of time a component is expected to operate satisfactorily.

service manual:
A FAA approved manual issued by the manufacturer of an aircraft or component that describes the approved methods of servicing and repairing the aircraft or component.

S

servicing:
The filling of an aircraft with consumables such as fuel, oil, and compressed gases to predetermined levels, pressure, quantities, or weights.

servo:
A device used to convert a small movement into one of greater movement or force.

servo tab:
A tab directly actuated by the aircraft control system that, when deflected, causes the control surface or other surface to which it is attached to be deflected or moved by the air forces acting on the tab. Sometimes called a Flettner tab or flying tab.

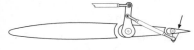

SERVO TAB

sesquiplane:
A type of biplane where the area of one of the wings (usually the lower) is less than one half of the other.

setback:
The distance from the mold point to the bend tangent line.

set screw:
A plain screw used principally for locking adjustable parts in position.

Seyboth fabric tester:
A patented, hand-operated device for testing the strength of installed aircraft fabric. This is accomplished by measuring the amount of force required to punch a hole in the fabric with the tester.

SFAR:
Special Federal aviation regulation.

s-glass:
(Silica/alumina/magnesia) Structural glass, used as fiber

reinforcement, designed to give high tensile strength.

shaded pole motor:
A low-torque AC induction motor whose rotating field is provided by the inductive action of shading poles on diametrically opposed pole pieces.

shaft horsepower (SHP):
Horsepower rating used for turboshaft engines. Determined using a dynamometer.

shear:
Stress exerted on a material that tends to slide it apart.

shear nut:
A thin nut used with clevis bolts to prevent the bolt from falling out. Shear nuts are suitable only for shear loads and must not be used with tensile load applications.

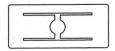

SHEAR NUT

shear pin:
A specially designed pin installed in the drive shaft of some engine-driven pumps to protect the accessory drive train in case of pump seizure. If the pump seizes, the pin will shear.

shear section:
A narrow section in the drive shaft of some engine-driven pumps. Designed to shear in case of pump seizure, the shear section will protect the engine accessory drive train from damage.

shear strength:
In materials, the stress required to produce fracture in the plane of a cross section, the conditions of loading being such that the directions of force and of resistance are parallel and opposite although their paths

are offset a specified minimum amount.

sheet holders:
Fasteners that can be quickly installed in or removed from a single side of a material that must be held tightly in place while maintaining hole alignment as holes are being drilled and fasteners installed.

sheet metal:
Metal of any thickness up to $1/8$ inch. Metal of greater thickness is considered plate.

shelf life:
The length of time a material, substance, product, or reagent can be stored under specified environmental conditions and continue to meet all applicable specification requirements and/or remain suitable for its intended function.

shielded cable:
An electrical conductor encased inside a braided metal shielding. The shielding is grounded and will intercept radiated electrical energy and conduct it to ground rather than cause radio interference.

shielded pair:
A line consisting of parallel conductors separated from each other and surrounded by a solid dielectric.

shim:
1. Very thin sheets of metal made in precise thickness and used between parts to obtain desired fits. Sometimes they are peelable laminated shims to be pulled off to the desired thickness.
2. A thin strip, usually made of metal, placed between adjacent surfaces to allow adjustment for fit. Shims are often laminated so that a closer adjustment can be secured by peeling off individual layers.

shimmy damper:
Any of various devices attached to a castering wheel to damp oscillation about the castering axis. Sometimes referred to as a *shimmy dampener*.

shock absorber:
A device built into the landing gear of an aircraft to absorb the energy of the impact of landing.

shock cord:
A strong, many-stranded rubber cord encased in a braided fabric sheath, used, e.g., as a shock absorber on certain light planes or as a launching device for gliders.

shock mounts:
A shock absorbing device used to mount engines, instruments, and other components to the airframe so that there will be a minimum amount of vibration transmitted to or from them.

shock strut:
A shock-absorbing landing gear strut.

shock wave:
A compression wave formed when a body moves through the air at a speed greater than the speed of sound.

shop head:
The second head of a rivet that is formed at the time of driving.

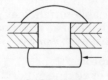

SHOP HEAD

short circuit:
An unintentional current path between two components in a circuit or between a component and ground; usually caused by a circuit malfunction.

S

short stack:
A type of reciprocating engine exhaust system that utilizes a short stack bolted directly to each cylinder exhaust port.

shot peening:
Cold working the surface of a metal by metal-shot impingement.

shoulder bolts:
A special type of bolt where the threaded portion is smaller than the shank.

show:
Unless the context otherwise requires: to show to the satisfaction of the Administrator. *(FAR 1)*

Shower of Sparks®:
A type of induction vibrator system used with some Bendix magnetos.

shrink fit:
A class of fit made when the outer member is expanded by heating to fit over a shaft, and then contracts or shrinks tightly to the shaft when cooled.

shrinking block:
A sheet metal forming tool that holds metal to prevent buckling as it is hammered during the shrinking process.

shunt:
A resistive device placed in parallel with another component. Appreciable current may flow through it and an appreciable voltage may exist across it.

shunt motor:
A type of electric motor that has the field coils connected in parallel with the armature. Used in low torque applications.

shunt resistor:
A resistor that is connected in parallel with the main circuit.

shunt wound generator or motor:
Machines in which the armature and field windings are connected in parallel (shunt) with each other.

shutoff valve:
A valve that operates fully open or fully closed.

shuttle valve:
A directional control valve on the wheel that directs hydraulic system pressure into the brake for normal action. If the system pressure is lost, the valve will direct emergency system pressure into the brake cylinders.

sight gauge:
A glass tube or window used to show the quantity of fluid in a reservoir or tank.

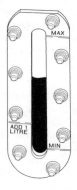

SIGHT GAUGE

sight line:
Line located at a distance equal to the radius of the brake measured outward from the bend tangent line beneath the clamping bar. This distance can most conveniently be calculated and measured from the edge of the metal.

sign status matrix (SSM):
A portion of the ARINC 429 data word provides information, which might be common to several peripherals

silicon:
A metallic element that, in its pure state, is used as a semiconductor.

silicon controlled rectifier (SCR):
A semiconductor device that functions as an electrically controlled switch.

silicone rubber:
An elastic material made from silicone elastomers. It is used with fluids which attack other natural or synthetic rubbers.

silicon, n-type:
Silicon doped by an impurity having five valence electrons.

silicon, p-type:
Silicon doped by an impurity having three valence electrons.

silver plating:
A finish used on locknuts to be used at high temperatures up to 1,400°F. It has excellent lubricating characteristics. Silver resists galling and seizing of mating parts when subjected to heat or heavy pressure.

silver solder:
An alloy of silver, copper, and nickel used for hard soldering. It produces a joint that is stronger than soft solder, but not as strong as some forms of brazing.

simple flap:
See *plain flap*

simplex fuel nozzle:
Single-orifice channels through which highly atomized and accurately shaped sprays of fuel go into the combustion chamber.

simplex operation:
Operating method in which transmission is made possible alternatively in each direction of a telecommunication channel, for example, by means of manual control.

simplified schematic:
Wiring illustration with intermediate depth and scope

sine:
In a triangle, the ratio of the length of the side opposite to the

measured angle to the length of the hypotenuse.

sine wave:
1. The curve traced by the projection on a uniform time scale of the end of a rotating arm, or vector. Also known as a *sinusoidal wave*.

2. The basic synchronous alternating waveform for all complex waveforms.

single-acting actuator:
A linear hydraulic or pneumatic actuator that uses fluid power for movement in one direction, and a spring force for its return.

single engine:
1. An aircraft with one engine.

2. A twin-engine aircraft operating with one engine failed.

single flare:
A type of flare used for rigid tubing in which the end of the tube is flared, but not doubled back over itself. See *double flare*.

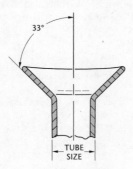

SINGLE FLARE

single-phase alternating current:
This term refers to a simple current, alternating in direction. Commercial single-phase current follows a sine wave. Such a current requires only two conductors for its circuit. Most common commercial frequencies are 50 and 60 cycles per second.

S

single-point fueling:
A method of fueling the aircraft from a single point. This is generally accomplished at one location under the wing and may involve a panel with valves and gauges to direct the fuel to the various tanks. Also called *pressure fueling.*

single-pole, double-throw switch (SPDT):
An electrical switch capable of establishing three conditions in one circuit.

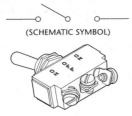

(SCHEMATIC SYMBOL)

SINGLE-POLE,
DOUBLE-THROW SWITCH

single-pole, single-throw switch (SPST):
An electrical switch capable of establishing two conditions in one circuit.

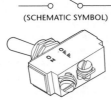

(SCHEMATIC SYMBOL)

SINGLE-POLE,
SINGLE-THROW SWITCH

single-servo brakes:
Brakes that use the momentum of the aircraft to wedge the lining against the drum and assist in braking when the aircraft is rolling forward.

single-sideband emission:
An amplitude modulated emission with one sideband only.

single wire electrical system:
Uses the airframe to distribute negative voltage

sintered metal:
See *powder metallurgy*

sitka spruce:
The standard species of wood for aircraft use.

sizing:
A generic term for compounds which are applied to yarns to bind the fibers together and stiffen the yarn to provide abrasion resistance during weaving. Starch, gelatin, oil, wax, and man-made polymers such as polyvinyl alcohol, polystyrene, polyacrylic acid, and polyacetatates are employed.

skid control generator:
The device that is mounted inside the axle, is keyed to the wheel, and senses the speed of wheel rotation. The rotation is converted into an electrical signal that is used by the anti-skid system.

ski plane:
An airplane whose wheels have been replaced with skis so that it can be operated from snow and ice.

Skydrol®:
A proprietary name for a brand of fire resistant hydraulic fluids with a phosphate ester base.

slag:
A non-metallic residue that forms on molten metal as a result of the combining of impurities.

slat:
A leading edge high lift device. Slats extend forward from the wing leading edge during slow speed flight. They help maintain proper airflow and increase lift.

SLAT

slinger ring:
A ring mounted around the hub of a propeller into which deicing fluid is directed and then slung out onto the blades to prevent the formation of ice.

slippage mark:
A mark that has been painted on to determine if relative movement has occurred. Slippage marks may be seen to identify movement between tires and wheels, or between instrument glass and the case.

slipper-type piston:
A type of piston used in older aircraft engines, whose sides are concave.

slip ring:
1. Contacts that are mounted on the shaft of a motor or generator to which the rotor windings are connected and against which the brushes ride.

2. Devices for making electric connections between stationary and rotating contacts.

slipstream:
Current of air driven back by the propeller.

sloshing sealer:
A synthetic rubber sealant poured into fuel tanks to seal the tank and prevent leaks.

slotted flap:
A flap that exposes a slot between itself and the wing when deflected, or a flap consisting of a number of slim surfaces, or slats, fastened together with slots between them.

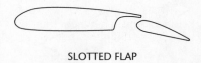

SLOTTED FLAP

slow blow fuse:
A special type of fuse designed to allow a momentary overload, but it will open when sustained excess current flows.

sludge chamber:
In a reciprocating engine, spool-shaped tubes pressed into the hollow crankpins or plugs pressed into each end of the crankpin that serve as sludge removers.

slug:
1. Forging stock for one workpiece cut to length.

2. Metal removed when punching a hole in a forging. Also called a *punchout*.

small aircraft:
Aircraft of 12,500 pounds or less, maximum certificated takeoff weight. *(FAR 1)*

smile:
The marring of aircraft skin, other than superficial, resulting from the driving of rivets. May require special rework. Also called *eyebrows*.

smoke detector:
A system that warns the flight crews of the presence of smoke in any of the protected areas aboard the aircraft. Several types of systems are currently in use.

smoking rivet:
Caused by fretting corrosion where oxygen or other corrosive agents enter in loose areas around the rivets attacking unprotected surfaces.

snap ring:
A small spring-loaded device that fits into a groove, either inside or outside of a shaft or inside a hole. Spring tension holds the ring in place.

S

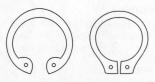

SNAP RINGS

snubber • spar

snubber:
The portion of a hydraulic actuator that arrests the motion of the piston at the end of its stroke to cushion the stopping action.

soaking:
Holding the part being heat treated at the selected temperature for a prolonged period of time to allow that temperature to become uniform throughout the part.

soapstone:
A soft mineral with a soapy feeling, and composed essentially of talc. Used to mark steel parts prior to welding.

sodium bicarbonate:
Baking soda. It is used to neutralize electrolyte spilled from lead acid batteries.

soft ground:
A connection to ground through an impedance sufficiently high to limit current flow to safe levels for personnel (normally 5 milliamperes).

soft faced hammer:
A hammer manufactured with a soft face to prevent marring machined or finished surfaces. The face may be made from plastic, brass, copper, lead or rawhide. Generally the face material is replaceable.

soft solder:
An alloy of lead and tin used to join non-structural metal parts or to increase the electrical conductivity of a twisted wire joint.

solder bridge:
Solder that spans a gap and connects another conductive pattern.

soldering:
A process of joining metallic surfaces with solder without melting of the base metals.

solenoid:
A type of electrically operated switch.

solid:
One of the three states of matter; it has definite volume and shape. Ice is the solid form of water.

solid-state device:
An electronic device that operates by the movement of electrons within a solid piece of semiconductor material.

solution heat treatment:
A heat treatment in which an alloy is heated to a sufficiently high temperature to permit many or all of the alloying elements to become randomly dispersed throughout the metal.

sonic venturi:
An inline venturi that is used as a duct pressure-limiting device in air cycle systems to control the speed and pressure of the bleed air.

space wave:
Radio waves that travel directly from the transmitter to the receiver and remain in the troposphere.

spaghetti:
Common name for the insulating rubber or plastic tubing used to cover wires.

spalling:
Cracking or flaking off of small particles of metal, usually in thin layers, from the surface.

spar:
Any principal structural member in an airfoil, running from tip to tip or root to tip.

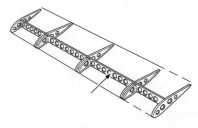

SPAR

220

spark plug, all-weather:

A shielded spark plug in which the ceramic is recessed into the shell so a resilient grommet on the harness lead can provide a watertight seal. All-weather spark plugs are easily identified by three-quarter-inch, twenty-thread-per-inch shielding.

spark plug, cold:

A spark plug in which the nose insulator provides a short path for heat to travel from the center electrode to the shell. Cold spark plugs are used in high compression engines to minimize the danger of pre-ignition.

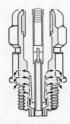

SPARK PLUG (COLD)

spark plug, fine-wire:

A spark plug using platinum or iridium electrodes. The small electrodes allow the firing end cavity to be open to provide better scavenging of lead oxides from the plug. Heat transfer characteristics of the fine wires prevent their overheating.

spark plug, hot:

A spark plug with a long nose insulator in which the heat transferring from the center electrode into the shell has a long path to travel. Hot spark plugs are used in engines which operate relatively cool, and they keep the center insulator hot enough to prevent accumulation of lead oxides.

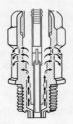

SPARK PLUG (HOT)

spark plug, massive-electrode:

Spark plugs using two, three, or four large nickel-alloy ground electrodes.

spark plug, resistor:

A composition resistor installed in the barrel of most shielded spark plugs. The resistor limits the current that is stored in the capacitive effect of the shielding and minimizes electrode erosion.

spark plug, shielded:

A spark plug completely encased in a steel shell. The radiated energy from the spark is conducted to ground through the shielding, preventing radio interference.

spark plug bushing:

A bronze or steel insert in the cast-aluminum head of a cylinder into which the spark plug is screwed.

spark test:

An old timers method of identifying various ferrous metals. The piece of metal is held against a grinding wheel and can be identified by the sparks that are thrown off. Each metal has distinct spark characteristics.

special VFR conditions:

Meteorological conditions that are less than those required for basic VFR flight in controlled airspace and in which some aircraft are permitted flight under visual flight rules. (FAR 1)

S

special VFR operations:
Aircraft operating in accordance with clearances within controlled airspace in meteorological conditions less than the basic VFR weather minima. Such operations must be requested by the pilot and approved by ATC. *(FAR 1)*

specific fuel consumption (SFC):
The amount of fuel, measured in pounds per hour, consumed or required by an engine for each horsepower or pound of thrust developed.

specific gravity:
The ratio of the weight of a given volume of a material to the same volume of pure water.

specific heat:
The ratio of the amount of heat required to raise the temperature of a body one degree, compared with the amount of heat required to raise the temperature of an equal mass of water one degree.

specific thrust:
A ratio of mass airflow and net thrust. One means of comparison between engines.

Spectrometric Oil Analysis Program (SOAP):
A system of oil analysis in which a sample is burned in an arc and the resulting light is examined for its wavelengths. This test can determine the amount of the different metals suspended in the oil, and can give an indication of an impending engine failure.

speed brakes:
A type of control system that extends from the aircraft structure into the slipstream to produce drag and slow the aircraft.

speeder spring:
The spring in a centrifugal governor used to establish the reference force. It is opposed by the centrifugal force of the spinning flyweights.

speed of light:
The speed at which light travels in a vacuum; 186,282 miles per second.

speed of sound:
The speed at which sound travels; 760 m.p.h. at sea level under standard atmospheric conditions.

spider:
That portion of a propeller assembly used to support the propeller blades.

splined shaft:
A shaft with machined groves made to accept matching ridges. Engine crank shafts are splined to accept propellers. Splines are machined to SAE standards.

split flaps:
1. A plate or surface hinged to the bottom of a wing, usually near the trailing edge, deflected downward for increased lift and drag.

2. An upper-surface aileron.

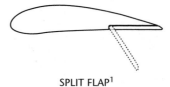

SPLIT FLAP[1]

split lock keys:
A type of split, tapered cylindrical wedges used to lock the valve spring retainers to the stem of a poppet valve in a reciprocating engine. Also called *valve keepers.*

split lockwasher:
A heavy spring steel lockwasher split at an angle across the face and twisted. The spring action of the washer provides enough friction to keep the nut from vibrating loose.

split parallel:
Power distribution systems used on some modern four-engine aircraft

spoiler:
A plate, series of plates, comb, tube, bar, or other device that projects into the air stream about a body to break up, or spoil, the smoothness of flow, especially such a device that projects from the upper surface of an airfoil, giving an increased drag and decreased lift. A projecting member on an aerodynamically designed body used to break down the airflow around the body so as to slow down its movement or decrease its lift.

spongy brakes:
A brake malfunction caused by air in the hydraulic fluid. This can generally be corrected by bleeding the brakes.

sponson:
A flange, or stub, projecting from the side of a flying boat hull to increase the beam of the hull and improve the lateral stability of the aircraft on water.

spot facing:
A drilling machine operation using the counter bore tool to smooth and square the surface of a part around a hole to allow a bolt or screw head to seat properly.

spot welding:
A type of electrical resistance welding where electrical current is passed through sheets of metal stacked together. When the metal between the electrodes melts, it joins the sheets.

spray bar:
A type of afterburner fuel nozzle that protrudes into the exhaust stream.

spray dust:
Spray dust results when a spray gun is held too far from the work, especially when a highly volatile thinner is used. It is caused when solid particles in the coating material dry while traveling from the nozzle to the surface being sprayed. Insufficient thinning or too high air pressure may also cause spray dust. Corrected by spraying at lower air pressures at distances of 6 to 8 inches from the work or by increasing the thinner content.

spreader bar:
The horizontal bar separating the floats of a twin-float seaplane.

springback:
The amount that metal springs back after being bent through a specific angle. This characteristic must be allowed for when calculating bends.

spring tab:
A tab attached to a control surface and actuated through a control linkage spring-loaded in such a manner that the tab supplies a certain amount of the force necessary to move its control surface. Its action and use are similar to those of the servo tab, but the springs incorporated in the control system work so as to make the tab supply only a part, rather than all, of the force required to move its surface.

spur and pinion gearing:
A type of reduction gearing that allows one shaft to turn slower than another shaft.

spur gear:
A gear having teeth parallel to the axis of the shaft on which it is mounted.

spurious domain (of an emission):
The frequency range beyond the out-of-band domain in which spurious emissions generally predominate.

spurious emission:
Emission on a frequency or frequencies that are outside the necessary bandwidth whose level may be reduced without affecting the corresponding transmission of information. Spurious emissions include harmonic

S

emissions, parasitic emissions, intermodulation products and frequency conversion products, but exclude out-of-band emissions.

spur planetary gearing:
A gear reduction system that has a large driving gear attached to a shaft, a large stationary gear called a bell gear and a set of small spur planetary gears mounted on a carrier ring.

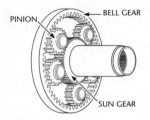

SPUR PLANETARY GEARING

squat switch:
An electrical switch mounted on the landing gear that will prevent the inadvertent retraction of the landing gear when the aircraft is on the ground. Also known as the *safety switch* or *weight-on-wheels switch*.

squeeler tip blade:
An area of reduced thickness at the tip of a turbine engine blade that is designed to wear away rather than damage the shroud if it makes contact.

squelch:
A circuit in a communications receiver that holds the output volume down until a signal is received.

squib:
A small explosive device that is electrically detonated to discharge the contents of a fire extinguisher bottle when the pilot activates the fire extinguisher switch.

SSALS:
Simplified short approach light system. *(FAR 1)*

SSALSR:
Simplified short approach light system with runway alignment indicator lights. *(FAR 1)*

stabilator:
A type of movable horizontal tail surface. It acts as a horizontal stabilizer and elevator combined. When the cockpit control is moved, the complete stabilator is moved to raise or lower the leading edge, thus changing the angle of attack and the amount of lift on the tail surfaces.

stability:
The ability of an aircraft to maintain its attitude or to resist displacement, and if displaced, to develop forces and moments tending to restore the original condition.

stabilizer:
The fixed tail surfaces.

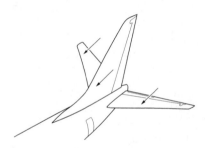

STABILIZER

stacking:
The lamination sequence in which the warp surface of one ply is laid against the fill surface of the preceding ply.

stagger:
The longitudinal relationship of the wings of a biplane. If the upper wing is forward of the lower, the stagger is said to be positive.

staggered ignition:
Dual ignition timed so that the two firing impulses do not occur at the same time.

stainless steel:
Steels that are corrosion and heat resistant and contain a minimum of 10 percent to 12 percent chromium. Other alloying elements are often present.

stall:
The reduction of airflow (speed) to the point where the airfoil stops producing lift.

stall strip:
A small triangular strip added to the root portion of the wing. It creates enough disturbance to stall the root before the tip at high angles of attack. The result is a much more gentle stall with some aileron control. If the stall strips were removed, a complete wing stalling would result.

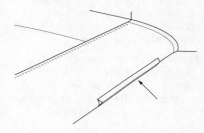

STALL STRIP

stall warning transmitter:
A device which produces a signal to warn the pilot of an impending stall.

standard atmosphere:
The atmosphere defined in U.S. Standard Atmosphere, 1962 (Geopotential altitude tables) Temperature: 59°F (15°C), pressure at sea level: 29.92 in. Hg 1013.2 milibars, 14.69 p.s.i., speed of sound: 761.6 m.p.h., 1225.35 k.p.h., 661.7 K. (FAR 1)

standard day:
Atmospheric pressure 29.92 inches of mercury 1,013.25 mb, at mean sea level altitude, and a temperature of 59°F.

standard frequency and time signal service:
A radio communication service for scientific, technical and other purposes, providing the transmission of specified frequencies, time signals, or both, of stated high precision, intended for general reception.

standard parts:
Items that are manufactured to AN (Air Force/Navy), NAS (National Aerospace Standard), or MS (Military Standard) specification. Bolts, nuts, rivets, and other standard hardware items are examples.

standard practices:
The procedures and practices normally used during aircraft maintenance, troubleshooting, and repair

standpipe:
Pipe located in a reservoir where the main hydraulic system draws its fluid.

starboard side:
Right side of an aircraft, looking forward.

starter-generator:
A unit found on turbine engines that combines the function of the starter and generator.

starter solenoid:
An electrically operated switch that uses a small amount of current to activate the high current starter circuit.

state of charge:
The condition or amount of charge in a battery.

static air temperature (SAT):
The temperature of the undisturbed air surrounding the aircraft

static charge:
A charge of static electricity.

S

225

static discharger:
A specially treated, fibrous wick attached to the trailing edge of a wing or other surface to discharge static electricity in flight. Sometimes referred to as static wick.

static electricity:
The accumulation of an electrical charge on a person or object due to friction, wind, or induction.

static pressure:
Atmospheric pressure measured at a point where there is no external disturbance and the airflow is smooth.

static system:
See *pitot-static system*

static thrust:
Thrust produced by a turbine engine that is not moving through the air.

static wick:
See *static discharger*

station:
1. The location of a point on an aircraft identified in inches from the datum.
2. One or more transmitters or receivers or a combination of transmitters and receivers, including the accessory equipment, necessary at one location for carrying on a radio communication service, or the radio astronomy service.

stationary gear:
Sometimes referred to as ring gear.

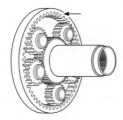

STATIONARY GEAR

stator:
The part of an assembly that remains stationary with respect to a rotating part. Stator vanes are a stationary set of airfoils in a compressor.

STC:
See *supplemental type certificate*

stealth:
Low-visibility aircraft with little or no radar signature.

steam gauge:
A term applied to any mechanical-type analog gauge used in aircraft.

steel:
An alloy of iron and carbon.

stellite:
An extremely hard and wear-resistant metal used for valve faces and stem tips. It contains cobalt, tungsten, chromium, and molybdenum.

step-down transformer:
A device used to step voltages down. There are more turns of wire in the primary winding than in the secondary winding.

stick shaker:
A device attached to the control column of larger aircraft that vibrates the column to warn of impending stall.

Stoddard solvent:
A low flash point petroleum product used for general cleaning, e.g., mineral spirits.

stoichiometric mixture:
Having the exact proportions required for complete combustion.

STOL aircraft:
Short takeoff and landing. Aircraft capable of taking off and landing in a much shorter distance than most aircraft.

stop drill:
A hole drilled at the end of a crack to prevent further growth.

stopway:
An area beyond the takeoff runway, no less wide than the runway and centered upon the extended centerline of the runway, able to support the airplane during an aborted takeoff, without causing structural damage to the airplane, and designated by the airport authorities for use in decelerating the airplane during an aborted takeoff. *(FAR 1)*

straight polarity:
The arrangement of direct current arc welding leads in which the work is the positive pole and the electrode is the negative pole of the welding arc.

strain hardening:
An increase in hardness and strength caused by plastic deformation at temperatures lower than the recrystallization range.

stranded conductor:
A conductor composed of a group of wires. The wires in a stranded conductor are usually twisted together and not insulated from each other.

stratosphere:
Atmospheric layer located between the troposphere and the ionosphere; it has little effect on radio waves.

strength-to-weight ratio:
Relationship between the strength of a material and its weight per cubic inch, expressed as a ratio. Basis for comparing the desirability of various materials for use in airframe construction and repair. Neither strength nor weight alone can be used as a means of true comparison.

stress corrosion:
Corrosion of the intergranular type that forms within metals subject to tensile stresses that tend to separate the grain boundaries.

stress relieving:
A process of reducing internal residual stresses in a metal object by heating to a suitable temperature and holding for a proper time at that temperature. This treatment may he applied to relieve stresses induced by casting, quenching, normalizing, machining, cold working, or welding.

stretching:
A sheet metal forming operation.

stringer:
A slender, lightweight, lengthwise, fill-in structural member in a fuselage, wing, nacelle, etc., serving to reinforce and give shape to the skin.

structural modal oscillations:
An undesired effect created by turbulence, which causes bending of the fuselage around the wing area

strut:
The external bracing on a wing.

STRUT

stub cable:
A 4-wire cable used to connect the TC to the current mode coupler on an ARINC 629 subsystem

stud:
A headless bolt having threads on each end. One end normally has coarse threads for screwing into a casting while the other end has fine threads to accept a nut.

sublimation:
Process by which a gas is changed to a solid or a solid to a gas without going through the liquid state.

subsonic:
Below the speed of sound.

S

227

substrate:
Layer of metal underlying a coating, regardless of whether the layer is basis metal.

substrate (of a microcircuit or integrated circuit):
The supporting material upon, or within, which the elements of a microcircuit or integrated circuit are fabricated or attached.

subtrahend:
A quantity or number to be subtracted from another.

sump jar:
A small jar in the vent line of a battery box containing a pad wet with a chemical such as bicarbonate of soda or boric acid. Fumes given off by the battery as it charges will by neutralized by this material before they are vented overboard.

superalloys:
A term broadly applied to iron-base, nickel-base, and cobalt-base alloys that are often quite complex and exhibit elevated-temperature mechanical properties and oxidation resistance.

supercharger:
An internally or externally driven air compressor used to provide additional pressure to the induction air so the engine can produce more power.

superheterodyne receiver:
A type of receiver that uses a mixer to convert the RF echo to an IF signal for amplification.

superhigh frequency:
The band of frequencies from 3 gigahertz to 30 gigahertz.

supersonic:
Speed greater than the speed of sound.

superstructure:
The framework attached to an aircraft truss structure to provide the desired aerodynamic shape. It is usually covered with lightweight sheet metal or aircraft fabric.

supplemental type certificate (STC):
A certificate authorizing an alteration to an airframe, engine, or component that has been granted a Type Certificate.

suppressed carrier single-sideband emission:
A single-sideband emission in which the carrier is virtually suppressed and not intended to be used for demodulation.

surface corrosion:
Corrosion that occurs on the surface of a metal and is characterized by a general dulling of the surface.

surface heat treatment:
See *case hardening*

surface plate:
1. An accurately machined and scraped flat metal piece (usually of cast iron) used to check the flatness of surfaces.

2. A plate with a flat surface upon which parts are assembled, laid out, and inspected. Plates today are being made of cast iron, glass, and marble. Cast iron being used to the greatest extent.

surface tape:
Strips of fabric tape used to cover seams, rib stitching, and other areas of a fabric covered aircraft.

surface tension:
1. That property, due to molecular forces, by which the surface of all liquids tends to bring the contained volume into a form having the least superficial area.

2. The property of a liquid by which the surface film of a liquid tends to form into a sphere. Surface tension affects the ability of a liquid to wet a surface.

surfactant:
Surface active agent. A substance that tends to reduce the surface tension of a liquid in which it is dissolved.

surge:
A momentary rise of pressure in a system.

surging:
A change in engine r.p.m. or engine power in an oscillating manner. This is usually caused by a malfunction in the fuel control system.

survival craft station:
A mobile station in the maritime mobile service or the aeronautical mobile service intended solely for survival purposes and located on any lifeboat, life-raft or other survival equipment.

sustaining speed:
The speed at which a turbine engine can keep itself running without having to depend on power from the starter.

swaging:
Forming a taper or a reduction on metal products such as rod and tubing by forging, squeezing or hammering.

swamping resistor:
A resistor used to increase or "broaden" the bandwidth of a circuit.

swash plate:
Rotating member, usually circular, set on a shaft and acting like a cam.

sweat solder:
A method of soldering where both pieces are tinned with solder, put together, and the joint is heated.

sweptback wing:
A backward slant from root to tip (or inboard end to outboard end) of an airfoil, or of the leading edge or other reference line of an airfoil. Sweepback usually refers to a design in which both the

leading and trailing edges of the airfoil have a backward slant.

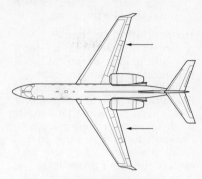

SWEPTBACK WING

swept forward wing:
A forward slant from root to tip (or inboard end to outboard end) of an airfoil, or of the leading edge or other reference line of an airfoil.

swirl vanes:
Air circulation vanes that surround the fuel nozzles in a turbine engine to aid in ignition and combustion.

symmetrical:
The condition where both halves of an object are the same.

symmetrical laminate:
A composite laminate in which the sequence of plies below the laminate midplane is a mirror image of the stacking sequence above the midplane.

synchronization gap (SG):
A time period common to all transmitters on the ARINC 629 data bus.

synchronous motor:
1. An AC motor whose rotor is activated by DC. It is characterized by constant speed and requires squirrel-cage windings or some other method to be self-starting.

2. Maintaining an operational relationship between the

S

designated master propeller and the slave propellers that causes their angle and rate of rotation to be the same.

synchrophasing system:
A propeller system that is used on multi-engine aircraft to synchronize phasing of each propeller. The engines all turn at the same r.p.m. and the propellers rotate in such a way that a master blade on each propeller keeps the same relative position in its rotation as the master blade on each of the other propellers.

synthetic fibers:
Man-made fibers as opposed to natural fibers.

synthetic oil:
Lubricating oil with a synthetic base rather than a petroleum base. It is extensively used in turbine engines.

synthetic vision:
A computer-generated image of the external scene topography from the perspective of the flight deck that is derived from aircraft attitude, high-precision navigation solution, and database of terrain, obstacles and relevant cultural features. *(FAR 1)*

synthetic vision system:
An electronic means to display a synthetic vision image of the external scene topography to the flight crew.

SYNCHROPHASING SYSTEM

Tt

tab:

An auxiliary airfoil or similarly shaped surface attached to a control surface.

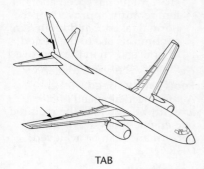

TAB

TACAN:

Ultra-high frequency tactical air navigational aid. *(FAR 1)*

tachometer:

An instrument that indicates, usually in revolutions per minute, the rotational speed of an engine, of a helicopter rotor, etc.

tachometer generator:

1. A small AC or DC generator, sometimes referred to as a rate generator, that converts its shaft speed into an electrical output. The tachometer is frequently used in servo systems to sense the velocity of a load.

2. An instrument that measures the rate at which a shaft is turning.

tack:

Stickiness of an adhesive or filament reinforced resin prepreg material.

tack coat:

A very light coat of material sprayed on a surface and allowed to stay until the solvents evaporate; it is then covered with the full, wet coat of material.

tack rag:

1. A rag, slightly damp with thinner, used to wipe a surface after it has been sanded to prepare it for the application of the next coat of finish.

2. Commercially available cloth that is coated with a wax and used before painting to pick up any dust on the surface.

tack weld:

A weld made to hold parts of a weldment in proper alignment until the final welds are made.

tacky:

A sticky or gluey surface.

tagout:

Specific practices and procedures to safeguard employees from the unexpected startup of machinery and equipment during service or maintenance activities.

tail boom:

An outrigger or spar connecting the tail surfaces to a pod-type fuselage.

tail cone:

The rearmost part of an aircraft fuselage.

TAIL CONE

tail dragger:

See *conventional gear*

tail pipe:

That portion of a turbine engine exhaust system through which the gases leave the aircraft.

tail rotor • tandem rotor system

tail rotor:
On some rotary-wing aircraft, a rotor, usually an anti-torque rotor, located at the tail used to provide directional control.

tail section:
The part of the airplane to which the rudder and elevators are attached. The tail has vertical and horizontal stabilizers to keep the airplane from turning about its lateral axis. Also called *empennage*.

tail skid:
1. A skid that was the forerunner of the tail wheel and supported the tail of the aircraft during ground operations.
2. A reinforcement designed to absorb the shock of the tail striking the ground on takeoff, used on some modern jet aircraft.

tail wheel:
The auxiliary wheel located at the rear of the fuselage on aircraft having a conventional landing gear arrangement. It is used for support and steering when the aircraft is on the ground.

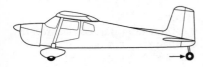

TAIL WHEEL

takeoff:
The part of the flight during which the airplane gains flying speed and becomes airborne.

takeoff power:
1. With respect to reciprocating engines, means the brake horsepower that is developed under standard sea level conditions, and under the maximum conditions of crankshaft rotational speed and engine manifold pressure approved for the normal takeoff, and limited in

continuous use to the period of time shown in the approved engine specification.
2. With respect to turbine engines: the brake horsepower that is developed under static conditions at a specified altitude and atmospheric temperature, and under the maximum conditions of rotor shaft rotational speed and gas temperature approved for the normal takeoff, and limited in continuous use to the period of time shown in the approved engine specification. *(FAR 1)*

takeoff safety speed:
A referenced airspeed obtained after lift-off at which the required one-engine-inoperative climb performance can be achieved. *(FAR 1)*

takeoff thrust:
With respect to turbine engines: the jet thrust that is developed under static conditions at a specific altitude and atmospheric temperature under the maximum conditions of shaft rotational speed and gas temperature approved for the normal takeoff, and limited in continuous use to the period of time shown in the approved engine specification. *(FAR 1)*

takeoff weight:
The weight of the aircraft at takeoff.

tandem rotor system:
A helicopter using two main rotors located in a fore and aft arrangement, turning in such a direction that they will cancel the torque of each other.

TANDEM ROTOR SYSTEM

tandem wing configuration:
A configuration having two wings of similar span mounted in tandem. *(FAR 1)*

tang:
The part of a file that fits into a handle.

tangent:
Making contact at a single point or along a line; touching but not intersecting.

tank circuit:
1. A parallel-resonant circuit.
2. Tuned circuit used to temporarily store energy.

tap:
A tool used to cut threads on the inside of a round hole.

tap drill:
The size of twist drill used to drill the hole before threads are cut using a tap. Charts are available that will show the proper size tap drill to be used for each size of tapped hole.

taper:
1. A uniform increase or decrease in the size or diameter.
2. A gradual reduction in either the chord length or thickness of an airfoil, blade, or the like, especially such a reduction from root to tip. The term usually refers to chord length unless otherwise indicated.

tapered crankshaft:
A crankshaft where the propeller is mounted by fitting it to a tapered end rather than a flange or spline.

tapered punch:
A hand punch that is tapered over its length and is often used to align parts for the installation of bolts or screws.

tapered roller bearing:
A bearing in which the inner- and outer-race bearing surfaces are cone shaped. Such bearings will withstand both radial and thrust loads.

taper pin:
Hardware used in movable joints that carry shear loads and where the absence of clearance space between members is essential.

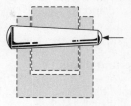

TAPER PIN

taper reamer:
A special type of reamer to accurately cut the sides of a tapered hole.

taper sand:
A sanding process to produce a uniform taper in a skin for the production of a scarf joint. See also *scarf joint*.

tapped hole:
A hole that has internal threads to receive a screw, bolt, or stud.

tapped resistor:
A wire-wound, fixed resistor having one or more additional terminals along its length, generally for voltage-divider applications.

tappet:
The part of the reciprocating engine valve train that rides on the face of the cam and transmits a reciprocating motion to the pushrods. This motion is then transferred to the rockers and opens and closes the valves. Also may be referred to as lifters or lifter bodies depending on other design criteria.

tare weight:
The weight of all extra items on a weighing scale platform that are not a part of the item being

weighed, such as jacks, blocks, and chocks. The weight of these items, when included in the scale reading, is deducted to obtain the actual weight of the aircraft.

tarmac:
A hard surfaced area of an airport used for aircraft parking, tie-down, and servicing.

TAS:
True airspeed. *(FAR 1)*

tautening dope:
Any of several types of aircraft dopes that when applied to the fabric produce tautness by shrinkage. This type of dope is required if the fabric in not tautened by other means, such as heat.

taxi:
To move an aircraft on the ground under its own power.

taxi light:
Lighting designed to provide illumination on the ground while taxiing or towing the aircraft to or from a runway, taxi strip, or in the hangar area. Often mounted on the non-steerable part of the nose landing gear and also mounted in the recessed areas of the wing leading edge, often in the same area with a fixed landing light.

TBO:
Time between overhauls.

TCAS:
A traffic alert and collision avoidance system. *(FAR 1)*

TCAS I:
A TCAS that utilizes interrogations of, and replies from, airborne radar beacon transponders and provides traffic advisories to the pilot. *(FAR 1)*

TCAS II:
A TCAS that utilizes interrogations of, and replies from airborne radar beacon transponders and provides

traffic advisories and resolution advisories in the vertical plane. *(FAR 1)*

TCAS III:
A TCAS that utilizes interrogation of, and replies from, airborne radar beacon transponders and provides traffic advisories and resolution advisories in the vertical and horizontal planes to the pilot. *(FAR 1)*

TDZL:
Touchdown zone lights. *(FAR 1)*

technical standard order (TSO):
An FAA approval covering the manufacture of a component for installation on a type-certificated aircraft.

tee fitting:
A plumbing fitting in the shape of the letter T.

TEE FITTING

Teflon®:
A proprietary name for a fluorocarbon resin used to make hydraulic and pneumatic seals and backup rings.

telephony:
A form of telecommunication primarily intended for the exchange of information in the form of speech.

TEMAC:
Trailing edge of mean aerodynamic chord.

temperature coefficient of resistance:
The rate of change in resistance per degree centigrade of temperature change.

tempering:
A heat-treating process used to relieve the stresses produced by hardening and to impart certain qualities, such as toughness. Sometimes called drawing.

template:
A guide, gauge, or pattern for checking dimensions or locations.

tensile load:
An external force tending to lengthen or stretch an object.

tensile strength:
The property of a metal which resists force applied to pull it apart.

tensiometer:
A tool used for measuring cable tension.

tension regulator:
Device installed in an aircraft control system to maintain a constant cable tension, regardless of changes in temperature.

terminal:
An electrical connection.

terminal controller (TC):
An ARINC 629 subsystem that moves data to and from the LRU memory.

terminal gap (TG):
Period unique for each transmitter connected to the ARINC 629 data bus.

terminal strip:
An insulating base or slab equipped with terminals for connecting wiring. Also called a *terminal board*.

terne plate:
Thin sheets of steel that have been coated with lead for corrosion control.

test cell:
A facility that contains both a control room and an engine room used for testing engines. Test cells are often fixed structures made of concrete or other durable materials.

test club:
See *club propeller*

tetraethyl lead (Pb(C$_2$H$_5$)$_4$):
A heavy, oily, poisonous liquid mixed into aviation gasoline to increase its critical pressure and temperature.

tetrode:
A vacuum tube having four active electrodes.

TGT:
Total gas temperature.

T-handle:
A T-shaped handle used for turning sockets.

theoretical pitch:
Same as the geometric pitch of propellers.

thermal:
Of or pertaining to heat or temperature.

thermal anti-icing system:
An aircraft surface heated to prevent the formation of ice. This is usually limited to the leading edges of wings and tail surfaces and the inlets to turbine engines.

thermal circuit breaker:
A circuit breaker using contacts mounted on a bimetallic strip that opens when an excessive amount of current flows through it causing heating.

thermal coefficient of resistance:
The amount of change in electrical resistance of a material with a change in temperature.

thermal conductivity:
The ability of a material to conduct heat. The time rate of flow of heat through a unit area normal to the temperature gradient per unit of temperature difference.

T

thermal cutout switch:
A type of switch that opens at a pre-determined temperature.

thermal decomposition:
A chemical action where the material is decomposed into a simpler substance by the action of heat.

thermal efficiency:
The ratio of the brake horsepower produced by the engine to the horsepower available in the fuel being burned.

thermal expansion:
Expansion caused by increase in temperature; may be linear or volumetric.

thermal fatigue:
Fracture resulting from the presence of temperature gradients that vary with time in such a manner as to produce cyclic stresses in a structure.

thermal insulator:
Materials that are poor conductors of heat.

thermal-magnetic trip element:
A single circuit breaker trip element that combines the action of a thermal and a magnetic trip element.

thermal relief valve:
A type of pressure relief valve installed in some hydraulic systems to prevent excessive pressure buildup due to thermal expansion of the fluid.

thermal runaway:
A condition in nickel-cadmium batteries that occurs when the cell resistances become unbalanced and allow some cells to take more current, which reduces their resistance further. This action can continue until serious damage or explosion occurs. Also called *vicious cycling*.

thermal shock:
The development of a steep temperature gradient and

accompanying high stresses within a structure.

thermal shunt:
See *hint sink*

thermal stress:
Stresses in metal resulting from non-uniform distribution of heat.

thermistor:
A semiconductor device whose resistance varies with temperature.

thermocouple:
A device composed of two pieces of dissimilar metal joined where heat is to be applied (the hot junction) and connected to an electrical measuring instrument (the cold junction). The application of heat will cause a measurable electrical current to flow in the circuit.

thermometer:
A device for measuring temperature or degrees of heat or cold; may depend upon the expansion of mercury or liquids or change in electrical conductivity.

thermoplastic:
Capable of being repeatedly softened by an increase of temperature and hardened by a decrease in temperature.

thermoplastic resin:
A plastic that repeatedly can be softened by heating and hardened by cooling through a temperature range characteristic of the plastic, and when in the softened stage, can be shaped by molding or extrusion.

thermosafety discharge indicator:
The red blowout disc located on the outside of the aircraft fuselage or engine nacelle that indicates if the fire detection system has been discharged due to overpressure resulting from excessive heat.

thermoset:
A plastic that changes into a

substantially infusible and insoluble material when cured by application of heat or chemical means. Once cured, a thermoset cannot be returned to the uncured state.

thermosetting resin:
Any type of resin that sets by chemical means and cannot be reheated and reformed.

thermostatic bypass valve:
A temperature sensing valve in an engine oil cooler that is used to direct oil around or through the cooler to maintain proper oil temperature.

thermoswitch fire detector:
A type of fire detector switch that closes at a pre-set temperature to activate the fire warning light.

thickness gauge:
See *feeler gauge*

thinner:
A solvent mixed with dope or paint to reduce its viscosity.

third-class lever:
A type of simple machine where the effort is applied between the fulcrum and the resistance. The human arm is an example of a third class lever.

thixotropic agent:
A substance added to a resin to increase its resistance to flow. See *microballoons*.

thread:
1. A helical projection of uniform section on the internal or external surface of a cylinder or cone.

2. The operation of cutting a screw thread.

thread chaser:
A tool used to remove contamination from a threaded device.

thread insert:
Any of a number of types of devices that are inserted into soft or brittle materials to provide

greater strength and minimize wear.

THREAD INSERT

thread pitch:
The distance from a point on one screw thread to a corresponding point on the next thread.

thread plug gauge:
A type of go/no go gauge used for checking threads.

three-phase system:
Electricity transmitted as three single phase currents, that is, three separate currents following separate sine curves, each at 60 cycles (or other frequency) per second, but with the peaks of their individual curves one-third of a cycle apart. At least three (sometimes four) conductors are required for three-phase alternating current.

three-view drawing:
A type of drawing generated by orthographic projection that uses three views to portray an object.

throatless shear:
A heavy duty, bench-mounted shear used for cutting large sheets of metal.

throttle:
The valve in a fuel metering device that determines the amount of the fuel-air mixture that is fed into the engine.

throttle ice:
Ice formed at, or near, the throttle of an engine from freezing of water vapor in the air that has undergone an expansion.

thrust:
Reaction force typically measured in pounds.

thrust, gross:
The thrust developed by the engine, not taking into consideration any presence of initial airmass momentum.

thrust, net:
The effective thrust developed by the engine during flight, taking into consideration the initial momentum of the air mass prior to entering the influence of the engine.

thrust, static:
Same as gross thrust without any initial airmass momentum present due to the engine's static condition.

thrust bearing:
The bearing in a reciprocating engine that absorbs propeller thrust loads.

thrust bending force:
The force on a propeller blade that bends it forward during takeoff and at high thrust settings.

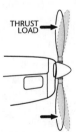

THRUST BENDING FORCE

thrust horsepower:
The amount of horsepower that the engine-propeller combination transforms into thrust.

thrust line:
An imaginary line passing through the center of the propeller hub, perpendicular to the plane of propeller rotation.

thrust loads:
Loads imposed on the crankshaft and bearings by the propeller pulling or pushing the aircraft.

thrust reverser:
A mechanical device installed in or behind the tail pipe of a turbine engine to deflect the exhaust gases forward. This is normally used to shorten the landing roll.

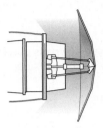

HOT STREAM-TYPE THRUST REVERSER

thrust specific fuel consumption:
The fuel that the engine must burn per hour to generate 1 pound of thrust.

thrust-weight ratio:
A ratio used to describe engine performance. It is calculated by dividing the engine's thrust output by the engine weight without fuel.

thumb nut:
A round nut, the outside circumference of which is knurled to provide a firm grip.

tie wrap:
See *ty-rap*

tiltrotor:
A hybrid aircraft with characteristics of both an airplane and a rotorcraft. It utilizes a rotating drivetrain configuration that uses rotors to provide lift for takeoff and then rotate 90°, converting the vertical lift rotors to forward thrust rotors. The drivetrain then rotates back to vertical for landing. The tiltrotor is equipped with wings to provide lift during forward flight.

time between overhauls (TBO):
A recommendation of the manufacturer of an aircraft engine

or accessory as to the amount of time that the engine or accessory can operate under average conditions before it should be overhauled.

time change item:
Any component that must be replaced after a specific time in service.

time in service:
With respect to maintenance time records, means the time from the moment an aircraft leaves the surface of the earth until it touches it at the next point of landing. *(FAR 1)*

timing disc:
A device mounted on the propeller or accessory drive to indicate degrees of crankshaft rotation. It is used for magneto or valve timing.

timing lights:
Used to help determine the exact instant that the magneto points open. There are two general types of timing lights in common use. Both have two lights and three external wire connections. Although both have internal circuits that are different, their function is much the same. Technicians should be very careful as one type indicates lights-on when the points open, the other indicates lights-off when the points open.

timing tolerance fault:
Occurs when the rise or fall of a digital signal responds too slowly to be within specifications of the data bus standard

Time-Rite indicator:
A brand of piston position indicator used for magneto and valve timing of reciprocating engines.

tinning:
Coating of a surface with a thin uniform layer of solder.

tin snips:
Common term for hand operated metal shears.

tip cap:
A removable cap on a helicopter rotor blade used to hold balance weights.

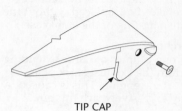

TIP CAP

tip fin:
See *winglet*

tip pocket:
See *tip cap*

tip speed:
The speed of the outermost part of a rotating airfoil.

toe-in:
Aircraft wheels that tend to converge at the front. Toe-in will cause excessive wear on the inside of the tire.

tolerance:
The difference between the minimum and maximum allowable dimension for a part. The sum of the + and – values shown on the drawing.

toluol:
A commercial grade of toluene, which is a liquid aromatic hydrocarbon similar to benzene but less volatile, toxic, and flammable.

tool steel:
A general classification for high-carbon steel that can be heat treated to a hardness required for metal cutting tools, such as punches, dies, drills, taps, reamers, and so forth.

T

top dead center (TDC):
The position of the piston when it has reached its uppermost limit of travel.

top overhaul:
On a reciprocating engine, to repair or replace to serviceable limits, those parts that can be repaired or replaced without the dismantling of the crankcase.

torching:
Long plumes of flame extending from the exhaust stack of a turbine engine. This is caused by an excessively rich mixture.

toroidal wound coil:
A electrical coil wound around a ring or doughnut-shaped core.

torque:
A force that produces, or tends to produce, rotation.

torque bending force:
The result of torque on the propeller blade that tends to bend it in the opposite direction of rotation.

TORQUE BENDING FORCE

torque limited:
A limitation placed on the drive train of a helicopter with regards to the power input.

torque links:
The hinged linkage between the piston and cylinder of an oleo strut. The piston is free to move in and out, but it is not able to rotate. Also called *scissors* or *nutcrackers*.

torquemeter:
1. A hydromechanical torque measuring device usually located in the reduction gear section of the engine. The measurement is read as torque foot pounds or percent of torque.

2. An indicator used on some large reciprocating or turboprop engines to indicate the amount of torque the engine is producing.

torque multiplier:
A tool used to multiply a torque force beyond what is found with conventional torque wrenches. Often used to torque the retaining nut(s) on a helicopter main rotor.

torque nose:
Mechanism in the nose section of an engine that senses engine torque and operates the torquemeter.

torque tube:
Tubular member of an aircraft control system used to transmit torsional movement to the control.

torque wrench:
A calibrated hand tool used to measure the amount of torque applied to a bolt or nut.

torsion:
An external stress that produces twisting within a body.

total gas temperature (TGT):
Measured gas temperature at a specific plane at the inlet to first stage stators, or between first stage stators and the rotor. EGT is the more common location.

toughness:
Ability of a metal to absorb energy and deform plastically before fracturing. It is usually measured by the energy absorbed in a notch impact test, but the area under the stress-strain curve in tensile testing is also a measure of toughness.

toxic:
Harmful, destructive, deadly, poisonous.

trace:
An amount large enough to be detected but not to be measured.

tracer:
A fiber, tow, or yarn added to a prepreg for verifying fiber alignment and for distinguishing warp fibers from fill fibers.

track:
The path followed by the tip of a propeller or rotor blade as it rotates.

TRACON:
Terminal Radar Approach Control Facility.

tractor propeller:
Propeller mounted on the front of the drive shaft of a conventional airplane.

Traffic Alert and Collision Avoidance System (TCAS):
Traffic Alert and Collision Avoidance System is an instrument integrated into other systems in an aircraft cockpit. It is an onboard system of hardware and software that together provide a set of electronic eyes so the pilot can "see" the traffic situation in the vicinity of the aircraft. Information comes from the Air Traffic Control Radar Beacon System (ATCRBS) transponder, or from an ATC Mode S transponder.

traffic pattern:
The traffic flow that is prescribed for aircraft landing at, taxiing on, or taking off from, an airport. *(FAR 1)*

trailing edge:
Edge of an airfoil over which the airflow passes last.

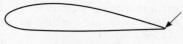

TRAILING EDGE

trailing edge flap:
Sections of the trailing edge of a wing that may be bent down or extended in flight to increase the camber of the airfoil.

tram:
See *trammel*

trammel:
The process used to square up the trusses in a wing.

trammel points:
Locations along the spar of a truss-type wing that are used to verify correct alignment of the structure prior to reapplying the fabric covering. This process is accomplished using a tool called a trammel.

trammels:
A form of dividers consisting of a beam upon which the legs can be adjusted and clamped. Used for work beyond the range of regular dividers.

transducer:
1. An electro-acoustical device for converting electrical energy into acoustical energy and vice versa.

2. An electrical device that either takes electrical energy and changes it into mechanical movement or mechanical movement and changes it into electrical energy.

3. Any device that is capable of converting energy from one form to another.

4. Device actuated by power from one system and supplying power to a second system.

transfer gearbox:
A gearbox driven from the main rotor shaft, which, in turn, drives the accessory gearbox.

transfer punch:
A special type of punch sold in sets with specific outside diameters. When inserted in a

T

hole of that diameter, they are able to mark the exact center of the hole on the new piece below the existing hole.

transformer:
A device composed of two or more coils linked by magnetic lines of force and used to transfer energy from one circuit to another.

transformer rectifier (TR):
A device to change AC to DC as well as changing the voltage.

transient:
A sudden signal change of short duration characterized by a steep wavefront that, when plotted against time, would appear markedly different from the waveforms immediately preceding and following it. Step-function is the term properly used in connection with establishing ratings.

transient conditions:
Conditions that may occur briefly while accelerating or decelerating or while passing through a specific range of engine operation.

transient currents:
These currents are of short duration, generated by sudden changes in the electrical or magnetic conditions existing in an electrical or magnetic circuit.

transistor:
A semiconductor device with three or more elements.

transistor voltage regulator:
A voltage regulator that uses a transistor to control the flow of field current, but uses vibrating points to sense the voltage and control the transistor.

transistorized voltage regulator:
A type of voltage regulator that uses a transistor to control the field current. A zener diode senses the voltage to be controlled.

translational lift:
Lift force exerted on the rotor

blades of a helicopter when increased speed is imparted to the blades or when their angle of attack is changed going from one type of flight to another, such as from hovering to forward flight.

translucent:
Capable of transmitting light but with sufficient distortion to prevent the perception of distinct images. A window that is fogged over is an example.

transmissive display:
LCD containing a dedicated light source mounted to the rear of the display.

transmit interval (TI):
A common period for all transmitters on the ARINC 629 data bus.

transmitter:
Equipment that generates and amplifies an RF carrier, modulates the RF carrier with intelligence, and radiates the signal into space.

transonic airplane:
An airplane designed to fly within the range of transonic speeds. The limits are variously set from as low as 550 miles per hour to as high as 900 miles per hour.

transonic flight:
Aircraft flying at approximately the speed of sound.

transpiration cooling:
A method of cooling blades and vanes in turbine engines by passing air through their porous walls from the inside to the outside.

transponder:
A radar beacon consisting principally of an antenna, receiver, and transmitter that emits signals only when triggered by the pulses of an interrogating radar set.

transport category aircraft:
Aircraft built and certified under 14 CFR Part 25.

transverse:
Situated or lying across; crosswise.

transverse pitch:
See *rivet gauge*

transverse wave:
A wave in which particle motion is perpendicular to the direction of propagation.

trapezoid:
A plane, four-sided geometric figure having only two sides parallel.

triac:
A three-terminal device that is similar to two silicone-controlled rectifiers back-to-back with a common gate and common terminals. Although similar in construction and operation to the SCR, the triac controls and conducts current flow during both alternations of an AC cycle.

trickle charging:
A constant current charging method that uses only a small amount of current.

tricycle landing gear:
The airplane's landing wheels arranged with two under the wings and one under the nose.

TRICYCLE LANDING GEAR

trigger pulse:
In radar, pulses that are used to initiate specific events.

trigonometry:
Deals with relationships that exist between the lengths of the three sides and the three angles of a triangle. While trigonometry can become very complex, for the purposes of the aircraft technician, the primary concern is with right triangles.

tri-jet:
An aircraft propelled by three jet engines.

trim tab:
A tab that is deflected to a position where it remains to keep the aircraft in the desired trim.

trimotor:
An airplane with three engines.

triode:
A three-electrode electron tube containing a plate, a cathode, and a control grid.

trip-free circuit breaker:
A circuit protection device which will open the circuit when a current overload exists, regardless of the position of the control handle.

triplane:
An airplane having three main supporting structures (e.g., wings).

TRIPLANE

trivalent impurity:
An impurity that, when added to a semiconductor, accepts one electron from a neighboring atom and creates a hole in the lattice structure of the crystal.

tropopause:
A location in the atmosphere that lies above the troposphere and below the stratosphere.

troposphere:
The lowest layer of the earth's atmosphere where most weather occurs.

troubleshooting:
The process of locating and diagnosing faults in equipment by means of systematic checking or analysis.

troubleshooting manual (TSM):
Designed specifically for system troubleshooting

true airspeed (TAS):
1. The speed at which an aircraft is moving relative to the surrounding air.

2. The airspeed of an aircraft relative to undisturbed air. True airspeed (TAS) is equal to equivalent airspeed (EAS) multiplied by $(\rho O/\rho)^{1/2}$. *(FAR 1)*

true air temperature (TAT):
A measure of the air temperature as it is compressed by the moving aircraft.

true altitude:
The actual height of an object above mean sea level.

true power:
The actual power that exists in an AC circuit. The product of the voltage, current, and power factor.

truss fuselage:
An aircraft fuselage constructed in such a manner that all members of the truss can carry both tension and compression loads.

truth table:
A table listing all possible combinations of inputs and the corresponding output of a Boolean function such as AND, OR, NOT, IMPLIES, XOR, NANS, NOR. Truth tables can be used as a means of representing a function or as an aid in designing a circuit to implement it.

TSO:
Technical standard order.

tubing:
A rigid hollow piece of metal through which wiring or fluids may pass.

tuned circuit:
1. A circuit consisting of inductance and capacitance that can be adjusted for resonance at a desired frequency.

2. A circuit that is used as a filter that passes or rejects specific frequencies.

3. An LC circuit used as a frequency-determining device.

tungsten inert gas welding (TIG):
See *gas tungsten arc welding (GTAW)*

tungsten steel:
A type of steel that includes tungsten in the alloy mixture. It is used in the manufacture of cutting tools because of its hardness.

tunnel diode:
A heavily doped semiconductor device that has high gain and fast switching capabilities.

turbine:
A rotary device actuated by impulse or reaction of a fluid flowing through the vanes or blades arranged around a central shaft.

turbine bucket:
A common term for the blades on a turbine wheel.

turbine disc:
The metal disc to which the turbine blades are attached.

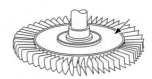

TURBINE DISC

turbine discharge pressure:
The total pressure at the discharge of the low-pressure turbine in a dual turbine axial flow engine.

turbine engine:
An engine in which a vaned wheel is made to turn by the force of vapor. See also *gas turbine engine.*

turbine inlet guide vanes:
The guide vanes in the turbine section of the engine that prepare hot gases for the next stage of turbine blades.

turbine inlet temperature (TIT):
Temperature taken in front of the first stage turbine nozzle vanes. This is the most critical temperature.

turbine nozzle:
Stationary nozzle that discharges a jet of gas against the blades on the periphery of a turbine wheel.

turbo:
1. Short for turbocharger.
2. Short for turbine or related to a turbine.

turbocharger:
An external super-charger driven by exhaust gases. It is used to increase the pressure of the air going into the engine.

turbocompound engine:
A radial engine that uses a series of power recovery turbines to extract additional horsepower from the exhaust gases. The power recover turbines extract energy from the exhaust and transfer it back to the crankshaft through a series of gears and fluid drive couplings.

turbofan engine:
A gas turbine core engine that directs part of its compressor air through the engine core. The forward compressor fans direct part of their airflow around the turbine core, thereby providing direct thrust. This bypass air can provide up to 75 percent of the total engine thrust.

turbojet engine:
A turbine engine that produces its thrust entirely by accelerating air through the engine.

turboprop engine:
A turbine engine that drives a propeller through a reduction gearing arrangement.

turboshaft engine:
A turbine engine that is geared to an output shaft. It is usually found in rotorcraft and ground power equipment.

turbosupercharger:
A supercharger incorporating a turbine driven by exhaust gases from the engine to rotate the impeller. Another name for turbocharger.

turbulent flow:
Flow of fluid in an unsteady state.

turn and slip indicator:
A flight instrument that combines a bank indicator and a turn indicator in the same housing. Also called a *turn-and-bank indicator*.

turnbuckle:
A mechanical screw device consisting of two threaded terminals and a threaded barrel. One terminal has right-hand threads and the other has left-hand threads. The barrel has matching right- and left-hand threads internally. The end of the barrel with left-hand threads inside can usually be identified by either a groove or knurl around the end of the barrel.

TURNBUCKLE

turn coordinator:
An aircraft instrument that senses roll and yaw movement about the lateral and longitudinal axes.

turning error:
One of the errors inherent in a magnetic compass. It shows up only on north or south headings and causes the compass to lead or lag the actual turn.

turns ratio:
The ratio of the number of turns in one winding of a transformer to the number of turns in another winding.

turnstile antenna:
A type of antenna used in vhf communications that is omni directional and consists of two horizontal half-wave antennas mounted at right angles to each other in the horizontal plane.

TVOR:
Very high frequency terminal omnirange station. *(FAR 1)*

twenty-minute rating:
The amp-hour rating of a battery indicating the amount of current that can be drawn from it in order to discharge it in twenty minutes.

twin-engine:
An aircraft with two engines.

TWIN ENGINE

twin-row radial engine:
A radial engine having two rows of cylinders, one behind the other.

twist drill:
A metal cutting tool with a straight shank and deep spiral flutes in its sides.

two-cycle engine:
A type of reciprocating engine in which a power impulse occurs on each stroke of the engine.

type:
1. As used with respect to the certification, ratings, privileges, and limitations of airmen, means a specific make and basic model of aircraft, including modifications thereto that do not change its handling or flight characteristics. Examples include: DC–7, 1049, and F–27.

2. As used with respect to the certification of aircraft, means those aircraft which are similar in design. Examples include: DC–7 and DC–7C; 1049G and 1049H; and F–27 and F–27F.

3. As used with respect to the certification of aircraft engines means those engines which are similar in design. For example, JT8D and JT8D–7 are engines of the same type, and JT9D–3A and JT9D–7 are engines of the same type. *(FAR 1)*

type certificate data sheet:
The official specification for an aircraft, engine or propeller issued by the FAA.

ty-rap:
A patented nylon strap used to hold wire bundles together. Also called *tie wrap* or *zip tie*.

Uu

U-bolt:
A rod threaded on both ends and shaped like the letter U. U-bolts are used to fasten cable around a thimble.

ultimate load:
The amount of load applied to a part, beyond which the part will fail.

Ultra-High Frequency (UHF):
The band of frequencies from 300 megahertz to 3 gigahertz. See *very high frequency*.

ultrasonic:
1. Acoustics. Of or pertaining to frequencies above those that affect the human ear, i.e., more than 20,000 vibrations per second.

2. Of or pertaining to very high supersonic speeds, hypersonic.

ultrasonic cleaner:
Type of cleaning apparatus that transmits sound waves through a fluid. It is often used for cleaning filters and bearings.

ultrasonic inspection:
A comparison form of nondestructive inspection in which a pulse of ultrasonic energy is induced into the material being tested, and the time required for it to return to the transducer is measured and displayed on a meter or oscilloscope screen. If the probe passes from sound material to material containing a fault, the operator will be able to detect it.

ultraviolet lamp:
A lamp that produces light with a wavelength that is slightly shorter than that of visible light. Often used with non-destructive testing materials.

unapproved parts:
Parts that may be airworthy but lack the proper FAA documentation.

undercarriage:
A term used to describe the aircraft's landing gear.

UNDERCARRIAGE

undercut:
A groove melted into the base metal adjacent to the toe or root of a weld and left unfilled by weld metal.

underinflation:
A condition where tire pressure is less than that required. Underinflation causes the tire to wear rapidly and unevenly at the outer edges of the tread. An underinflated tire develops higher temperatures during use than a properly inflated tire. This can result in tread separation or blowout failure.

underspeed condition:
The condition that occurs when the propeller speed drops below the r.p.m. for which the governor is set.

undervoltage relay:
A circuit protection device that senses a low voltage condition and opens the circuit when the voltage drops below a predetermined value.

underwing fueling:
See *single-point fueling*

undrainable fuel:
Fuel that remains trapped in the system after draining.

U

undrainable oil:
Oil that remains trapped in the oil system when the oil is drained.

unfeather:
To turn (a propeller) from the feathered position.

uniform surface corrosion:
A general covering of corrosion in which the action has been even. No pits or localized damage have formed.

unijunction transistor:
A three-terminal, semiconductor device with a negative resistance characteristic that is used in switching circuits, oscillators, and wave-shaping circuits.

union:
A plumbing connector that attaches one piece of tubing to another.

UNION

unit:
1. An assembly or any combination of parts, subassemblies, and assemblies mounted together. Normally capable of independent operation.

2. A single object or thing.

United States (in a geographical sense):
1. The states, the District of Columbia, Puerto Rico, and the possessions, including the territorial waters.

2. The airspace of those areas. *(FAR 1)*

United States air carrier:
A citizen of the United States who undertakes directly by lease, or other arrangement, to engage in air transportation. *(FAR 1)*

universal-head rivets:
These were designed as a universal replacement for both the round- and brazier-head rivets. They were developed specifically for the aircraft industry. They look similar to modified brazier-head rivets. Universal-head rivets have a flat area on the head one-half times the shank diameter, a head diameter twice the shank diameter and a head height approximately 42.5 percent of the shank diameter.

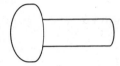

UNIVERSAL-HEAD RIVET

universal motor:
The universal motor consists of an armature and a set of field coils connected in a series. It can operate either on AC or DC and has the same speed and torque characteristics as the DC series motors. In the larger capacities, it has compensating windings like DC machines.

universal propeller protractor:
A type of protractor designed to be used to check propeller blade angles when the propeller is on a balancing stand or installed on the aircraft engine.

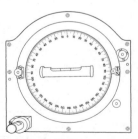

UNIVERSAL PROPELLER PROTRACTOR

unloading valve:
A pressure control valve used
in hydraulic systems to act as a
pressure-limiting device. When
the pressure reaches the set value,
the valve will re-route the fluid
back to the pump inlet.

unscheduled maintenance:
Maintenance done as a result of
discrepancies found by flight and
ground personnel.

unusable fuel:
Fuel left in the fuel system, which
cannot be consumed by the
engine. This amount is usually
given in the Aircraft Specifications
or Type Certificate Data Sheets.

unusable oil:
Oil that cannot be used by the
engine.

unwanted emissions:
Consist of spurious emissions and
out-of-band emissions.

updraft carburetor:
A type of carburetor in which the
air passes upward.

up link:
The frequency used to transmit a
signal from earth to a satellite.

upper deck pressure:
The pressure of the air (in
inches of mercury) between the
turbocharger compressor and
the throttle plate. This air may be
used not only for the powerplant
but also for the pressurization of
the cabin and the fuel injection
system.

upper sideband:
All of the sum frequencies above
the carrier.

upset head:
The end of the rivet that is formed
during installation.

usable fuel:
The portion of the total fuel load
that is available for consumption
by the aircraft in flight.

useful load:
The useful load of an aircraft is
determined by subtracting the
empty weight from the maximum
allowable gross weight. For
aircraft certificated in both the
normal and utility categories,
there may be two useful loads
listed in the aircraft weight and
balance records.

utility category airplane:
An airplane certificated for flight
that includes limited acrobatics.

U

V_1:
The maximum speed in the takeoff at which the pilot must take the first action (e.g., apply brakes, reduce thrust, deploy speed brakes) to stop the airplane within the accelerate-stop distance. V_1 also means the minimum speed in the takeoff, following a failure of the critical engine at VEF, at which the pilot can continue the takeoff and achieve the required height above the takeoff surface within the takeoff distance. *(FAR 1)*

V_2:
Takeoff safety speed. *(FAR 1)*

V_2min:
Minimum takeoff safety speed. *(FAR 1)*

VA:
Design maneuvering speed. *(FAR 1)*

vacuum:
Pressure less than atmospheric pressure expressed in inches of mercury (in. Hg).

vacuum bag:
The plastic or rubber layer used to cover the part so that a vacuum can be drawn.

vacuum bag molding:
A process in which the lay-up is cured under pressure generated by drawing a vacuum in the space between the lay-up and a flexible sheet placed over it and sealed at the edges.

vacuum pump:
An air pump mounted on an aircraft engine. The negative pressure produced by this pump is used to drive aircraft instruments.

valve clearance, cold:
The clearance between the valve stem and the rocker arm of an engine using solid valve lifters when the engine is cold.

valve clearance, hot:
The clearance between the valve stem and the rocker arm of an engine using solid valve lifters when the engine is at operating temperature.

valve core:
A spring-loaded, resilient check valve inside the valve stem that allows air to flow into a tire to inflate it and then traps the air, preventing its leaking out. The pin of the valve core may be depressed to release the air from the tire.

valve face:
The ground face of the intake or exhaust valve that makes contact with the ground seat in the cylinder when the valve is closed.

valve float:
Condition in which the frequency of the valve opening exactly corresponds to the resonant frequency of the valve spring. Under these conditions, the valve spring will exert no closing force.

valve grinding:
The process of resurfacing the face of the intake and exhaust valves of a reciprocating engine. This is done to restore the quality of their seal in the cylinder.

valve guide:
The insert in the cylinder that guides the valve during motion and holds it concentric to the valve seat.

valve lag:
The number of degrees of crankshaft rotation after bottom center at which the intake or exhaust valve opens or closes. For example, if the intake valve closes 60° after bottom center on the compression stroke it has a valve lag of 60°.

valve lap:
A period where both the intake and exhaust valves are open at the same time.

valve lapping:
A process using a fine abrasive to obtain a perfect seal between the valve and valve seat.

valve lead:
The number of degrees of rotation before bottom center at which the intake or exhaust valve opens or closes. For example, if an intake valve opens 15° before the piston reaches center on the exhaust stroke, it is said to have a 15° valve lead.

valve lift:
The distance that the valve is lifted off its seat.

valve overlap:
The angular distance of crankshaft rotation when the piston is passing center on the exhaust stroke when the intake and exhaust valves are both open.

valve radius gauge:
A gauge used to determine if a valve has the proper radius between the head and stem. Any change in this radius would indicate valve stretch.

valve seat:
A hardened ring of steel or bronze shrunk fit into the cylinder head to provide a surface on which the valve can seat.

valve springs:
Helical-wound steel wire springs that are used to close the poppet valves of a reciprocating engine.

valve spring tester:
A machine used during engine overhaul to test the condition of valve springs by measuring the force required to compress them to a specific height.

valve stretch:
Elongation of the valve stem usually caused by overheating.

valve timing:
The relationship between the crankshaft rotation and the opening and closing of the intake and exhaust valves.

vane:
A term generally used for stationary airfoils within a turbine engine.

vane type pump:
A type of constant displacement pump utilizing sliding vanes turning in an eccentric cavity to force fluid through the pump.

vapor-cycle air conditioning:
A closed-circuit refrigeration system used for air conditioning in which heat is extracted by refrigerant alternately being evaporated and condensed. Typically uses freon R12 or R134 as the refrigerant.

vaporize:
To change a liquid into a vapor.

vapor lock:
A stoppage or diminution of fuel flow in a system caused by fuel vapor in the lines.

vapor pressure:
That pressure of the vapor above a liquid required to prevent further evaporation of the liquid.

vaporizing tubes:
Devices used instead of fuel nozzles in some engines.

varactor:
A PN junction semiconductor, designed for microwave frequencies, in which the capacitance varies with the applied voltage.

varactor FM modulator:
An FM modulator that uses a voltage-variable capacitor (varactor).

variable capacitor:
A capacitor whose capacity can be changed.

V

variable displacement pump:
A pump whose output may
be varied by the pressure on
the system. For high-pressure
applications, this is usually done
by varying the stroke, either
actual or effective, of a piston-type
pump.

variable inlet guide vanes:
Movable devices located in front
of the first compressor rotor to
guide the angle of incidence of
the inlet air to the first compressor
rotor.

variable pitch propeller:
A propeller whose pitch may be
changed during flight.

variable resistor:
A resistor whose resistance can be
changed.

varsol:
A petroleum product used as a
solvent for cleaning parts.

V_B:
Design speed for maximum gust
intensity. *(FAR 1)*

V-block:
A hardened and ground block of
steel with a V-shaped cut in the
top to permit location of parts
for machining and inspection
operations.

V_C:
Design cruising speed. *(FAR 1)*

V_D:
Design diving speed. *(FAR 1)*

V_{DF}/M_{DF}:
Demonstrated flight diving speed.
(FAR 1)

vector:
A quantity with both magnitude
and direction.

vector generator:
Processor circuitry used to draw
lines on a CRT display

vegetable oils:
In early aviation, additives for
mineral-based oils had not yet

been invented. Many engines,
particularly rotary radial engines,
used a vegetable-based lubricant,
mainly castor oil. While castor oil
oxidized fairly readily and tended
to gum up, it did not wash away
with gasoline. Because rotary
engines used a fuel-distribution
system similar to a two-cycle
(crankcase induction), castor
oil worked for those engines.
However, rapid improvement in
mineral oil processing phased out
its use.

V_{EF}:
The speed at which the critical
engine is assumed to fail during
takeoff. *(FAR 1)*

velocity:
The distance an object travels per
unit of time.

veneer:
Thin sheets of wood used in the
manufacture of plywood and
laminated wood.

ventral fin:
A fin mounted to the underside
of an aircraft. Often added as
an additional contribution to
directional stability.

venturi:
A converging-diverging passage
for fluid, which increases the fluid
velocity and lowers its pressure; a
venturi tube.

vernier caliper:
A micrometer caliper with a
special vernier scale that allows
each one-thousandth of an inch
to be broken down into ten equal
parts, so one ten-thousandth of an
inch may be accurately read.

vertical axis:
An axis passing through an
aircraft from top to bottom and
usually passing through the
center of gravity. Also called a
normal axis.

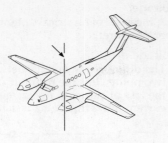

VERTICAL AXIS

vertical navigation:
An autopilot mode used to fly the selected altitude or glide path

vertical speed indicator (VSI):
A rate-of-climb indicator.

vertical stabilizer:
A fin mounted approximately parallel to the plane of symmetry of an airplane, airship, or other aircraft, to which the rudder, when present, is attached. Also called a *vertical fin*.

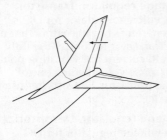

VERTICAL STABILIZER

vertical vibration:
A vibration in which the movement is in the vertical, or up and down, direction. An out of track main rotor may cause this type of vibration.

very high frequency (VHF):
The band of frequencies from 30 megahertz to 300 megahertz.

very low frequency (VLF):
The band of frequencies from 3 kilohertz to 30 kilohertz.

V_F:
Design flap speed. *(FAR 1)*

V_{FC}/M_{FC}:
Maximum speed for stability characteristics. *(FAR 1)*

V_{FE}:
Maximum flap extended speed. *(FAR 1)*

VFR:
Visual flight rules. *(FAR 1)*

VFR over-the-top:
With respect to the operation of aircraft: the operation of an aircraft over-the-top under VFR when it is not being operated on an IFR flight plan. *(FAR 1)*

V_{FTO}:
Final takeoff speed. *(FAR 1)*

V_H:
Maximum speed in level flight with maximum continuous power. *(FAR 1)*

VHF:
Very high frequency. *(FAR 1)*

vibration:
Repetitive back and forth movement.

virtual ground:
A point in a circuit that is at ground potential (0 V) but is not connected to ground.

viscometer:
An instrument used to measure the viscosity of a fluid.

viscosity:
The fluid friction, or the resistance to flow, of oil or other fluid.

viscosity index:
The measure of change in viscosity of oil with a change in temperature.

viscous:
Heavy, thick-bodied, gluey, or slow in motion.

visible line:
The line used for all lines on a drawing representing visible lines on the object.

visual inspection:
The qualitative observation of physical characteristics utilizing the unaided eye or with stipulated levels of magnification.

V_{LE}:
Maximum landing gear extended speed. *(FAR 1)*

V_{LO}:
Maximum landing gear operating speed. *(FAR 1)*

V_{LOF}:
Lift-off speed. *(FAR 1)*

V_{MC}:
Minimum control speed with the critical engine inoperative. *(FAR 1)*

V_{MO}/M_{MO}:
Maximum operating limit speed. *(FAR 1)*

V_{MU}:
Minimum unstick speed. *(FAR 1)*

V-NAV, VNAV:
Vertical Navigation

V_{NE}:
Never-exceed speed. *(FAR 1)*

V_{NO}:
Maximum structural cruising speed. *(FAR 1)*

voids:
Discontinuities in which there is a physical separation between opposite walls.

volatile liquids:
Liquids that are readily vaporizable at relatively low temperatures; explosive liquids.

volt:
The unit of electromotive force or electrical pressure. One volt is the pressure required to send 1 ampere of current through a resistance of 1 ohm.

voltage:
A measure of electrical potential or pressure.

voltage drop:
The difference in voltage between two points. It is the result of the loss of electrical pressure as current flows through a resistance.

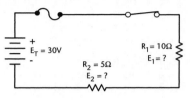

VOLTAGE DROP
(SCHEMATIC)

voltage regulator:
A device that automatically compensates for variations in line-power voltage, thus maintaining nearly constant voltage on the electrical circuit.

voltage regulator, transistor:
A voltage regulator for DC generators or alternators that uses a transistor to control the flow of field current but vibrating points to sense voltage and control the transistor. See also *transistor voltage regulator*.

voltage regulator, transistorized:
A voltage regulator for DC generators or alternators that uses a transistor to control the field current. A zener diode senses the voltage to be controlled. See also *transistorized voltage regulator*.

voltage regulator, vibrating-type:
A voltage regulator for DC generators or alternators that use vibrating points to sense voltage and provide a varying resistance for the generator field current.

voltage standing wave ratio (VSWR):
In a waveguide, the ratio of the electric field (voltage) at a maximum point to that of an adjacent minimum point.

voltmeter:
A meter used to measure voltage. Usually one function of a multimeter.

volt-ohm-milliameter (VOM):
See *multimeter*

volumetric efficiency:
Of an internal-combustion piston engine, the efficiency with which the engine draws the fuel air mixture into its cylinders, expressed, for example, as the ratio of the volume of the fuel-air mixture drawn in at inlet pressure and temperature to the piston displacement.

VOM:
Volt-Ohm-Milliammeter

VOR:
Very high frequency omnirange station. *(FAR 1)*

VORTAC:
Collocated VOR and TACAN.

vortex:
A circular, whirling movement of air forming a space in the center toward which anything caught in the vortex tends to move. See *wingtip vortices*.

vortex generators:
Small, low-aspect ratio airfoils mounted in pairs on the upper surface of aircraft wings. Their function is to bring high energy to the surface of the wing by keeping the air from separating from the surface of the wing, thereby delaying shock induced separation.

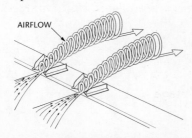

AIRFLOW

VORTEX GENERATORS

vortex interrupter system:
A high pressure stream of air that is directed into the area below and in front of a turbine engine when the aircraft is on the ground. Dissipates the vortex that can cause debris to be ingested into the engine. Used on engines that are mounted on the bottom of the wing.

VOX:
Voice

V_R:
Rotation speed. *(FAR 1)*

V_{REF}:
Reference landing speed. *(FAR 1)*

V_S:
The stalling speed or the minimum steady flight speed at which the airplane is controllable. *(FAR 1)*

V_{S0}:
The stalling speed or the minimum steady flight speed in the landing configuration. *(FAR 1)*

V_{S1}:
The stalling speed or the minimum steady flight speed obtained in a specific configuration. *(FAR 1)*

V_{SR}:
Reference stall speed. *(FAR 1)*

V_{SR0}:
Reference stall speed in the landing configuration. *(FAR 1)*

V_{SR1}:
Reference stall speed in a specific configuration. *(FAR 1)*

V_{SW}:
Speed at which onset of natural or artificial stall warning occurs. *(FAR 1)*

V-tail surface:
An empennage consisting of two fixed and two movable surfaces arranges in a V shape. These two surfaces have the same aerodynamic function as the traditional three surfaces.

V

V$_{TOSS}$:
Takeoff safety speed for category A rotorcraft. *(FAR 1)*

V-type engine:
A reciprocating engine with the cylinders arranged in two in-line banks generally set 60° apart. Most have 8 to 12 cylinders and may be either liquid-cooled or air-cooled. They are designated by a V, followed by a dash and the piston displacement in cubic inches, for example, V-1710.

VU number:
Specific number used to designate all panels and racks on Airbus aircraft

V$_X$:
Speed for best angle of climb. *(FAR 1)*

V$_Y$:
Speed for best rate of climb. *(FAR 1)*

Ww

WAAS:
1. Wide Area Augmentation System
2. A GPS enhancement designed to improve the integrity, accuracy, availability, and continuity of the basic satellite navigation system over a large area of coverage

wafer-type selector switch:
A rotary switch in which the contacts are arranged on levels. Each level (wafer) is electrically independent but mechanically connected by the shaft of the switch.

warning:
Calls attention to any methods, materials, or procedures that must be followed to avoid injury or death

warning area:
A warning area is airspace of defined dimensions, extending from three nautical miles outward from the coast of the United States, that contains activity that may be hazardous to nonparticipating aircraft. The purpose of such warning areas is to warn non-participating pilots of the potential danger. A warning area may be located over domestic or international waters or both. (FAR 1)

warning lights:
Annunciator lights to warn the flight crew of a dangerous situation or the failure of a system or component.

WARNING LIGHTS

warp:
The yarn running lengthwise in a woven fabric.

warp clock:
A composite fabrication and engineering symbol used as reference for aligning the warp yarns or tows in the desired direction.

warp direction:
The direction of the warp yarns or tows in a fabric or tape. The warp direction is parallel to the selvage edge.

warp surface:
The surface of a fabric that has a majority of warp fibers woven above the fill fibers.

Warren truss:
Named after Captain Warren (English), who adapted the type for bridges from a Belgian design. A rigid fuselage truss having diagonal braces between the longerons.

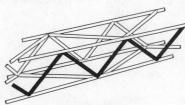

WARREN TRUSS

wash primer:
A self-etching primer used in aluminum or magnesium. It is often used to prepare the surface for zinc chromate primer.

washer:
A flat metal disc with a central hole. It is used to provide a smooth bearing surface for a nut or bolt to seat against.

wash-in:
A permanent warp or twist given a wing such that some specified or understood angle angle of attack (usually the geometric angle of attack) is greater at the tip than at the root.

wash-out:
A permanent warp or twist given a wing such that some specified or understood angle of attack (usually the geometric angle of attack) is smaller at the tip than at the root.

waste gate:
A valve by means of which a turbosupercharger is controlled. Exhaust gases in excess of the amount required are diverted through the valve and into the open before reaching the turbine. Also called a *blast gate*.

water break test:
A quality control test to confirm the lack of surface contamination by observing an unbroken film of water over the surface.

water injection:
Water or water-alcohol mixture that is injected into the cylinders of a reciprocating engine or into the combustion section of a turbine engine to remove some of the heat that would cause damage under conditions of full power operations.

waterline:
A horizontal reference plane from which vertical measurements in an aircraft may be taken.

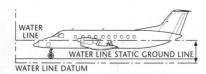

WATERLINE

water soluble:
Having the ability to dissolve in water.

watt:
The unit of electrical power that is the product of voltage and current.

watt hours:
Unit of measure based on cumulative power usage over a period of time. For example, if a 100-watt bulb consumes electrical energy for 20 hours, it has used 2,000 watt hours.

wattmeter:
A meter used to measure electrical power.

waveform:
The shape of the wave obtained when instantaneous values of an ac quantity are plotted against time in rectangular coordinates.

waveguide:
A rectangular, circular, or elliptical metal pipe designed to transport electromagnetic waves through its interior.

wavelength:
The distance, usually expressed in meters, traveled by a wave during the time interval of one complete cycle. It is equal to the velocity divided by the frequency.

wave soldering:
A process wherein printed boards are brought in contact with the surface of continuously flowing and circulating solder.

wear pads:
Used in brakes, steel pads that are riveted to the surfaces of the stationary disks, the pressure plate, and the back plate to provide a wearing surface against the sintered material on the rotating disks. It is more economical to replace the wear pads than the disks and the plates themselves.

Weber's theory:
A theory of magnetism that assumes that all magnetic material is composed of many tiny magnets. A piece of magnetic material that is magnetized has all of the tiny magnets aligned so that the north pole of each magnet points in one direction.

WEFT:
Wings, Engine(s), Fuselage, Tail. Method used during war time to learn an aircraft's major parts for recognition training.

weft:
The transverse threads or fibers in a woven fabric. Those fibers running perpendicular to the warp. Also called *fill, filling yarn,* or *woof.*

weighing points:
Specific locations on the aircraft where scales are placed for weighing purposes.

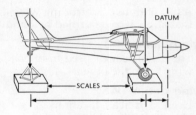

WEIGHING POINTS

weight-shift-control aircraft:
A powered aircraft with a framed pivoting wing and a fuselage controllable only in pitch and roll by the pilot's ability to change the aircraft's center of gravity with respect to the wing. Flight control of the aircraft depends on the wing's ability to flexibly deform rather than the use of control surfaces. *(FAR 1)*

weld bead:
A deposit of filler metal from a single welding pass.

welding:
Joining two or more pieces of material by applying heat or pressure, or both, with or without filler material, to produce a localized union through fusion or recrystallization across the interface.

welding rod:
Filler metal in wire or rod form used in gas welding and brazing processes and in those arc welding processes in which the electrode does not provide the filler metal.

weldment:
An assembly whose component parts are formed by welding.

Weston meter movement:
A moving coil-type analog meter movement.

wet cell:
A chemical cell in which the electrolyte is in liquid form.

wet grinder:
A type of precision grinding machine that uses a flow of liquid coolant to remove the heat of the grinding operation.

wet lay-up:
A method of making a reinforced product by applying a liquid resin system while the reinforcement is put in place.

wet sump engine:
An engine in which all of the oil supply is carried within the engine itself.

wet takeoff:
Engine operation when water injection is used.

wet wing:
A wing incorporating integral fuel tanks.

Wheatstone bridge:
An AC bridge circuit used to measure unknown values of resistance, inductance, or capacitance.

wheel well:
A place provided to stow the gear in the retracted position.

whip antenna:
A quarter wave antenna. It is normally vertically polarized.

windmilling:
The rotation of an aircraft propeller by air flowing over it with the engine not operating.

W

wing:
The main lifting surface of an airplane that generates lift by air flowing over it, thereby creating a low pressure area above it.

wing area:
The total wing area determined by multiplying the wing span by the wing chord.

wing chord:
An imaginary line between the leading and trailing edge of an airfoil section.

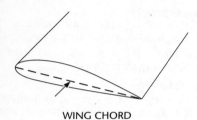

WING CHORD

wing fence:
A wall-like plate mounted on the upper surface of a wing to prevent spanwise airflow. Wing fences have been used for many years with the advent of the sweptback wing.

wing fillet:
A streamlined fairing between the wing and the fuselage.

wing heavy:
A condition in flight where one wing has a tendency to fly lower than the other. This can be corrected by properly adjusting the aircraft rigging.

winglet:
In its simplest form, a winglet is a vertical extension of the wing. It keeps the air from sliding off the end of the wing. *(FAR 1)*

wing leveler:
A simple autopilot system used to provide guidance along only the longitudinal axis of the aircraft.

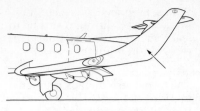

WINGLET

wing loading:
The ratio of the weight of the fully loaded aircraft to the total wing area.

wing nut:
A nut with two protruding wings that allow it to be turned by hand.

wingspan:
The distance measured from one wing tip to the other.

wing station (WS):
Used to indicate locations longitudinally along the wings of the aircraft

wingtip vortices:
1. Circular patterns of air created by an airfoil when generating lift. Vortices from medium to heavy aircraft may be extremely hazardous to small aircraft.

2. An area of extreme turbulence below an aircraft in flight. It is caused by the high-pressure air below the wing spilling over the wing tips into the low pressure above the wing.

wingwalkers:
Personnel assigned and positioned to observe wingtips and tails, rotor blades, empennage, etc., for clearance of obstacles, structures and other aircraft. In addition to being in position to see tips and tails, they should also be able to see and communicate with the driver of the towing vehicle or other person in charge of the towing operation.

wire gauge:
A device used to measure the diameter of wire.

wire identification number:
A label placed on all wires three inches or longer

wire routing chart:
Used to locate wire bundles that run through the aircraft

wire-wound resistor:
A type of electrical resistor whose base has a winding of high resistance wire and is covered with baked-on ceramic material.

wiring diagram:
Very specific diagrams with details on wires, connectors, and pin numbers for a given system

wiring manual:
Contains various diagrams, charts, lists and schematics needed to maintain the various electrical/electronic systems on the aircraft

wobble pump:
A hand-operated fluid pressure pump. The name comes from the action of operating the pump.

Woodruff key:
A hardened piece of metal shaped in a half circle on one side and flat on the other side. The key fits into a semi-circular furrow to prevent a wheel from turning on a shaft.

workability:
The ease with which wood, metal or plastic may be formed or shaped.

work hardening:
See *strain hardening*

work life:
The period during which a compound, after mixing with a catalyst, solvent, or other compounding ingredient, remains suitable for its intended use.

wrist pin:
A hardened and polished steel pin that attaches the small end of a connecting rod into a piston.

wrought iron:
A commercially pure form of iron with minute slag inclusions that make it soft, tough, and malleable.

wye connection:
A three-phase connection in which each winding is connected to a command ground forming a connection that resembles the letter Y. See *Y connection*.

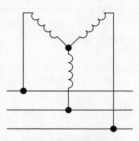

WYE CONNECTION

W

261

Xx

X-axis:
1. In composite laminates, an axis in the plane of the laminate which is used as the zero degree reference for designating the angle of a lamina.
2. In a gyro, the spin axis of the gyro.

X-band radar:
The frequency range between 8,000 and 12,500 Mhz.

XDCR, XDUCER:
Transducer

xenon:
A heavy, colorless, inert, chemical, gas element.

xero-radiography (RT):
A process using the photoconductive property of amorphous selenium to produce a radiological image, instead of photographic film.

X-FEED:
Crossfeed

XMIT:
Transmit

X-ray:
Electromagnetic radiation of extremely short wavelength, capable of penetrating solid objects and exposing photographic film.

X-Y plane:
In composite laminates, the reference plane parallel to the plane of the laminate.

Yy

yarn:
A generic term for strands or bundles of continuous filaments or fibers, usually twisted and suitable for making textile fabric.

yaw:
Rotation about the vertical axis of the aircraft.

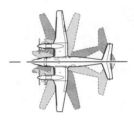

YAW

yaw damper:
Automatic control system for the rudder in transport and larger executive aircraft to reduce Dutch roll tendency. Dutch roll can be a very unpleasant experience for passengers.

Y-axis:
1. In composite laminates, the axis in the plane of the laminate which is perpendicular to the X-axis.
2. In a gyro, an axis through the center of gravity and perpendicular to the spin axis.

Y connection:
The connections of a three-phase AC alternator in which one end of each of the three windings is common. See *wye connection.*

yellow arc:
An instrument marking indicating a caution range.

y-valve:
The oil drain valve for a dry sump engine. It derives its name from its shape. One arm of the Y goes to the pressure pump inlet of the engine, one arm to the oil reservoir, and the lower arm is fitted with a shut-off valve, and is the point from which the oil may be drained from the reservoir. Fuel for oil dilution is introduced in the y-valve.

Zz

Z:
Impedance

Zahn cup:
A special cup of definite size and shape with a hole in its bottom. It is used to measure the viscosity of a material by the number of seconds required for the cup to empty.

Z-axis:
1. In composite laminates, the reference axis normal to the plane of the laminate.

2. In a gyro, an axis through the center of gravity and mutually perpendicular to both the X (spin) and Y axes.

zener diode:
A semiconductor device that allows free electron flow in one direction and restricts flow in the opposite direction until a specific voltage has been reached.

zerk fitting:
A type of fitting with a ball-head design feature used to fit the head of a grease gun. The fitting incorporates an internal check valve to prevent grease from exiting the fitting during normal operation.

zero adjustment:
The adjustment of an instrument to a zero point.

zero fuel weight (ZFW):
The zero fuel weight is the maximum allowable weight of a loaded aircraft without fuel. Included in the zero fuel weight is the weight of cargo, passengers, and crew. All weights in excess of the zero fuel weight must consist of usable fuel.

zero lash lifters:
See *hydraulic valve lifter*

zinc chromate primer:
A popular corrosion-inhibiting primer used on metal aircraft parts. It serves as a good bond between the metal and the finish that is applied.

zone numbers:
Zone numbers on drawings are similar to the numbers and letters printed on the borders of a map. They are there to help locate a particular point. To find a point, mentally draw horizontal and vertical lines from the letters and numerals specified; the point where these lines would intersect is the area sought.

zoning:
A reference system designed by the Air Transport Association (ATA) to further identify the location of components on large aircraft

zulu time:
See *Greenwich mean time*

Zyglo® inspection:
Proprietary name for a type of dye penetrant inspection utilizing a penetrant visible under ultraviolet light.

X
Y
Z

Markings by Country

COUNTRY	CODE	COUNTRY	CODE	COUNTRY	CODE
Afghanistan	YA	Croatia	9A	Israel	4X
Algeria	7T	Cuba	CU	Italy	I
Angola	D2	Cyprus	5B	Jamaica	6Y
Anguilla	VP-A	Czech Republic	OK	Japan	JA
Antigua and Barbuda	V2	Democratic People's Republic of Korea	P	Jordan	JY
Argentina	LQ, LV	Democratic Republic of the Congo	9Q	Kazakhstan	UP
Armenia	EK			Kenya	5Y
Aruba	P4	Denmark	OY	Kuwait	9K
Australia	VH	Djibouti	J2	Kyrgyzstan	EX
Austria	OE	Dominica	J7	Lao People's Democratic Republic	RDPL
Azerbaijan	4K	Dominican Republic	HI		
Bahamas	C6	Ecuador	HC	Latvia	YL
Bahrain	A9C	Egypt	SU	Lebanon	OD
Bangladesh	S2	El Salvador	YS	Lesotho	7P
Barbados	8P	Equatorial Guinea	3C	Liberia	A8
Belarus	EW	Eritrea	E3	Libya	5A
Belgium	OO	Estonia	ES	Liechtenstein (plus national emblem)	HB
Belize	V3	Ethiopia	ET		
Benin	TY	Falkland Islands (Malvinas)	VP-F		
Bermuda	VP-B, VQ-B			Lithuania	LY
		Fiji	DQ	Luxembourg	LX
Bhutan	A5	Finland	OH	Macedonia, Republic of	Z3
Bolivia	CP	France	F		
Bosnia/Herzegovina	E7	Gabon	TR	Madagascar	5R
Botswana	A2	Gambia	C5	Malawi	7Q
Brazil	PP, PR, PT, PU	Georgia	4L	Malaysia	9M
		Germany	D	Maldives	8Q
Brunei Darussalam	V8	Ghana	9G	Mali	TZ
Bulgaria	LZ	Greece	SX	Malta	9H
Burkina Faso	XT	Grenada	J3	Marshall Islands	V7
Burundi	9U	Gibraltar	VP-G	Mauritania	5T
Cambodia	XU	Guatemala	TG	Mauritius	3B
Cameroon, Republic of	TJ	Guinea	3X	Mexico (plus national emblem)	XA, XB, XC
Canada	C, CF	Guinea Bissau	J5		
Cape Verde	D4	Guyana	8R	Micronesia, Federated States of	V6
Cayman Islands	VP-C	Haiti	HH		
Central African Republic	TL	Honduras	HR	Monaco	3A
		Hungary	HA	Mongolia	JU
Chad	TT	Iceland	TF	Montenegro	4O
Chile	CC	India	VT	Montserrat	VP-M
China	B	Indonesia	PK	Morocco	CN
Columbia	HK, HJ	Iran, Islamic Republic of	EP	Mozambique	C9
Comoros	D6			Myanmar	XY, XZ
Congo	TN	Iraq	YI	Namibia	V5
Cook Islands	E5	Ireland	EI, EJ	Nauru	C2
Costa Rica	TI	Isle of Man	M	Nepal	9N
Côte d'Ivoire	TU			Netherlands	PH

Markings by Country - continued

COUNTRY	CODE	COUNTRY	CODE	COUNTRY	CODE
Netherlands Antilles	PJ	Serbia	YU	Tonga	A3
New Zealand	ZK, ZL, ZM	Seychelles	S7	Trinidad and Tobago	9Y
		Sierra Leone	9L	Tunisia	TS
Nicaragua	YN	Singapore	9V	Turkey	TC
Niger	5U	Slovakia	OM	Turkmenistan	EZ
Nigeria	5N	Slovenia	S5	Turks and Caicos	VQ-T
Norway	LN	Solomon Islands	H4	Uganda	5X
Oman	A4O	Somalia	6O	Ukraine	UR
Pakistan	AP	South Africa	ZS, ZT, ZU	United Arab Emirates	A6
Palau	T8			United Kingdom	G
Panama	HP	Spain	EC	United Kingdom Colonies and Protectorates (see individual countries)	VP, VQ, VR
Papua New Guinea	P2	Sri Lanka	4R		
Paraguay	ZP	St. Helena, Ascension and Tristan da Cunha	VQ-H		
Peru	OB				
Philippines	RP	St. Kitts and Nevis	V4	United Republic of Tanzania	5H
Poland	SP	St. Lucia	J6		
Portugal	CR, CS	St. Vincent and the Grenadines	J8	United States of America	N
Qatar	A7	Sudan	ST	Uruguay	CX
Republic of Korea	HL	Suriname	PZ	Uzbekistan	UK
Republic of Moldova	ER	Swaziland	3D	Vanuatu	YJ
Romania	YR	Sweden	SE	Venezuela	YV
Russian Federation	RA	Switzerland (plus national emblem)	HB	Vietnam	XV
Rwanda	9XR			Virgin Islands	VP-L
Samoa	5W	Syrian Arab Republic	YK	Yemen	7O
San Marino	T7	Tajikistan	EY	Zambia	9J
São Tomé and Príncipe	S9	Thailand	HS	Zimbabwe	Z
Saudi Arabia	HZ	Togo	5V		
Senegal	6V, 6W				

Markings by Code

CODE	COUNTRY	CODE	COUNTRY	CODE	COUNTRY
3A	Monaco	9Y	Trinidad and Tobago	H4	Solomon Islands
3B	Mauritius	A2	Botswana	HA	Hungary
3C	Equatorial Guinea	A3	Tonga	HB	Liechtenstein *(plus national emblem)*
3D	Swaziland	A4O	Oman		
3X	Guinea	A5	Bhutan	HB	Switzerland *(plus national emblem)*
4K	Azerbaijan	A6	United Arab Emirates		
4L	Georgia	A7	Qatar	HC	Ecuador
4O	Montenegro	A8	Liberia	HH	Haiti
4R	Sri Lanka	A9C	Bahrain	HI	Dominican Republic
4X	Israel	AP	Pakistan	HJ	Columbia
5A	Libya	B	China	HK	Columbia
5B	Cyprus	C	Canada	HL	Republic of Korea
5H	United Republic of Tanzania	C2	Nauru	HP	Panama
		C5	Gambia	HR	Honduras
5N	Nigeria	C6	Bahamas	HS	Thailand
5R	Madagascar	C9	Mozambique	HZ	Saudi Arabia
5T	Mauritania	CC	Chile	I	Italy
5U	Niger	CF	Canada	J2	Djibouti
5V	Togo	CN	Morocco	J3	Grenada
5W	Samoa	CP	Bolivia	J5	Guinea Bissau
5X	Uganda	CR	Portugal	J6	St. Lucia
5Y	Kenya	CS	Portugal	J7	Dominica
6O	Somalia	CU	Cuba	J8	St. Vincent and the Grenadines
6V	Senegal	CX	Uruguay		
6W	Senegal	D	Germany	JA	Japan
6Y	Jamaica	D2	Angola	JY	Jordan
7O	Yemen	D4	Cape Verde	JU	Mongolia
7P	Lesotho	D6	Comoros	LN	Norway
7Q	Malawi	DQ	Fiji	LQ	Argentina
7T	Algeria	E3	Eritrea	LV	Argentina
8P	Barbados	E5	Cook Islands	LX	Luxembourg
8Q	Maldives	E7	Bosnia and Herzegovina	LY	Lithuania
8R	Guyana	EC	Spain	LZ	Bulgaria
9A	Croatia	EI	Ireland	M	Isle of Man
9G	Ghana	EJ	Ireland	N	United States of America
9H	Malta	EK	Armenia		
9J	Zambia	EP	Iran, Islamic Republic of	OB	Peru
9K	Kuwait	ER	Republic of Moldova	OD	Lebanon
9L	Sierra Leone	ES	Estonia	OE	Austria
9M	Malaysia	ET	Ethiopia	OH	Finland
9N	Nepal	EW	Belarus	OK	Czech Republic
9Q	Democratic Republic of the Congo	EX	Kyrgyzstan	OM	Slovakia
		EY	Tajikistan	OO	Belgium
9U	Burundi	EZ	Turkmenistan	OY	Denmark
9V	Singapore	F	France	P	Democratic People's Republic of Korea
9XR	Rwanda	G	United Kingdom	P2	Papua New Guinea

Markings by Code - continued

CODE	COUNTRY	CODE	COUNTRY	CODE	COUNTRY
P4	Aruba	TT	Chad	VR	United Kingdom Colonies and Protectorates
PH	Netherlands	TU	Côte d'Ivoire		
PJ	Netherlands Antilles	TY	Benin	VT	India
PK	Indonesia	TZ	Mali	XA	Mexico *(plus national emblem)*
PP	Brazil	UK	Uzbekistan		
PR	Brazil	UP	Kazakhstan	XB	Mexico *(plus national emblem)*
PT	Brazil	UR	Ukraine		
PU	Brazil	V2	Antigua and Barbuda	XC	Mexico *(plus national emblem)*
PZ	Suriname	V3	Belize		
RA	Russian Federation	V4	St. Kitts and Nevis	XT	Burkina Faso
RDPL	Lao People's Democratic Republic	V5	Namibia	XU	Cambodia
		V6	Micronesia, Federated States of	XV	Vietnam
RP	Philippines			XY	Myanmar
S2	Bangladesh	V7	Marshall Islands	XZ	Myanmar
S5	Slovenia	V8	Brunei Darussalam	YA	Afghanistan
S7	Seychelles	VH	Australia	YI	Iraq
S9	São Tomé and Príncipe	VP	United Kingdom Colonies and Protectorates	YJ	Vanuatu
SE	Sweden			YK	Syrian Arab Republic
SP	Poland	VP-A	Anguilla	YL	Latvia
ST	Sudan	VP-B	Bermuda	YN	Nicaragua
SU	Egypt	VP-C	Cayman Islands	YR	Romania
SX	Greece	VP-F	Falkland Islands (Maldives)	YS	El Salvador
T7	San Marino			YU	Serbia
T8	Palau	VP-G	Gibraltar	YV	Venezuela
TC	Turkey	VP-L	Virgin Islands	Z3	Macedonia, Republic of
TF	Iceland	VP-M	Montserrat	Z	Zimbabwe
TG	Guatemala	VQ	United Kingdom Colonies and Protectorates	ZK	New Zealand
TI	Costa Rica			ZL	New Zealand
TJ	Cameroon			ZM	New Zealand
TL	Central African Republic	VQ-B	Bermuda	ZP	Paraguay
TN	Congo	VQ-H	St. Helena, Ascension and Tristan da Cunha	ZS	South Africa
TR	Gabon			ZT	South Africa
TS	Tunisia	VQ-T	Turks and Caicos	ZU	South Africa